D1376440

Emerson's Library

EMERSON'S LIBRARY

Walter Harding

State University College
Geneseo, New York

Published for the Bibliographical Society of the
University of Virginia

———

The University Press of Virginia
Charlottesville

© 1967 by the Rector and Visitors
of the University of Virginia

The University Press of Virginia

First published 1967

Library of Congress Catalog Card Number: 67-17628
Printed in the United States of America

For

William Gilman
Scholar, humanitarian, friend

67149

Preface

This is a companion volume to my *Thoreau's Library* (Charlottesville, 1957). I was astounded when I embarked on the earlier work to discover that no catalogue of Emerson's library had ever been published despite the fact that, unlike Thoreau's, Emerson's library is still almost intact. It is in the Concord Antiquarian Society in Concord, Massachusetts, just across the street from Emerson's home, and an excellent card catalogue of the library, prepared by Morrison C. Haviland of Harvard University, is in existence.

The present work is based directly on Haviland's card catalogue in the Antiquarian Society, although a number of changes have been made to make the entries conform to modern library style. In addition, I have shortened the entries to include basically the author, short title, place of publication, publisher, date, and, when indicated, the pagination. Names of editors, translators, and illustrators have been retained. The presence of autographs and annotations in the volumes is indicated, as is the provenance of the volumes when known. A few of the items could not be fully identified. These were, in most cases, reprints or clippings of reviews from unidentified periodicals or mutilated editions of works whose card descriptions did not fit those listed in standard library catalogues. Occasional errors were found in the Haviland catalogue. When these could be checked, and even sometimes when they could not be, they were corrected.

The Haviland catalogue includes many volumes now in the Concord Antiquarian Society collection that were owned by other members of the Emerson family than Ralph Waldo. Since all these volumes were moved to the Antiquarian Society directly from the Emerson home, and since ownership of a volume by another member of his immediate family did not negate the possibility that Emerson used it as much as any volume he had acquired himself, I have included in this catalogue all such volumes published before Emerson's death in 1882.

Emerson's library in the Antiquarian Society collection is remarkably complete. (Books containing annotations are now at the Houghton Library, Harvard, for safekeeping, having been replaced in most instances with other copies of the same edition.) Few volumes from his library can be found elsewhere. In fact, the only other group of Emerson's books that is really worth separate mention is the one in the Concord Free Public Library. Emerson was one of the six members of the library committee when the Concord Free Public Library was established in 1873, just as he had been active in the work of its predecessor, the Concord Town Library, for many years. In the first two years of the new library Emerson donated a large number of books, and he contributed further books occasionally for the remainder of his life.[1] Since many of these volumes were obviously taken from Emerson's personal library, I have included all his donations to the Concord Free Public Library in this list.

Also included are the few books from Emerson's library that have turned up in the pages of *American Book Prices Current,* the books listed in Kenneth Cameron, "Books No Longer in Emerson's Library" (*The Tran-*

[1]See Kenneth Cameron, "Emerson's Aid to Concord Libraries," in his *The Transcendentalists and Minerva* (Hartford: Transcendental Books, 1958), III, 863-70, referred to hereafter as "Cameron, III."

scendentalists and Minerva, III, 855-62), and a few other books that I have had the good fortune to note in my research. For the volumes not in the Antiquarian Society collection, I have noted either the present or the most recently known location.

The entries are arranged alphabetically, generally by author; the catalogue itself is followed by an index of titles, editors, translators, and the like.

So numerous have been the people who have assisted me in this project that I despair of being able to acknowledge every one of them. I do, however, wish particularly to express my gratitude to the members of the Ralph Waldo Emerson Memorial Association for their permission to edit and publish this catalogue; to the Research Foundation of the State University of New York for a grant-in-aid to assist in the photographing of the Haviland catalogue and in the typing of my manuscript; to William Jackson (whose sudden death before the publication of this book is a serious loss to the bibliographical world) of the Houghton Library of Harvard University for his assistance in obtaining a copy of the Haviland catalogue; to Mrs. Dorothy Nyren and Mr. William Buckley for providing a check list of the Emerson books in the Concord Free Public Library; to Professor William Gilman of the University of Rochester for providing me with material from as-yet-unpublished portions of *The Journals and Miscellaneous Notebooks of Ralph Waldo Emerson* (Cambridge, Mass.: Harvard University Press, 1960-   ), which he and his staff are editing; to Miss Betty Beaumont, Mrs. Raffaele D. Catanzariti, Miss Brenda Dockery, Mrs. Raymond Emerson, Mr. Edward W. Forbes, Miss Freda Hark, Mrs. Howard Kent of the Concord Antiquarian Society, the late Professor Perry Miller of Harvard University, Mrs. Caleb Wheeler, the late Professor Stephen Whicher of Cornell University, and Mr. John Cook Wyllie of the Bibliographical Society of the University of Virginia, for their many and varied types of assistance. All students of Transcendentalism are indebted to Professor Kenneth W. Cameron of Trinity College for his pioneer work in Emerson scholarship in his many and various books and articles and in his *Emerson Society Quarterly,* but I owe a special debt to him for his interest in this project and the many clues he offered me in running down stray books from Emerson's library. Miss Joy Williams of the Alderman Library of the University of Virginia regularized the bibliographical descriptions throughout the catalogue—a major undertaking for which not only I, but also all future users of the list, am indebted.

Geneseo, New York   WALTER HARDING
January 12, 1967   University Professor of English
                                                  State University of New York

Contents

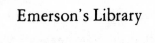

Emerson's Library

"I am filling my house with books which I am bound to read, and wondering whether the new heavens which await the soul (after the fatal hour) will allow the consultation of these."

–Ralph Waldo Emerson, *Journal,* July 21, 1870

A

A., A. AND A. M.   Aurora, a volume of verse.   London: Henry
S. King, 1875.   v, 266 pp.

ABBOTT, JACOB.   The corner stone.   Very greatly improved
and enl.   With numerous engravings.   New York:
Harper, 1858.   xii, 380 pp.

———.   History of King Alfred of England.   New York:
Harper, 1849.   270 pp.
Inscription: Ellen Emerson from her Uncle George, Jan. 1,
1850.

———.   The young Christian.   Rev. ed.   New York:
American Tract Society, 1832.   xi, 323 pp.

ABERCROMBIE, JOHN.   The philosophy of the moral feelings.
New York: J. & J. Harper, 1833.   xiii, 210 pp.

ACADÉMIE FRANÇAISE, PARIS.   ... Complément du Dictionnaire
de l'Académie francaise... publié sous la direction d'un
membre de l'Académie française, par Narcisse Landois...
et Louis Barré.   [Paris: Firmin Didot frères, 184-?]
[4] pp.
Prospectus.

———.   ... Souscription spéciale en faveur de toutes les
fortunes.   Edition complète et officielle du Dictionnaire
de l'Académie francaise, précédée d'un discours sur la
langue française, par M. Villemain...   [Paris: Firmin
Didot frères, 18—?]   [4] pp.
Prospectus.

ACOLLAS, ÉMILE. Nécessité de refondue l'ensemble de nos codes et notamment le code Napoléon au point du vue de l'idée démocratique. Appendice contenant le code civil de la convention. 2. éd. Paris: Guillaumin, 1866. 193 pp.

ACOSTA, JOSEPH. Masoth Hayojim. The burdens of the nations. From the 2d London ed. Book I. Cambridge: Hilliard and Metcalf, 1821. 27 pp.

Bound with: Webster, Daniel. A discourse delivered at Plymouth, December 22, 1820. Boston, 1821.

ADAM, ALEXANDER. Roman antiquities.

In 1821 Emerson lent a copy of this book to one of his classmates (Cameron, III, 856). The first American edition appeared in Philadelphia in 1807. Other editions were published in New York in 1814 and 1819.

——. ——. With numerous notes, and improved indices, by James Boyd. 6th ed. Glasgow: Blackie, 1835. xi, 528 pp.

Autograph.

ADAMS, JOHN QUINCY. An address, delivered at the request of the committee of arrangements for celebrating the anniversary of independence at the city of Washington on the fourth of July, 1821, upon the occasion of reading the Declaration of Independence. Cambridge: Hilliard and Metcalf, 1821. 34 pp.

Autograph.

Bound with: Webster, Daniel. A discourse delivered at Plymouth, December 22, 1820. Boston, 1821.

——. An eulogy on the life and character of James Monroe, fifth President of the United States. Delivered at the request of the Corporation of the City of Boston, on the 25th of August, 1831. Boston: J. H. Eastburn, 1831. 100 pp.

Bound with: Webster, Daniel. Speech ... on the 14th January, 1814. Alexandria, 1814.

——. An oration addressed to the citizens of the town of Quincy, on the fourth of July, 1831, the fifty-fifth anniversary of the independence of the United States of America. Boston: Richardson, Lord and Holbrook, 1831. 40 pp.

Bound with: Webster, Daniel. Speech...on the 14th January, 1814. Alexandria, 1814.

——. Oration on the life and character of Gilbert Motier de Lafayette. Delivered at the request of both Houses of the Congress of the United States before them, in the House of Representatives at Washington, on the 31st December, 1834. Washington: Gales and Seaton, 1835. 94 pp.
Bound with: Everett, Edward. Speech...March 9, 1826. Washington, 1826.

ADAMS, WILLIAM. Conversations on The shadow of the cross. New York, 1844. 42 pp.
Bound with the author's The shadow of the cross. New York, 1847.

——. The shadow of the cross, an allegory. 3d American ed., with engravings from original designs, by Chapman. New York: General Prot. Episcopal S. S. Union, Daniel Dana, Jr., Agent, 1847. 96 pp.

The Advent harp, designed for believers in the speedy coming of Christ. Boston: J. V. Himes, 1849. 466 pp.
Autograph: Ellen Emerson.

AESCHINES. The oration of Aeschines against Ctesephon, with notes by J. T. Champlin. Cambridge: John Bartlett, 1850. xii, 182 pp.
Text in Greek.
Autograph and notes: C. Emerson, Mar. 1862. [?]

AESCHYLUS. Tragoediae. Ad exemplar Glasgvense accvrate expressae. Editio stereotypa. Lipsiae: Tavchnitii, 1819. 320 pp.
Text in Greek.
Autograph: 1822.

——. Aeschylus. Tr. by R. Potter. New York: Harper, 1834. lxxi, 342 pp.
Autograph.

——. The seven tragedies of Aeschylus, literally tr. into English prose with notes critical and explanatory...3d ed., rev. and cor. Oxford: J. Vincent, 1843. 281 pp.
Autograph.

Aesthetic papers. Ed. by Elizabeth P. Peabody. Boston: The Editor, 1849. iv, 248 pp.

Affirmations.   First [-fifth] part.   [n.p., 18—?]   16, 8, 8,
8 pp.
>Caption title.
>Pts. 1-2 continuously paged.
>Bound with: Lane, Charles.   A classification of science and
>arts.   London, 1826.

——.   Copy 2.   Has only pt. 4.

AGASSIZ, LOUIS.   Address delivered on the centennial anniversary of the birth of Alexander von Humboldt, under the
auspices of the Boston Society of Natural History.   With
an account of the evening reception.   Boston: Boston
Society of Natural History, 1869.   107 pp.
>Note includes summary of R. W. E.'s remarks.

——.   A journey in Brazil.   Boston: Ticknor and Fields,
1868.   xix, 540 pp.
>Inscription by author to R. W. E.

——.   Lake Superior: its physical character, vegetation,
and animals, compared with those of other and similar
regions.   With a narrative of the tour, by J. Elliot Cabot.
And contributions by other scientific gentlemen.   Boston:
Gould, Kendall and Lincoln, 1850.   x, 428 pp.
>Inscription from J. E. Cabot to Emerson, and notes.

——.   Methods of study in natural history.   Boston:
Ticknor and Fields, 1863.   viii, 319 pp.
>Inscription.

AGOULT, MARIE CATHERINE SOPHIE (DE FLAVIGNY),
Comtesse d'.   Dante et Goethe; dialogues par Daniel
Stern [pseud.].   Paris: Librairie académique Didier,
1866.   425 pp.

——.   Esquisses morales; pensées, réflexions et maximes,
par Daniel Stern [pseud.].   3. éd., rev. et augm.   Paris:
J. Techener, 1839.   viii, 331 pp.
>Inscription.

AGUILAR, GRACE.   [Home influence: a tale for mothers and
daughters.   New York: Harper, 18—?]   vii, 411 pp.
>Copy imperfect: t.p., and all before p. [iii]wanting.

——.   The mother's recompense: a sequel to Home influence.   39th thousand.   New York: D. Appleton, 1865.
iv, 499 pp.

AINSWORTH, ROBERT. [English-Latin dictionary. Dictionum liber secundus. Latinarum scilicet notationes variasque significationes justo ordine tradens, allatisque exemplis e classicis scriptoribus singulas confirmans.] 2 v. in 1.
Probably the second volume, with t.p. missing, of An abridgment of Ainsworth's dictionary, English and Latin, designed for the use of schools, by Thomas Morell. Carefully corrected and improved from the last London quarto ed. by John Carey. Philadelphia: U. Hunt, 1820.
Signature: William Emerson.

AKENSIDE, MARK. The pleasures of imagination, a poem, in three books. Boston: Thomas B. Wait and Sons, 1816. 90 pp.
Autographs: Feb. 1817, and notes.

AKERMAN, JOHN YONGE. Some account of the possessions of the Abbey of Malmesbury in the days of the Anglo-Saxon kings; with remarks on the ancient limits of the forest of Braden. Communicated to the Society of Antiquaries. London: J. B. Nichols, 1857. 59 pp.
Inscription slip inserted.

ALAMANNI, LUIGI. La coltivazione, poema. Londra, 1780. xxxxiii, 238 pp.
Presented to the Concord Free Public Library in Feb. 1874. Autograph, R. W. Emerson.

ALBREE, GEORGE. Things of the kingdom, a series of essays. Philadelphia: J. B. Lippincott, 1881. 276 pp.
Letter from the author's son laid in, in front.

Album. New Haven: Durrie & Peck & N. & S. S. Jocelyn, 1826.
A blank book with verse, prose quotations, and notes written in; some sheets inserted.
Autograph: Ellen L. Tucker—verses mainly by or to her.
Includes some verses supposedly by R. W. E.

——. [n.p., n.d.]
Plates depict youthful instructive entertainments. Autograph: Edward, 1850.

ALCOTT, AMOS BRONSON. Concord days. Boston: Roberts Bros., 1873. vii, 276 pp.
Inscription: May 1873.

——. Conversations with children on the Gospels; conducted and ed. by A. Bronson Alcott... Boston: James Munroe, 1836–37. 2 v.
> Vol. 1 has quotation from Schiller in Alcott's hand. Inscription: v. 1, R. W. Emerson from his friend A. Bronson Alcott; v. 2, R. W. Emerson (in Alcott's hand).

——. Emerson. Cambridge: Priv. Print., 1865. 62 pp.

——. New Connecticut, an autobiographical poem. Boston: Priv. Print., 1881. 158 pp.
> Inscription by Alcott to R. W. E., Aug 27, '81.

——. Sonnets and canzonets. Boston: Roberts Bros., 1882. iv, 149 pp.
> Inscription: 14 Apr. 1882.

——. ——. Boston: Roberts Bros., 1882. iv, 151 pp.
> Inscription by author to Mrs. E., July 1882.

——. Table-talk. Boston: Roberts Bros., 1877. xi, 178 pp.
> Inscription: 20 May 1877.

——. Tablets. Boston: Roberts Bros., 1868, iv, 308 pp.

ALCOTT, LOUISA MAY. Flower fables. Boston: G. W. Briggs, 1855. 182 pp.
> Inscription: For Ellen Emerson from the author. Letter inserted from L. M. Alcott.

——. ——. Copy 2.
> Dedicated to Ellen T. Emerson.
> Signature: Emerson (in Ellen's hand).

——. Kitty's class-day. "A stitch in time saves nine." Boston: Loring, 1868. 12 pp.

ALDRICH, THOMAS BAILEY. ...Cloth of gold, and other poems. Cloth of gold. Friar Jerome's beautiful book. Interludes. Baby Bell and other poems. Judith. Sonnets. Boston: James R. Osgood, 1874. ix, 183 pp.
> Inscription by author to R. W. E.

[ALER, PAUL.] Gradus ad Parnassum; sive, Novus synonymorum, epithetorum, versuum, ac phrasium poeticarum thesaurus... Ab uno e Societate Jesu. Hanc ed., valdè emendatam, et tam sexcentis testimoniis à T. Morell laudatis, quàm multis aliis adauctam, summâ curà re-

censuit Adamus Dickinson.   Edinburgi: Typis academicis,
excudebat C. Stewart, impensis Stirling & Slade, 1821.
viii, 673 pp.

The Alexandrian; a republication of valuable literary and
scientific works... no. 24, 26–27.   New York: Wm.
Pearson, 1834.   1 v.

ALGER, WILLIAM ROUNSEVILLE.   The poetry of the East.
Boston: Whittemore, Niles, and Hall, 1856.   viii, 280 pp.
Inscription.

ALLINGHAM, WILLIAM.   Fifty modern poems.   London: Bell
and Daldy, 1865.   viii, 183 pp.
Autograph.

——.   Laurence Bloomfield in Ireland, a modern poem.
London: Macmillan, 1864.   viii, 290 pp.
Errata slip inserted at p. [1].
Inscription and autograph.

——.   Poems.   London: Chapman and Hall, 1850.   xii,
297 pp.
Inscription and notes.

——.   Rambles by Patricius Walker [pseud.].   London:
Longmans, Green, 1873.   xi, 345 pp.
Inscription: W. Allingham, April 17, 1873.

AMERICAN ACADEMY OF ARTS AND SCIENCES, BOSTON.   Memoirs.   New ser., v. 10, pt. 1.   Cambridge: Welch and
Bigelow; Boston: Metcalf and Dakin, 1868.   351 pp.

——.   Proceedings.   New ser., v. 1 (whole ser., v. 9), May,
1873–May, 1874.   Boston: John Wilson, 1874.   367 pp.

The American naturalist, a popular illustrated magazine of
natural history.   Ed. by A. S. Packard, Jr., E. S. Morse,
A. Hyatt and F. W. Putnam.   v. 3.   Salem, Mass.: Peabody Academy of Science, 1870.   viii, 693 pp.

——.   Ed. by A. S. Packard, Jr., and F. W. Putnam, E. S.
Morse and A. Hyatt, associate editors.   v. 4.   Salem,
Mass.:   Peabody Academy of Science, 1871.   xii,
775 pp.

AMERICAN ORIENTAL SOCIETY.   Proceedings.   October, 1867.
[New Haven?, 1867?]   xii pp.

AMERICAN SOCIAL SCIENCE ASSOCIATION.   ... Constitution, address, and list of members of the American Association for the Promotion of Social Science, with the questions proposed for discussion; to which are added minutes of the transactions of the Association.   July, 1866.
Boston: Wright & Potter, 1866.   64 pp.

AMERICAN UNITARIAN ASSOCIATION.   Day unto day...   Boston, 1875.   xviii, 367 pp.

——.   Hymn and tune book, for the church and the home...
Boston, 1871 [c1868].   xxxvi, 329 pp.
   Autograph: Emerson (in Ellen's hand).

——.   ——.   Copies 2-7.
   Copy 7: Ellen T. Emerson stamped on outside.

——.   ——.   Rev. ed.   Boston, 1880 [c1877].   398 pp.

——.   Hymns and tunes.   Selected from the revised edition of the Hymn and tune book for the church and the home.
Boston, [18—?].   [64] pp.

——.   ——.   Copy 2.

——.   Services for congregational worship.   Rev. ed.
Boston, 1877.   118 pp.
   Autograph: Ellen T. Emerson.

——.   Social hymn and tune book, for the conference and prayer-meeting, and the home, with services and prayers.
Boston, 1877.   155 pp.
   Ms. prayer in envelope, laid in.

The American's guide: comprising the Declaration of Independence; the Articles of Confederation; the Constitution of the United States; and the constitutions of the several states composing the Union...   Philadelphia: Towar & Hogan, 1828.   478 pp.

AMES, FISHER.   Works.   Comp. by a number of his friends. To which are prefixed notices of his life and character... [by J. T. Kirkland].   Boston: T. B. Wait, 1809.   xxxi, 519 pp.
   Autograph.

ANDERSEN, HANS CHRISTIAN.   Bilderbuch ohne Bilde. Vollständige vom Verfasser besorgte Ausgabe.   7. Aufl. New York: Leypoldt & Holt, 1869.   61 pp.

——. The story of my life. Now first tr. into English, and containing chapters additional to those published in the Danish ed., bringing the narrative down to the Odense festival of 1867. Author's ed. London: Sampson Low and Marston, 1871. xii, 569 pp.

ANDREWS, ETHAN ALLEN. First lessons in Latin; or, An introduction to Andrews and Stoddard's Latin grammar. 3d ed. Boston: Crocker and Brewster, 1839. 216 pp.
Autograph and notes.

[ANDREWS, JULIA C.] Breakfast, dinner, and tea: viewed classically, poetically, and practically. Containing numerous curious dishes and feasts of all times and all countries. Besides three hundred modern receipts... New York: D. Appleton, 1860. xi, 351 pp.

ANDREWS, LANCELOT. Nineteen sermons concerning prayer. The first six shewing the nature of prayer, as a preparative thereunto; the residue a large and full exposition upon the Lords Prayer. Cambridge: Roger Daniel, 1641. 450 pp.

ANDRONICUS RHODIUS. *Spurious works.* The paraphrase of an anonymous Greek writer (hitherto published under the name of Andronicus Rhodius) on the Nicomachean ethics of Aristotle. Tr. from the Greek by W. Bridgman. London: Printed by C. Whittingham, 1807. 478 pp.
Given to the Concord Free Public Library by Emerson in Aug. 1873 (Cameron, III, 866).

ANGELO, *pseud.* Sculpture-poetry. New York: Hurst, [c1881]. iv, 373 pp.

Anna; or, Passages from the life of a daughter at home. New York: Robert Carter, 1865. xxi, 342 pp.
Autograph: Ellen T. Emerson.

——. New York: Robert Carter & Bros., 1867. xxi, 342 pp.
Autographed slip mounted on t.p.: S. W. Stephen. Autograph: Ellen T. Emerson. Letter from E. Cabot to Ellen E. regarding book.

Annual of scientific discovery; or, Yearbook of facts in science and art, exhibiting the most important discoveries and improvements in mechanics, useful arts, natural philosophy, chemistry, astronomy, meteorology, zoölogy, botany, mineralogy, geology, geography, antiquities, together with a list of recent scientific publications; a classified list of patents; obituaries of eminent scientific men; an index to important papers in scientific journals, reports, etc.   Ed. by David A. Wells... and George Bliss, Jr.   Boston: Gould, Kendall, and Lincoln, 1850.

Annual of scientific discovery; or, Year-book of facts in science and art, for 1852, exhibiting the most important discoveries and improvements...; notes on the progress of science during the year 1851, etc., etc.   Ed. by David A. Wells.   Boston: Gould and Lincoln, 1852.   xxiv, 408 pp.
   Signature: R. W. Emerson.

ANTHOLOGIA GRAECA.   The Greek anthology, as selected for the use of Westminster, Eton, and other public schools. Literally tr. into English prose, chiefly by George Burges...   To which are added metrical versions by Bland, Merrivale, and others, and an index of references to the originals.   London: H. G. Bohn, 1852.   vii, 518 pp.
   Notes and autograph.

ANTHON, CHARLES.   A system of Latin versification, in a series of progressive exercises, including specimens of translation from English and German poetry into Latin verse...   New York: Harper, 1845.   327 pp.
   Autographs: Charles Emerson; William Emerson, Staten Island; and notes.

ANTIMASONIC PARTY, MASS. CONVENTION, BOSTON, 1829–30. An abstract of the proceedings of the Anti-Masonic State Convention of Massachusetts, held in Faneuil Hall, Boston, Dec. 30 and 31, 1829, and Jan. 1, 1830.   Boston: John Marsh, 1830.   32 pp.

———.   A brief report of the debates in the Anti-Masonic State Convention of the Commonwealth of Massachusetts, held in Faneuil Hall, Boston, December 30, 31, 1829, and January 1, 1830.   Boston: John Marsh, 1830.   48 pp.

[APPLETON, THOMAS GOLD.] Faded leaves. Boston: Roberts
Bros., 1872. ix, 150 pp.
> Inscription by author, 27 Feb. 1872.

——. A Nile journal. Illus. by Eugene Benson. Boston:
Roberts Bros., 1876. 307 pp.
> Inscription.

——. Syrian sunshine. Boston: Roberts Bros., 1877.
308 pp.

——. Windfalls... Boston: Roberts Bros., 1878.
364 pp.

Appletons' Railroad and steamboat companion: being a travellers' guide through the United States of America, Canada,
New Brunswick, and Nova Scotia... Illus. by 30 maps,
engraved on steel, including four plans of cities, and embellished with twenty-six engravings, by W. Williams.
New York: D. Appleton; Philadelphia: G. S. Appleton,
1849. 313 pp.
> Signature: R. W. Emerson.

APULEIUS MADAURENSIS. The metamorphosis; or, Golden ass,
and philosophical works. Tr. from the original Latin, by
Thomas Taylor... London: R. Triphook and T. Rodd,
1822. xxiv, 400 pp.
> Autograph.

ARABIAN NIGHTS. Arabian nights entertainments, carefully
revised and occasionally corrected from the Arabic. To
which is added, a selection of new tales, now first tr.
from the Arabic originals. Also, an introduction and
notes, illustrative of the religion, manners, and customs
of the Mahummedans, by Jonathan Scott... Philadelphia: R. W. Pomeroy, 1826. 6 v.
> Set incomplete: v. 2–6 wanting.

Archaeologia; or, Miscellaneous tracts, &c. London: Society of Antiquaries, 1832. 136 pp.

ARCHAEOLOGICAL INSTITUTE OF AMERICA. ...First annual
report of the Executive Committee, with accompanying
papers, 1879–80. Presented at the annual meeting of the
Institute, Boston, May 15, 1880. Cambridge: John Wilson, 1880. 163 pp.

ARIOSTO, LODOVICO. Orlando furioso. Milano: Dalla
società tipografica de'classici italiani, 1812–14. 5 v.
Autographs.

ARISTOPHANES. The comedies, tr. into familiar blank verse,
with notes, preliminary observations on each play, etc., by
C. A. Wheelwright... To which is added a dissertation
on the old Greek comedy from the German of Wachsmuth...
Oxford: D. A. Talboys, 1837. 2 v.
Autographs.

ARISTOTLE. Nicomachean ethics. Tr., with notes, original
& selected; an analytical introduction; and questions for
the use of students, by R. W. Browne... London: Henry
G. Bohn, 1850. lxxxi, 347 pp.

——. Ὄργανον. Aristotelis Stagiritae peripateticorvm
principis organvm, hoc est, libri omnes ad logicam perti-
nentes, Graecè & Latinè... Ed. tertia... Genevae:
Ex typis Vignonianis, 1605. 895 pp.

——. Treatise on rhetoric, literally translated from the
Greek. With an analysis by Thomas Hobbes, and a series
of questions. New ed., to which is added, a supplementary analysis containing the Greek definitions. Also
the Poetics of Aristotle, literally tr., with a selection of
notes, an analysis, and questions, by Theodore Buckley... London: Henry G. Bohn, 1850. iv, 500 pp.
Note and autograph.

ARMIG, S. P. Mundorum explicatio; wherein are couched the
mysteries of the external, internal and eternal worlds...
Also the explanation of an hieroglyphical figure. A
sacred poem. London: Lodowick Lloyd, 1663. 332 pp.

ARNIM, BETTINA (BRENTANO) VON. Correspondence of
Fräulein Günderode and Bettine von Arnim... Boston:
T. O. H. P. Burnham, 1861. xii, 344 pp.

——. Dies Buch gehört dem König. Berlin: E. H.
Schroeder, 1843. viii, 307 pp.
Autograph.

[——.] Goethe's correspondence with a child... London:
Longman, Orme, Brown, Green, and Longmans, 1839. 3 v.
Autographs.

[——.] ——. 1st American, from the London ed. Lowell: Daniel Bixby, 1841. 2 v.
> Inscription and notes.

——. Die Günderode... Grünberg und Leipzig; W. Leonsohn, 1840. 2 v.
> Autograph.

——. Günderode... Boston: E. P. Peabody, 1842. xii, 106 pp.

ARNIM, GISELA VON. Wie es unterdessen Daheim war, dramatische Erzâhlung. Berlin: Wilhelm Hertz, 1875. x, 410 pp.

ARNOLD, SIR EDWIN. The light of Asia; or, The great renunciation (Mahâbhinishkramana). Being the life and teaching of Gautama, prince of India and founder of Buddhism (as told in verse by an Indian Buddhist). London: Trübner, 1879. xiii, 238 pp.
> Inscription: Oct. 1879. Clippings laid in at p. 7.

——. The poets of Greece. London: Cassell, Petter, and Galpin, 1869. xiv, 226 pp.
> Inscription: Sept. 1869.

ARNOLD, MATTHEW. Essays in criticism. Boston: Ticknor and Fields, 1865. xv, 506 pp.
> Inscription: from J(ames?) T. F(ields?), June 1865.

——. ——. London: Macmillan, 1865. xix, 302 pp.
> Inscription: From E. Lyell Standey, March 1865.

——. On translating Homer: last words. A lecture given at Oxford. London: Longman, Green, Longman and Roberts, 1862. 69 pp.
> Inscription.

——. Poems. A new and complete ed. Boston: Ticknor and Fields, 1856. 336 pp.
> Notes and autograph.

——. ——. The first vol.: Narrative and elegiac poems. London: Macmillan, 1869. vi, 276 pp.
> Inscription: Feb. 1871.

——. ——. The second vol.: Lyric, dramatic, and elegiac poems. New and complete ed. London: Macmillan, 1877. vii, 312 pp.

Art. IV. 1. Researches into the physical history of mankind.
By James Cowles Prichard... Third edition. London,
1836–47. Five volumes... 2. The natural history of
man... 3. Appendix to the first edition of The natural
history of man. London, 1845... [n.p., 1847.] pp.
49–82.
  Apparently a review extracted from a periodical. Inscription.

ASSOCIATION OF AMERICAN GEOLOGISTS AND NATURALISTS. Re-
ports of the first, second, and third meetings of the As-
sociation of American Geologists and Naturalists, at
Philadelphia, in 1840 and 1841, and at Boston in 1842.
Embracing its proceedings and transactions. Boston:
Gould, Kendall and Lincoln, 1843. · viii, 544 pp.

ATHENAEUM CLUB, LONDON. Rules and regulations, list of
members, and donations to the library, 1846; with supplement for 1847. London, 1847. 132, 46 pp.

The atheneum; or, Spirit of the English magazines. 3d ser.,
v. 3–[4], Oct. 1829–April 1830; [April–Oct., 1830]. Boston: John Cotton. 2 v. in 1.
  Autograph: L. J. Emerson.

ATKINSON, WILLIAM PARSONS. On the right use of books, a
lecture. Boston: Roberts Bros., 1878. 65 pp.
  Inscription. Letter from author laid in at front, 3 April 1879.

The Atlantic monthly, a magazine of literature, art, and politics. v. 1–v. 12, no. 64, Nov. 1857–Dec. 1863. Boston:
Phillips, Sampson; London: Trübner. 12 v.
  Notes (v. 1–5, 8) and signatures of R. W. E.
  In July 1873 Emerson gave copies of v. 20–22, 24–26,
1867–70, to the Concord Free Public Library (Cameron, III,
866).

The Atlantic monthly. Index. v. 1–38, 1857–76. I. Index
of articles. a. General articles. b. Editorial departments.
II. Index of authors. Boston: H. O. Houghton; New York;
Hurd and Houghton, 1877. 106 pp.

Atlantis; ein Monatsschrift zur Vermittelung der deutschen
und amerikanischen Kultur und Literatur. Hrsg. und
redigirt von Chr. Essellen. Bd. 9, Sept. 1858. New
York: L. Hauser, 1858. 240 pp.

[Atlas.] Boston: Cummings & Hilliard, [1820?]. [I].
Romanum imperium. —[II]. Italia antiqua. —[III]. Graecia
antiqua. —[IV]. Asia Minor antiqua.

[AUDIN, JEAN MARIE VINCENT.] Guide du voyageur en
France, ... par Richard [pseud.]. ... 14. éd. ...
Paris: Audin, 1831. viii, 352 pp.
    Autograph.

AUGUSTINUS, AURELIUS, *Saint.* The confessions of S. Augustine; rev. from a former translation by E. B. Pusey,
with illus. from S. Augustine himself. Oxford: John
Henry Parker, J. G. F.; London: J. Rivington, 1840.
xxxvi, 363 pp.
    Inscription on flyleaf: R. Waldo Emerson with the love of his
    sister E.

——. Meditationes, Soliloquia, et Manvale. Accesserunt
Meditationes b. Anselmi, Meditationes d. Bernardi et
idiotae [pseud.] viri docti contemplationes De amore
divino. Paris: A. Jouby, 1864. pp. 233–444.

——. Meditations, his Treatise of the love of God, So-
liloquies, and Manual. With select contemplations from
St. Anselm and St. Bernard. Tr. by Geo. Stanhope. ...
London: J. Nunn, Radwell and Montin, 1818. iv, 419 pp.
    Signature: R. W. Emerson.

AURELIUS ANTONINUS, MARCUS. The meditations of Marcus
Aurelius Antoninus, with the Manual of Epictetus, and a
Summary of Christian morality. Freely tr. from the origi-
nal Greek, by Henry M'Cormac... London: Longman,
Brown, Green, and Longmans, 1844. 126 pp.
    Signature: R. W. Emerson.

——. The thoughts of the Emperor M. Aurelius Antoninus.
Tr. by George Long. Boston: Ticknor and Fields, 1864.
310 pp.
    Inscription by publisher to R. W. E.

AUSTIN, JANE (GOODWIN). Fairy dreams; or, Wanderings in
elfland. With illus. by Hammatt Billings. Boston: J. E.
Tilton, [ᶜ1859]. 216 pp.
    Inscription: Mrs. R. W. E. with regards of author, Dec. 1,
    1859.

AUSTIN, SARAH (TAYLOR), *tr.*   Fragments from German prose
   writers.   With biographical sketches of the authors.
   New York: D. Appleton, 1841.   xii, 353 pp.
      Notes and autograph.

AYTOUN, WILLIAM EDMONDSTOUNE.   Lays of the Scottish cav-
   aliers and other poems.   New York: Redfield, 1858.
   viii, 351 pp.

B

BABCOCK, WILLIAM HENRY.   Lord Stirling's stand, and other
poems.   Philadelphia: J. B. Lippincott, 1880.   213 pp.
Inscription by the author to R. W. E.

BABINGTON, E. R., *ed.*   Hidden sense.   Seek and find; or,
Double acrostics.   London: Frederick Warne; New York:
Scribner, 1867. 112 pp.
Inscription: Ellen T. Emerson from Aunt Lizzie, Jan. 1, 1868.

Baby's ride, and other stories.   Illus. by Ida Waugh.   New
York: McLaughlin Bros., 1882.

BACON, DELIA SALTER.   The philosophy of the plays of Shak-
spere unfolded.   With a preface by Nathaniel Hawthorne
...   Boston: Ticknor and Fields, 1857.   cx, 582 pp.
Autograph.   Note on recto of last leaf.

BACON, FRANCIS.   Essays, moral, economical, and political.
Boston: Bedlington, 1828.   218 pp.
Bound with: Locke, John.   A treatise on the conduct of
understanding. Boston, 1828.
Now in Concord Free Public Library.

——.   Works.   London: W. Baynes, 1824.   10 v.
Autographs and notes.

[BAGSTER, SAMUEL, AND SONS, *firm, publishers.*]   The harmony
of the four Evangelists, chronologically arranged, after
the manner of the Greek of Archbishop Newcome.   Reprinted from Bagster's celebrated Bible and issued by
Howard Gannett.   Boston, [18—?].   [4] pp.
This is laid in: Carpenter, Lant.   Harmony of the Gospels.
Boston, 1831.

BAILEY, EBENEZER. First lessons in algebra; being an easy introduction to that science, designed for the use of academies and common schools ... Rev. ed. Boston: Hickling, Swan & Brewer, 1860. xii, 254 pp.

BAILEY, PHILIP JAMES. The angel world, and other poems. Boston: Ticknor, Reed, and Fields, 1850. 114 pp.
Inscription: From W[illiam?] E. C[hanning?]

——. Festus, a poem. 3d ed. London: William Pickering, 1848. xvi, 367 pp.
Inscription and notes.

——. Nottingham Castle, an ode, historical and traditionary, on the opening of the castle as a permanent art museum. Nottingham: T. Forman, 1878. 8 pp.
Inscription.

[BAILEY, SAMUEL.] Essays on the formation & publication of opinions and on other subjects. 2d ed., rev. and enl. London: R. Hunter, 1826. xv, 320 pp.
Note on inside back cover, and autograph.

BAKER, BENJAMIN FRANKLIN. The new Haydn: a collection of hymn tunes, chants, sentences and anthems. Adapted for all the wants of public and private worship, and for the use of choirs, singing schools, musical societies and conventions. Together with a complete treatise on the principles of musical notation. Boston: Ticknor & Fields, 1866. 400 pp.
Notes: Ellen's.

BAKER & TILDEN, *publishers*. Map of the city of Boston and its environs executed under the direction of H. F. Wallace, state topographer. New York: Baker and Tilden, American Topographical Office, 1866. col. map.

BALL, BENJAMIN WEST. Elfin land, and other poems. Boston: J. Munroe, 1851. viii, 150 pp.
Inscription: R. W. Emerson from the author, 1851 (in R. W. E.'s hand).

BALZAC, HONORÉ DE. Ursule Mirouet. Bruxelles: Société belge de librairie, Hauman, 1842. 2 v.
Autographs.

BANCROFT, GEORGE.   A history of the United States, from
the discovery of the American continent ...   Boston:
Little, Brown, 1834–75.   10 v.
> Set incomplete: v. 3, 5, 6 wanting.
> Autographs: v. 7, From the author; v. 8, inscription; v. 9,
> printed inscription; v. 10, presented by publisher.

Bancroft's tourist guide: Yosemite, San Francisco and around
the Bay.   San Francisco, 1871.
> Given to Concord Free Public Library by Emerson in Feb.
> 1874 (Cameron, III, 866).

The Bank of England and the Act of 1844.   From a corre-
spondent.   [n.p., n.d.]
> Galley sheet (offprint).

BARBAULD, ANNA LETITIA (AIKIN), AND AIKIN, JOHN.   Evenings
at home; or, The juvenile budget opened, consisting of a
variety of miscellaneous pieces, for the instruction and
amusement of young persons, by Mrs. Barbauld and Dr.
Aikin.   4th American ed.   Philadelphia: Thomas T. Ash;
R. Wright, Printer, [18—?].   3 v.
> Set incomplete: v. 1, 2 wanting.

——.   Hymns in prose for children.   London: John Murray,
1864.   xii, 100 pp.   illus.
> Inscription: Edith Emerson with Uncle William's love, Dec.
> 1864.

——.   [Lessons for children: a primer.   Boston: E. P.
Peabody, 1841.]   vi, 100 pp.

——.   Works.   With a memoir by Lucy Aikin ...   Boston:
David Reed, 1826.   2 v.
> Set incomplete: v. 2 wanting.
> Inscription: R. W. Emerson to his Mother (in R. W. E.'s hand).

BARCHOU DE PENHOEN, AUGUSTE THÉODORE HILAIRE.   Histoire
de la philosophie allemande depuis Leibnitz jusqu'à
Hegel.   Paris: Charpentier, 1836.   2 v.
> Autograph.

BARLOW, GEORGE.   A life's love.   London: John Camden
Hotten, [1873?].   viii, 99 pp.

——.   Poems and sonnets.   London: John Camden Hotten,
1871.   3 v.

BARNES, WILLIAM.   Rural poems.   Boston: Roberts Bros.,
1869.   xi, 158 pp.
  Note laid in at p. 143.

[BARNETT, EZRA STILES.]   A sermon for children.   Boston:
Leonard C. Bowles, 1831.   18 pp.
  Bound with: The Christian teacher's manual.   Boston, 1828.

BARRETT, BENJAMIN FISKE.   Catholicity of the New Church
and uncatholicity of New-Churchmen.   New York: Mason
Bros., 1863.   312 pp.
  Given to Concord Free Public Library by Emerson. Withdrawn from circulation in 1921 (Cameron, III, 866).

——.   Letters on the divine trinity, addressed to Henry
Ward Beecher.   New York: Mason Bros., 1860.   viii,
137 pp.

BARRETT, THOMAS SQUIRE.   Examination of Gillespie: being
an analytical criticism of the arguement *a priori* for the
existence of a great first cause, as developed by W. H.
Gillespie in his "Necessary existence of God."   2d ed.
London: Provost, 1871.   iv, 48 pp.

BARTHÉLEMY, JEAN JACQUES.   Travels of Anacharsis the
Younger in Greece, during the middle of the fourth century
before the Christian aera.   Tr. from the French.   ...
London: G. G. and J. Robinson, 1796.   4 v.
  Tr. by William Beaumont.

——.   ——.   Maps, plans, views and coins, illustrative of
the Travels of Anacharsis the Younger in Greece, during
the middle of the fourth century before the Christian era.
London: G. G. and J. Robinson, 1796.   36 pp.
  Bookplate of William Emerson.

BARTLETT, JOHN.   Familiar quotations: being an attempt to
trace to their source passages and phrases in common use.
5th ed.   Boston: Little, Brown, 1868.   xii, 778 pp.
  Inscription: R. W. Emerson with regards of John Bartlett.

BARTOL, CYRUS AUGUSTUS.   Church and congregation, a plea
for unity.   Boston: Ticknor and Fields, 1858.   xxiv,
336 pp.
  Inscription: From the author.

———. Discourses on the Christian body and form. Boston: Crosby, Nichols; New York: C. S. Francis, 1853. vi, 376 pp.

Inscription: Mary M. Emerson from her friend Ann Tracy, April 26, 1853.

———. Discourses on the Christian spirit and life. Boston: Wm. Crosby and H. P. Nichols, 1850. iv, 344 pp.

Inscription: From author to R. W. E.

———. James T. Fields, a discourse in West Church, Boston. Boston: A. Williams, 1881. 21 pp.

———. Principles and portraits. Boston: Roberts Bros., 1880. 460 pp.

Signature: R. W. Emerson.

———. Radical problems. Boston: Roberts Bros., 1872. 407 pp.

Inscription.

———. The rising faith. Boston: Roberts Bros., 1874. iii, 386 pp.

———. The upper standing, a sermon preached in the West Church, Boston, March 3, 1872. Boston: Leonard C. Bowles, 1872. 11 pp.

———. The word of the spirit to the church. Boston: Walker, Wise, 1859. 86 pp.

Inscription: R. W. Emerson from C. A. B.

BARTON, F. B. An outline of the positive religion of humanity of A. Comte: love, order, progress. London: E. Truelove, 1867. 23 pp.

BARTON, WILLIAM PAUL CRILLON. Compendium flora Philadelphia, containing a description of the indigenous and naturalized plants found within a circuit of ten miles around Philadelphia. Philadelphia: M. Carey, 1818. 2 v.

BASTIAT, FRÉDÉRIC. Essays on political economy. [4th (people's) ed.] London: Provost, [1874]. iv, 234 pp.

BAXTER, RICHARD. The dying thoughts of Richard Baxter. Abridged by Benjamin Fawcett. New York: American Tract Society, [18—?]. vi, 132 pp.

BEAR, WILLIAM E.   The relations of landlord and tenant in England and Scotland.   London, New York: Cassell, Petter and Galpin, 1876.   131 pp.

BEARD, GEORGE MILLER.   Stimulants and narcotics; medically, philosophically, and morally considered.   New York: G. P. Putnam, 1871.   155 pp.
   Presented to Concord Free Public Library, by Edward W. Emerson, Dec. 21, 1887 (Cameron, III, 866).

BEATTIE, JAMES.   The minstrel; or, The progress of genius, and other poems.   New York: R. & W. A. Bartow; Richmond, Va.: W. A. Bartow, 1821.   216 pp.
   Autograph and notes.

BEAUMONT, FRANCIS, AND FLETCHER, JOHN.   Comedies and tragedies.   Never printed before.   And now published by the authours originall copies...   London: Humphrey Robinson, 1647.
   Autograph.

——.   The works of Beaumont and Fletcher.   With an introduction by George Darley ...   A new ed.   London, New York: George Routledge, 1872.   2 v.

BECHSTEIN, LUDWIG.   ... Märchenbuch, mit 87 Holzschnitten nach Originalzeichnungen von Ludwig Richter.   2. illustrierte Ausg.   Leipzig: Georg Wigand, 1857.   xi, 345 pp.
   Autograph: Ellen T. Emerson.

BEDA VENERABILIS.   Ecclesiastical history of England.   Also the Anglo-Saxon Chronicle ...   Ed. by J. A. Giles ...   London: Henry G. Bohn, 1847.   xliv, 515 pp.
   Autograph.

BEECHER, CATHERINE ESTHER.   ... Domestic receipt book, designed as a supplement to her Treatise on domestic economy.   10th ed.   New York: Harper, 1852.   xiii, 306 pp.

——.   A treatise on domestic economy, for the use of young ladies at home, and at school.   Rev. ed., with numerous additions and illustrative engravings.   3d ed.   New York: Harper, 1851.   369 pp.
   Autographs.   Signature: Lydian J. Emerson.

BEECHER, EUNICE WHITE (BULLARD). "Mrs. Henry Ward Beecher." Motherly talks with young housekeepers, embracing eighty-seven brief articles on topics of home interest, and about five hundred choice receipts for cooking, etc. New York: J. B. Ford, 1873. xx, 492 pp.

BELKNAP, JEREMY. A discourse intended to commemorate the discovery of America by Christopher Columbus, delivered at the request of the Historical Society in Massachusetts, on the 23d day of October, 1792, being the completion of the third century since that memorable event. To which are added, four dissertations, connected with various parts of the discourse, viz: 1. On the circumnavigation of Africa by the ancients. 2. An examination of the pretensions of Martin Behaim to a discovery of America prior to that of Columbus, with a chronological detail of all discoveries made in the 15th century. 3. On the question, whether the honey-bee is a native of America? 4. On the colour of the native Americans and the recent population of this continent. Boston: Apollo Press, 1792. 132 pp.
Signature: Ezra Ripley, and R. W. Emerson from his grandfather (in R. W. E.'s hand).

BELL, SIR CHARLES. The hand, its mechanism and vital endowments, as evincing design. A new ed. Philadelphia: Carey, Lea & Blanchard, 1835. xii, 213 pp.
Signature: R. W. E., and notes.

BELL, ROBERT, *ed*. Songs from the dramatists. London: John W. Parker, 1854. xii, 268 pp.
Notes.

BENJAMIN, SAMUEL GREEN WHEELER. The Atlantic islands as resorts of health and pleasure. New York: Harper, 1878. 274 pp.

——. Contemporary art in Europe. New York: Harper, 1877. 165 pp.

BENNETT, WILLIAM COX. Poems. A new ed. London: Routledge, Warne, and Routledge, 1862. xvi, 533 pp.

——. Prometheus the fire-giver; an attempted restoration

of the lost first part of the Prometheian trilogy of
Aeschylus.   London: Chatto & Windus, 1877.   63 pp.
  Inscription.

———. ———. Copy 2.

BERNARD DE CLAIRVAUX, *Saint*.   La vie de S. Bernard, pre-
mier abbé de Clairvaux, et père de l'eglise.   Divisée en
six livres, [dont les trois premiers sont traduits du latin
de trois celebres abbez de son temps, & contiennent
l'histoire de sa vie.   Et les trois derniers sont tirez de
ses ouvrages, & representent son esprit et sa conduitte].
Paris: Antoine Vitré, 1648.   764 pp.

BERRIAN, WILLIAM, *comp.*   Officium eucharisticum: a pre-
paratory office for the holy communion, with suitable
prayers at the administtation thereof.   New York: James
A. Sparks, 1846.   151 pp.
  Inscription: For Miss Knickerbocker with Dr. Berrian's regards.

BERTOCCHI, FULVIA.   Raccolta di no. 100 soggetti li più
rimarchevoli dell'istoria Romana inventati ed incisi da
Bartolomeo Pinelli Romano illustrata da Fulvia Bertocchi.
Roma: Presso Vincenzo Poggioli stampatore della
R. C. A., 1821.   87 pp.

BETHUNE, GEORGE AMORY.   The uncertainties of travel; a
plain statement by a certain traveller.   Boston: Priv.
Print., 1880.   43 pp.

BEWICK, THOMAS.   A history of British birds.   Newcastle: J.
Blackwell, 1847.   2 v.

———.   A memoir of Thomas Bewick, written by himself.
Embellished by numerous wood engravings, designed and
engraved by the author for a work on British fishes, and
never before published.   Newcastle-on-Tyne: Jane
Bewick; London: Longman, Green, Longman, and Roberts,
1862.   xix, 344 pp.
  Inscription from a worker (Jane Bewick?).

Bhăgvăt-Geētă; or, Dialogues of Krĕĕshnă and Ărjŏŏn.   Tr.
by Charles Wilkins.   London, 1785.
  Autographed by Emerson on t.p.   After Emerson's death the

volume was given to W. H. Channing by Edward Emerson.   It
is now owned by Mr. Thomas W. Streeter, Morristown, N.J.
(Cameron, III, 857).

BIBLE. *English. 1739.*   The Holy Bible, containing the Old
and New Testaments: newly translated out of the original
tongues, and with the former translations diligently compared and revised.   By His Majesty's special command.
Appointed to be read in churches.   Oxford: John Baskett,
1739.   2 v.
   Autographs: v. 1, Hannah Bliss hers giv^e by fath, Josh^a
Loring; v. 2, Elizabeth Lombard, Frances Lombard.

——.   *1764.*   [The Holy Bible, containing the Old and New
Testaments.   Edinburgh? 1764?]   1 v.
   Autograph and notes.   The Bible of the Rev. W. Emerson,
first chaplain of the Revolutionary Army, who died at his post
in 1776.

——.   *1770.*   The Holy Bible, containing the Old and
New Testaments; newly translated out of the original
tongues, and with the former translations diligently
compared and revised, by His Majesty's special command.   Appointed to be read in churches.   Oxford:
T. Wright and W. Gill, 1770.   3 v. in 1.
   Autograph.
   Emerson genealogy, 1796–1906, verso of t.p. and leaves
inserted in New Testament.

——.   *1818.*   The Holy Bible, containing the Old and
New Testaments; translated out of the original
tongues, and with the former translations diligently
compared and revised.   Boston: R. P. & C. Williams, 1818.   690, 209 pp.

——.   *1845.*   The Holy Bible, containing the Old and
New Testaments; translated out of the original
tongues, and with the former translations diligently
compared and revised.   New York: American Bible
Society, 1845.   669 pp.

——.   *1856.*   The English version of the Polyglot
Bible; containing the Old and New Testaments. With
the marginal readings, together with a copious and

original selection of references to parallel and illustrative passages ...   Philadelphia: J. B. Lippincott, 1856.   viii, 824, 256, 77 pp.

———. *1869.*   The Holy Bible, containing the Old and New Testaments; translated out of the original tongues, and with the former translations diligently compared and revised.   32d ed.   New York: American Bible Society, 1869.   2 v. in 1 (1284 pp.).

———. *Selections. 1849.*   The hieroglyphical Bible with devotional pieces for youth.   Containing four hundred cuts, by [J. A.] Adams.   New York: J. C. Riker, 1849.   209 pp.
>   Autograph: Ellen T. Emerson.

———. *O. T. Greek. 1824. Septuagint.*   Ἡ Παλαια Διαθήκη κατὰ τουσ ʹεβδομήκοντα.   Sev Vetvs Testamentvm Graecvm ivxta septvaginta interpretes ex avctoritate Sixti qvinti pontificis maximi editvm. Ivxta exemplar originale Vaticanvm, Romae editvm MDLXXXVII, qvo ad textvm accvratissime et ad amvssim necvsvm cvra et stvdio Leandri van Ess ... Ed. stereotypa.   Lipsiae: Sumtibvs et typis Caroli Tavchnitii, 1824.   1022 pp.
>   Signature: R. W. Emerson.

———. *O. T. Selections. Latin. 1693.*   Genesis sive Mosis prophetae liber primus.   Ex translatione Joannis Clerici, cum ejusdem paraphrasi perpetua, commentario philologico, dissertationibus criticis quinque et tabulis chronologicis.   Amstelodami: Abrahamum Wolfgangum, & Janssonio-Waesbergias, 1693.   568 pp.
>   Autograph: 1825.

———. *O. T. Apocrypha. English.* [18—?]   The Apocrypha according to the authorized version.   Oxford: University Press, [18—?].   [232] pp.
>   Inscription.

———. *O. T. Historical books. Latin. 1708.*   Veteris Testamenti libri historici, Josua, Judices, Rutha,

Samuel, Reges, Paralipomena, Esdnas, Nehemias et
Esthera; ex translatione Joannis Clerici; cum
ejusdem commentario philologico, dissertationibus
criticis, et tabulis chronologicis.   Amstelodami:
Apud Henricum Schelte, 1708.   720 pp.
   Autograph.

———. *O. T. Poetical books. Latin.* *1731.*   Veteris
Testamenti libri hagiographi, Jobus, Davidis Psalmi,
Salomonis Proverbia, Concionatrix & Canticum
Canticorum, ex translatione Joannis Clerici; cum
ejusdem commentario philologico in omnes memoratos
libros, et paraphrasi in Jobum ac Psalmos.
Amstelaedami: Apud R. & J. Wetstenios & G. Smith,
1731.   750 pp.
   Autograph.

———. *O. T. Prophets. Latin.* *1731.*   Veteris
Testamenti Prophetae, ab Esaia ad Malachiam usque,
ex translatione Joannis Clerici; cum ejusdem commentario philologico et paraphrasi in Esaiam,
Jeremiam, ejus Lamentationes et Abdiam; disserta-
tione Joh. Smith De prophetia et ipsius auctoris De
poesi Hebraeorum.   Amstelaedami: R. & J.
Wetstenios & Gul. Smith, 1731.   xxix, 632 pp.
   Autograph.

———. *O. T. Psalms. English.* *1741.*   The Psalms,
hymns, and spiritual songs of the Old and New
Testament, faithfully translated into English metre,
for the use, edification, and comfort of the saints in
publik and private, especially in New-England ...
18th ed.   London: F. Osborn, and T. Longman, 1741.
90 pp.
   Bound with: The Holy Bible.   Oxford, 1739.

———. *1831.*   A new translation of the book of Psalms,
with an introduction, by George R. Noyes.   Boston:
Gray and Bowen, 1831.   xxviii, 232 pp.
   Inscription by Ellen T. Emerson July 1887.

———. *1840.*   The book of Psalms, translated out of

the original Hebrew, and with the former translations diligently compared and revised. New York, 1840. 112 pp.

Bound with: The New Testament. New York, 1840.

———. *O. T. Pseud. 1713.* Codex pseudepigraphus Veteris Testamenti, collectus castigatus, testimoniisque, censuris & animadversionibus illustratus à Johanne Alberto Fabricio ... Hamburgi: Sumptu Christiani Liebezeit, 1713. Vol. 1 only.

Inscription and autograph: R. Waldo Emerson from his brother Wm.

———. *N. T. Gospels. English. 1811.* The four Gospels, translated from the Greek. With preliminary dissertations, and notes critical and explanatory, by George Campbell ... With the author's last corrections ... Boston: W. Wells, and Thomas B. Wait, 1811. 4 v.

Bookplate of Isaac Hurd, 1812.
Inscription: v. 1, gift of J. H. to R. W. E., 1812.

———. *1820.* A translation of the New Testament, by Gilbert Wakefield. From the 2d London ed. Cambridge: Hilliard and Metcalf, 1820. 2 v.

Autographs: v. 1, signature and quotation from Goethe in hand of R. W. E.; v. 2, notes and signature of R. W. E.

———. *1827.* The New Testament of Our Lord and Savior Jesus Christ, tr. out of the original Greek and with the former translations diligently compared and revised. [5th ed.] Stereotyped by Baker & Greele, Boston. New York: American Bible Society, 1827. 315 pp.

Signature: E. T. Emerson.

———. *1828.* The New Testament in the common version conformed to Griesbach's standard Greek text. Boston: Boston Daily Advertiser, 1828. [402] pp.

Signature: R. W. E.

———. *1840.* The New Testament of Our Lord and Saviour Jesus Christ, tr. out of the original Greek, and with the former translations diligently compared

and revised. [5th ed.] New-York: Redfield &
Lindsay, 1840. 431 pp.
　　Autograph. Signature: Fanny Haskins.

——. *1881*. The New Testament of Our Lord and
Savior Jesus Christ, tr. out of the Greek, being the
version set forth A.D. 1611, compared with the most
ancient authorities and revised A.D. 1881. Printed
for the Universities of Oxford and Cambridge. Oxford: University Press, 1881. xviii, 332 pp.

——. *French*. Le nouveau testament de notre
seigneur Jésus-Christ. Paris: Institution biblique-
catholique, [18—?]. 584 pp.

——. *Greek*. *Selections*. *1716*. Ἡ Καινὴ Διαθήκη.
Novum Testamentum, in quo tum selecti versiculi
1900, quibus omnes Novi Testamenti voces con-
tinentur, asteriscis notantur; tum omnes & singulae
voces, semel vel saepius occurrentes, peculiari nota
distinquuntur. Auctore Johanne Leusden, profes-
sore. Lugduni Batavorum: Sumptibus societatis,
1716. 504 pp.
　　Autographs.

——. *1798*. Novvm Testamentvm Graece perpetva
annotatione illvstratvm. Editionis Koppianae.
Vol. VII. Gottingae: Io. Christian Dieterich, 1798-
1803. 2 v. in 1.
　　Pte. 2 published by Henricum Dieterich.
　　Contents:—[pte. 1] Complectens epistolas Pavlli ad
Timothevm Titvm et Philemon.—[pte. 2] Complectens
epistolas Pavlli ad Philippenses et Colossenses.

——. *1800*. Ἡ Καινὴ Διαθήκη. Novum Testamentum
... Editio prima Americana. Wigorniae, Mass.:
Isaias Thomas, Jun., 1800. 478 pp.
　　Copy of first American edition of the New Testament in
Greek given to Emerson by his half-uncle, D. B. Ripley,
in 1813. Emerson's autograph, dated 1816, beneath which
he has written "Harvard University, 1817."
　　Now owned by George Goodspeed of Boston, Mass.
(Cameron, III, 856).

——. 'Η Καινὴ Διαθήκη.   Novum Testamentum
Graece ex recensione Jo. Jac. Griesbachii cum
selecta lectionum varietate.   Tom. II, Pars II.
Lipsiae: Sumptibus G. J. Göschen, 1806.   pp. 535-
615.
Signature: W. Emerson.

——. *1809.* 'Η Καινὴ Διαθήκη.   Novum Testamentum
Graece, ex recensione Jo. Jac. Griesbachii cum
selecta lectionum varietate ...   Lipsiae: Sumtibus
G. J. Göschen, 1809.   2 v. in 1.
Autograph: R. W. Emerson.

——. *1810.*   Novvm Testamentvm Graece perpetva
annotatione illustratvm.   Editionis Koppianae.
Vol. IX.   Complectens epistolas catholicas.
Fascicvl. II.   Exhibens vtramqve epistolam Petri.
Continvavit Davides Ivlivs Pott ...   Edito altera.
Göttingae: Henrici Dieterich, 1810.
Bound with: Fasc. 1, 1816.

——. *1816.*   Novvm Testamentvm Graece perpetva
annotatione illvstratvm.   Editionis Koppianae.
Vol. IX.   Complectens epistolas catholicas.
Fascicvl. 1.   Exhibens epistolam Iacobi.
Continvavit D. Davides Ivlivs Pott.   Editio tertia
avctior et emendatior.   Göttingae: Henricvm
Dieterich, 1816.   viii, 355 pp.
Signature: R. W. Emerson.

——. *1823.*   Novum Testamentum Graece perpetua
annotatione illustratum a Io. Beniam Koppe ...
Vol. VI.   Complectens epistolas Pauli ad Galatas
Ephesios Thessalonicenses.   Edit. Tertia emendata
et aucta curavit Th. Chr. Tychsen.   Göttingae:
Henricum Dieterich, 1823.   xx, 460 pp.
Signature: R. W. Emerson.

——. *1823.*   Novvm Testamentvm Graece.   Perpetva
annotatione illvstratvm.   Editionis Koppianae.
Vol. VIII.   Complectens epistolam Pavlli ad
Hebraeos.   Continvavit Ioannes Henricvs Heinrichs
...   Editio altera auctior passim et emendatior.

Göttingae: Henricvm Dieterich, 1823. xxii, 255 pp.
2 signatures: R. W. Emerson.

——. *1824.* Novvm Testamentvm Graece. Perpetva
adnotatione illvstratvm a Ioh. Beniamin Koppe.
Volvmen IV. Complectens epistolam Pavli ad
Romanos. Editionem tertiam. Novis observa-
tionibvs et excvrsibvs avctam, cvravit Christophorvs
Fridericvs Ammon. Göttingae: Dieterichianis, 1824.
415 pp.
Signature: R. W. Emerson.

——. *1824.* Novum Testamentum. Textum Graecum
Griesbachii et Knappii denuo recognovit, delectu
varietatum lectionis testimoniis confirmatarum,
adnotatione cum critica tum exegetica et indicibus
historico et geographico, vocum Graecarum infre-
quentiorum, et subsidiorum criticorum exegetico-
rumque instruxit Joannes Severinus Vater ... Halis
Saxonum: Gebaueriana, 1824. vi, 835 pp.
Signature: R. W. Emerson.

[BIDDLE, HORACE PETERS.] Glances at the world, 1864–
1865, by Hieronymus Anonymous [pseud.] ...
Mundus: Cadmus Faustus, 5874 [i.e. 1866?]. 141 pp.
Ms. note on t.p.: Logansport, Indiana.

[——.] Glances at the world, by Hieronymus Anonymous [pseud.] ... Mundus: Cadmus Faustus, 5878
[i.e. 1873?]. 371 pp.

Black anthology.
Emerson's will, drawn April 14, 1876, leaves to his
daughter Edith the book of selections "known in my family
as the 'Black Anthology' " (Cameron, III, 858).

BLAIR, HUGH. Lectures on rhetoric and belles lettres.
Emerson lists this as a book which he lent to one of his
Harvard classmates in 1821 (Cameron, III, 856).

BLAKE, WILLIAM. Songs of innocence and of experience, shewing the two contrary states of the human
soul. London: W. Pickering, and W. Newbery, 1839.
xxi, 74 pp.
Inscription and notes in Emerson's hand: R. W. Emerson
from his friend E. P. P.

[BLAND, EDITH (NESBIT) "MRS. HERBERT BLAND."] The lily and the cross.   New York: G. P. Dutton; London: Griffith, Farran, Okeden & Welsh, [18—?]. [16] pp.

The blessed hope ...   London: Williams and Norgate, [1881].   viii, 236 pp.
  Inscription inserted and note.

BLOCK, LOUIS JAMES.   Exile, a dramatic episode.   St. Louis: G. I. Jones, 1880.   120 pp.
  Inscription: 22 July 1880.

BLODGET, LORIN.   The commercial and financial strength of the United States, as shown in the balances of foreign trade and the increased production of staple articles.   Philadelphia: King & Baird, [1865].   56 pp.

BLOEDE, GERTRUDE.   Poems, by Stuart Sterne [pseud.]. New York: Nich. Muller, 1874.   x, 244 pp.

BLOOD, BENJAMIN PAUL.   The anaesthetic revelation and the gist of philosophy ...   Amsterdam, N. Y., 1874.   37 pp.

[_____.]   The bride of the iconoclast, a poem.   Suggestions toward the mechanical art of verse.   Boston: J. Munroe, 1854.   131 pp.

BOCCACCIO, GIOVANNI.   The decameron; or, Ten day's entertainment, of Boccaccio, tr. from the Italian. To which are prefixed, remarks on the life and writings of Boccaccio [by E. Dubois] and an advertisement, by the author of Old Nick, a piece of family biography, etc.   London: J. F. Dove, 1820.   579 pp.
  Notes.

_____.   Vita di Dante Alighieri.   Milano: Giovanni Silvestri, 1823.   126 pp.
  Autograph and note.

BODENSTEDT, FRIEDRICH MARTIN VON.   Die Lieder des Mirza-Schaffy [pseud.] mit einem Prolog von Friedrich Bodenstedt.   6. Aufl.   Berlin: Koniglichen Geheimen Oberhofbuchdruckerei, 1859.   xxiv, 200 pp.

BOEHME, JAKOB.   The remainder of books written by
Jacob Behme viz. I. The first apologie to Balthazac
Tylcken ... II. The second apologie in answer to
Balthazar Tylcken ...   III. The fouer complexions
...   IV. The considerations upon Esaiah Stiefels
booke ... V. The apologie in answer to Esaiah
Stiefel ...   VI. The apologie in answer to Gregory
Rickter ... VII. Twenty-five epistles ...   Eng-
lished by John Sparrow.   London: Giles Calvert,
1662.   various pagings.
> Inscription: From W. B. Green.

———.   The works of Jacob Behmen, the Teutonic
theosopher ...   To which is prefixed, the life of
the author.   With figures, illustrating his Principles,
left by William Low.   London: M. Richardson, 1764.
4 v.
> Autographs.

BOLINGBROKE, HENRY SAINT-JOHN.   The works of the late
Rt. Hon. Henry St. John, Lord Viscount Bolingbroke.
London: Daniel Mallet, 1754.   5 v.
> Autographs of William Emerson.

BONER, CHARLES.   The new dance of death and other
poems.   London: Chapman and Hall, 1857.   50 pp.

Book of worship, for the congregation and the home,
taken principally from the Old and New Testaments.
8th ed.   Boston: Crosby, Nichols; New York:
Charles S. Francis, 1858.   viii, 174, iv, 476 pp.
> Inscription: Ellen from her Mother, Jan. 1, 1859.

[BOOTH, DAVID.]   The art of brewing.   [London, 1829?]
64 pp.   Bound with: [Needham, M.]   On the manufacture of iron.   [London, 1831.]

BOREL, THÉODORE.   Le comte Agénor de Gasparin.
6. éd.   Paris: J. Bonhoure, 1879.   xi, 152 pp.
> Printed presentation slip.

BORROW, GEORGE HENRY.   Lavengro, the scholar, the
gipsy, the priest.   New York: G. P. Putnam, 1851.
> Signature: pt. 1, R. W. Emerson; pt. 2, R. W. E.

———. The Romany Rye; a sequel to "Lavengro."
New York: Harper, 1857. 141 pp.
Autograph.

———. The Zincali; or, An account of the gypsies of
Spain. With an original collection of their songs
and poetry. New-York: Wiley and Putnam, 1842.
2 v. in 1.
Inscription: From Thomas Delff.

BOSSU, JEAN BERNARD. Nouveaux voyages aux Indes
occidentales, contenant une relation des différens
peuples que habitent les environs du grand Fleuve
Saint-Louis, appellé vulgairement le Mississipi [sic],
leur religion; leur governement; leur moeurs; leur
guerres, & leur commerce. Amsterdam: D. J.
Changuion, 1769. 2 v. in 1.
Inscription: T. Carlyle (Chelsea) to R. W. Emerson
(Concord) in Carlyle's hand.

BOSSUET, JACQUES BENIGNE. Discours sur l'histoire
universelle; dupuis le commencement du monde
jusqu'à l'empire de Charlemagne ... Éd. stéréotype. Paris: Didot, 1803. 2 v.
Autographs: C. C. Emerson.

BOSTON. CITY COUNCIL. Celebration of the centennial
anniversary of the battle of Bunker Hill. With an
appendix containing a survey of the literature of the
battle, its antecedents and results. Boston, 1875.
174 pp.

———. ... Celebration of the centennial anniversary of
the evacuation of Boston by the British Army, March
17th, 1776. Reception of the Washington medal.
Oration delivered in Music Hall, and chronicle of the
siege of Boston, by George E. Ellis. Boston, 1876.
vi, 199 pp.

———. A memorial of Charles Sumner, from the city of
Boston ... Boston, 1874. 162 pp.

———. CHURCH OF THE DISCIPLES. Memorial of the
commemoration by the Church of the Disciples of the

fiftieth birth-day of their pastor, James Freeman
Clarke, April 4, 1860 ...   Boston: Prentiss &
Deland, 1860.   47 pp.

_____. FIRST CHURCH.   The commemoration by the First
Church in Boston of the completion of two hundred
and fifty years since its foundation, on Thursday,
November 18, 1880.   Also four historical sermons
...   Printed by order of the Society.   Boston: Hall
and Whiting, 1881.   xx, 218 pp.

_____. KING'S CHAPEL.   A liturgy collected for the use
of the church at King's Chapel, Boston ...   2d ed.,
with some alterations and additions.   Boston:
Joshua Belcher, 1811.   360 pp.
     On cover: Rev. Ezra Ripley, stamped in gold.

_____. PUBLIC LIBRARY.   ... A chronological index to
historical fiction including prose fiction, plays and
poems.   2d and enl. ed.   Boston, [1875].   iv,
32 pp.

BOSTON ATHENAEUM. LIBRARY.   Catalogue, 1807-1871
...   Boston, 1874-82.   5 v.

The Boston directory, embracing the city record, a general directory.   No. 71, for the year commencing
July 1, 1875.   Boston: Sampson, Davenport, [1875].
1408 pp.

BOSTON FEMALE ANTI-SLAVERY SOCIETY.   Report, with a
concise statement of events, previous and subsequent
to the annual meeting of 1835.   2d ed.   Boston,
1836.   108 pp.
     Cover title: Right and wrong.

The Boston medical and surgical journal.   Ed. by F. E.
Oliver.   Whole no. 1707, v. 63, no. 15, Thursday,
Nov. 8, 1860.   [Boston.] pp. 289-308.

BOSTON SOCIETY FOR THE DIFFUSION OF USEFUL KNOW-
LEDGE.   The American library of useful knowledge.
Published by authority of the Boston Society for the
Diffusion of Useful Knowledge.   Vol. 1.   Con-

taining Judge Story's, Mr. Wilisten's, and Mr.
Everett's lectures before the Mechanics' Institution
... Boston: Stimpson and Clapp, 1831.   320 pp.
  Autograph and notes.

BOSTON SOCIETY OF THE NEW JERUSALEM.   New Jerusalem
  tracts ... [no. 1-6.]   Boston: Allen and Goddard,
  1831.   6 nos. in 1 v.
    Contents:—Concerning the rich and poor in heaven.—
    That heaven consists of innumerable societies.—That
    there is a correspondence of heaven with all things of
    earth.—What the world of spirits is.—That the Lord rules
    the hells.—Concerning infants in heaven.

BOSWELL, JAMES.   The life of Samuel Johnson, comprehending an account of his studies, and numerous
  works, in chronological order; a series of his epistolary correspondence and conversations with many
  eminent persons; and various original pieces of his
  composition, never before published; the whole exhibiting a view of literature and literary men in Great
  Britain, for nearly half a century during which he
  flourished.   With copious notes and biographical illustrations, by Malone.   London: Jones & Co., 1827.
  ix, 580 pp.
    Autograph and notes.

BOTTA, ANNE CHARLOTTE (LYNCH).   Hand-book of universal literature, from the best and latest authorities.
  4th ed.   Boston: Ticknor and Fields, 1864.   xviii,
  567 pp.

BOUTELLE, ANN L.   Biographical sketch of Ann L.
  Boutelle.   Boston: Benjamin H. Greene, 1836.
  35 pp.

BOUTWELL, GEORGE SEWALL.   Reconstruction; speech of
  Hon. George S. Boutwell, of Massachusetts, in the
  House of Representatives, January 17, 1868.
  [Washington: Printed at the Congressional Globe
  Office, 1868.]   8 pp.
    Concerns House bill H. R. no. 439.

BOVEE, CHRISTIAN NESTELL. Intuitions and summaries of thought. Cambridge: Riverside Press, 1862 2 v.
Letter from author laid in, front of v. 1.

BOWDITCH, NATHANIEL. XXXII. An estimate of the height, direction, velocity and magnitude of the meteor, that exploded over Weston in Connecticut, December 14, 1807. With methods of calculating observations made on such bodies. [N.p., n.d.] pp. 213-245.
Apparently an article from a periodical. With this are two other articles numbered XXXIII and XXXIV: Analysis of sculpture of barytes, from Hatfield, Massachusetts, by John Corham, and Investigation of the apparent motion of the earth viewed from the moon, arising from the moon's librations, by James Dean.

BOWEN, ELI. The pictorial sketch-book of Pennsylvania; or, Its scenery, internal improvements, resources, and agriculture, popularly described. [1st ed.] Philadelphia: W. P. Hazard, 1852. 192 pp.

BOWLES, EMILY. In the Camargue. Boston: Loring, [1877]. 279 pp.

[BOWMAN, JAMES F.] The island home; or, The young castaways. Ed. by Christopher Romaunt [pseud.] Boston: Gould and Lincoln, 1852. xviii, 461 pp.

Boys' and girls' magazine and fireside companion. Ed. by Mrs. S[amuel] Colman ... [v. 2, 3, Aug., Oct. 1843.] Boston: T. H. Carter. pp. 253-287.

BRACKETT, ANNA CALLENDER. The education of American girls, considered in a series of essays. New York: G. P. Putnam's Sons, 1874. 401 pp.

BRADFORD, SAMUEL. Some incidents in the life of Samuel Bradford, Senior, by his son. Also, the autobiography or a brief narrative of the life of Samuel Bradford, Junior, to January 1, 1879. Printed, not published. Philadelphia, 1880. 79 pp.
Clipping inserted at p. 27. Inscription, May 1880.

BRADFORD, SARAH ELIZABETH (HOPKINS) "Mrs. J. M. Bradford." Scenes from the life of Harriet Tubman. Auburn, [N. Y.]: W. J. Moses, 1869. 132 pp.

BRAY, CHARLES. A manual of anthropology; or, Science of man, based on modern research. London: Longmans, Green, Reader and Dyer, 1871. xxiii, 358 pp.

——. The philosophy of necessity; or, Natural law as applicable to moral, mental, and social science. 2d ed., rev. London: Longman, Green, Longman & Roberts, 1863. viii, 446 pp.

BREMER, FREDRIKA. The bondmaid. Tr. from the Swedish by M. L. Putnam. Boston: James Munroe, 1844. vi, 112 pp.
> Inscription: From author to Mrs. Emerson, 1850.

BREWSTER, SIR DAVID. The life of Sir Isaac Newton. New York: J. & J. Harper, 1831. 323 pp.
> Autograph and notes.

BRIDGMAN, MARCUS FAYETTE. Mosses. Boston: A. Williams, 1877. 86 pp.

BRIDGMAN, WILLIAM, *tr.* Translations from the Greek, viz. Aristotle's synopsis of the virtues and vices, the similitudes of Demophilus, the golden sentences of Democrates, and the Pythagoric symbols with the explanations of Jamblichus. To which are added the Pythagoric sentences of Demophilus by Thomas Taylor ... London: R. Wilks [etc.], 1804. xvi, 135 pp.
> Autograph.

BRILLAT-SAVARIN, JEAN ANTHELME. Physiologie du goût; ou, Méditations de gastronomie, et à l'ordre du jour, dédié aux gastronomes parisiens, avec une notice sur l'auteur, édition accompagnée des ouvrages suivants, traité des excitants modernes par H. de Balzac. Anecdotes et fragments d'histoire culinaire par des amateurs. Pensées et préceptes, recueillis par un philosophe. Recettes et formules

par un Cordon-blue.   La gastronomie, poème, par
Berchoux.   L'art de diner en ville, poème, par
Colnet.   Paris: Charpentier, 1853.   xi, 525 pp.

BRITISH MUSEUM. DEPT. OF GREEK AND ROMAN ANTIQ-
UITIES.   Elgin and Phigaleian marbles.   London:
Charles Knight, 1833.   2 v.

BROCKIE, WILLIAM.   Indian philosophy, introductory
paper.   London: Trübner, 1872.   25 pp.

BRODRICK, GEORGE CHARLES.   English land and English
landlords; an enquiry into the origin and character of
the English land system, with proposals for its reform.   London: Pub. for the Cobden Club by Cassell,
Petter, Galpin, 1881.   viii, 515 pp.

BROOKE, HENRY.   Redemption, a poem.   A new ed.
London: Briscoe, 1817.   24 pp.
   Bound with: Lane, Charles.   A classification of sci-
   ence and arts ...   London, 1826.

The brothers; or, Consequences, a story of what happens
every day.   With an account of savings banks.
[Cambridge]: Hilliard and Metcalf, 1823.   63 pp.
   Bound with: The classical journal.   1830–31.

BROUGHAM, JOHN, AND ELDERKIN, John, *eds*.   Lotos
leaves: original stories, essays and poems by White-
law Reid, Wilkie Collins, Mark Twain, John Hay,
John Brougham ... and Alfred Tennyson ...   Boston: W. F. Gill, 1875.   xv, 411 pp.

[BROUGHAM AND VAUX, HENRY PETER BROUGHAM, *1st
Baron*.]   An account of Lord Bacon's Novum organon
scientiarum; or, New method of studying the sciences.   The first, or introductory part.   [London,
18—?]   40 pp.
————.   ————.   Copy 2.
   Copy imperfect: pp. 17–40 wanting.

BROWN, HOWARD NICHOLSON.   Sunday stories.   Boston:
Lockwood, Brooks, 1879.   220 pp.

BROWN, LEONARD.   Poems of the prairies.   3d ed.   Des
Moines: Mills, 1879.   viii, 68 pp.

[BROWN, SAMUEL.]   Art. V–1. Of man, six monograms:
by David Scott, S. A. Edinburg, ... 1831. 2. The
rime of the ancient mariner, illustrated, &c., by
David Scott .... Edinburgh and London, 1837.
[n.p., n.d., of article.]   pp. 133–157.
> Apparently an article extracted from a periodical.

BROWN, THEO.   Extracts from the letters of Theo.
Brown.   Worcester: Putnam & Davis, 1879.   iv,
106 pp.
> Letter from Mrs. Brown laid in at p. 73.

BROWN, THOMAS.   Lectures on the philosophy of the
human mind.   Philadelphia: John Grigg; Charleston,
S. C.: William P. Bason, W. Brown, 1824.   3 v.
> Set incomplete: v. 2–3 wanting.

[BROWNE, ALBERT GALLATIN.]   In memoriam, J. W. B.
[i.e. John White Browne].   Boston: Crosby,
Nichols, Lee, 1860.   iv, 90 pp.
> Inscription, R. W. E. from C. C. Shackford.

BROWNE, SIR THOMAS.   Christian morals.   2d ed.
With a life of the author, by Samuel Johnson, and explanatory notes.   London: Richard Hett, 1756.   lxi,
136 pp.

——.   Miscellaneous works.   With some account of
the author and his writing.   Cambridge: Hilliard
and Brown, 1831.   xxxii, 304 pp.
> Autograph.

——.   Religio medici, a letter to a friend, Christian
morals, Urn-burial, and other papers.   Boston:
Ticknor and Fields, 1862.   xviii, 432 pp.
> Inscription: Mr. Emerson with the editors sincere re-
> gards   Jan. 1st 1862, and notes.

——.   ... Religio medici, letter to a friend, &c., and
Christian morals, ed. by W. A. Greenhill ...   London: Macmillan, 1881.   lvi, 392 pp.
> Notes.

———. Works, including his life and correspondence;
ed. by Simon Wilkin ... London: W. Pickering,
1835–36 [v. 1: 1836]. 4 v.
>Inscription: R. Waldo Emerson, the gift of Concord
friends, 1839 (in Emerson's hand), and notes. Autograph
in v. 2.

[BROWNELL, HENRY HOWARD.] Lyrics of a day; or,
Newspaper-poetry, by a volunteer in the U. S. Service. 2d ed. New York: Carleton, 1864. ix, 192 pp.
>Inscription and notes.

BROWNING, ELIZABETH (BARRETT). Aurora Leigh. [Au-
thor's ed.] New York: C. S. Francis, 1857.
366 pp.
>Inscription deleted: Dec. 1856.

BROWNING, ROBERT. Men and women. Boston: Ticknor
and Fields, 1856. v, 351 pp.
>Autograph.

———. Poems. New ed. Boston: Ticknor and
Fields, 1859. 2 v.
>Autographs and notes.

BRUCE, WALLACE. The land of Burns. Illustrated by
James D. Smillie. Boston: Lee and Shepard; New
York: C. T. Dillingham, 1879.

BRUNO, GIORDANO. Opere di Giordano Bruno Nolano,
ora per la prima volta raccolte e pubblicate da Adolfo
Wagner ... Lipsia: Weidmann, 1830. 2 v.
>Autograph.

BRYANT, JOHN HOWARD. Poems. New York: D. Appleton, 1855. vi, 93 pp.
>Inscription: 18 Jan. 1866.

BRYANT, WILLIAM CULLEN. The embargo; or, Sketches
of the times, a satire. 2d ed., cor. and enl. Together with The Spanish revolution, and other poems.
Boston: E. G. House, 1809. 35 pp.
>Inscription: From P. Bryant to E. H. Mills.

———. Poems. New-York: E. Bliss, 1832. 240 pp.
>Autograph and notes.

BRYCE, JAMES BRYCE.   The Holy Roman Empire.   3d
ed., rev.   London: Macmillan, 1871.   xxvii, 424 pp.
Inscription.

BUCKMINSTER, JOSEPH STEVENS.   A sermon, delivered at
the interment of the Rev. William Emerson, pastor of
the First Church of Christ in Boston, who died May
12, 1811, in the forty-third year of his age.   Boston:
Joseph T. Buckingham, 1811.   24 pp.
Autograph: C. C. Emerson.

BULKELEY, PETER.   The Gospel-covenant; or, The
covenant of grace opened ...   Published according to order.   London: B. Allen, 1646.
432 pp.
Inscription: R. W. Emerson the gift of George F. Hoar
(in R. W. E.'s hand), and notes.

[BUNKER HILL MONUMENT ASSOCIATION.]   Circular, Sep-
tember 20, 1824.   [Boston, 1824.]   8 pp.
Bound with: Webster, Daniel.   A discourse delivered at
Plymouth, December 22, 1820 ...   Boston, 1826.

———.   Proceedings of the annual meeting, June 23,
1875, with the oration of Hon. Charles Devens, Jr.,
and an account of the centennial celebration, June
17, 1875.   Boston, 1875.   viii, 216 pp.
Inscription: To R. W. E. by Wm. H. Wheildon.

BUNN, MARGARET AGNES (SOMERVILLE).   A preliminary
dissertation on the mechanism of the heavens.
Philadelphia: Carey & Lea, 1832.   134 pp.
Autograph: R. W. Emerson 1832.

BUNYAN, JOHN.   Grace abounding to the chief of sinners,
Heart's ease in heart trouble, The world to come; or,
Visions of Heaven and Hell, and The barren fig-tree.
London: J. F. Dove, 1827.   viii, 408 pp.
Notes.

———.   The pilgrim's progress from this world to that
which is to come, delivered under the similitude of a
dream.   New York: American Tract Society, [184—?].
603 pp.
Autograph: Edward Waldo Emerson, July 10, 1856.

BUONARROTI, MICHEL ANGELO. Rime di Michelagnolo Buonarroti il vecchio, col comento di G. Biagioli. Parigi: Presso l'editore, 1821. xliv, 405 pp.
Autograph.

———. Rime e lettere di Michelagnolo Buonarroti; precedute dalla vita dell'autore scritta da Ascano Condivi. Firenze: G. Barbèra, 1860. xvii, 459 pp.

BURBIDGE, THOMAS, AND CLOUGH, ARTHUR H. Ambarvalia, poems. London: Chapman and Hall; Oxford: Francis Macpherson, 1849. 155 pp.
Autograph and markings.

BURBURY, MRS. E. J. How to spend a week happily. London: Darton & Hodge, 1864. 140 pp.
Autograph: Ellen T. Emerson.

BURKE, EDMUND. The beauties of Burke, consisting of selections from his works, by Alfred Howard. London: T. Davison. 211 pp.

———. Philosophical enquiry into the origin of our ideas of the sublime and beautiful, with an introductory discourse concerning taste. London: J. F. Dove, 1827. iv, 172 pp.
Autograph: C. C. Emerson.

———. Reflections on the Revolution in France. v. 2. London: [John Sharpe], 1820. 177 pp.
Autograph: Charles C. Emerson, 1826.

———. Works. Reprinted from the last London ed. Boston: Wells and Lilly, 1826-27. 7 v.
Autographs and notes.

BURKHARDT, CHARLES B. Fairy tales and legends of many nations, selected, newly told, and tr. Illus. by Walcutt, Cafferty, and others. New York: James Miller, 1847. 302 pp.

BURNHAM, BENJAMIN FRANKLIN. The martyr-crisis, a poem. Chicago: D. B. Cooke, 1861.
Inscription by the author.

BURNS, ROBERT. Poetical works. With the author's life, written by himself ... Philadelphia: Benjamin

Johnson, Jacob Johnson, & Robert Johnson, 1804.
2 v.

BURROUGHS, JOHN.   Notes on Walt Whitman, as a poet
and person.   2d ed.   New York: J. S. Redfield,
1871.   126 pp.

BURTON, ROBERT.   The anatomy of melancholy ... by
Democritus Junior [pseud.] ...   11th ed. cor.   To
which is now first prefixed, an account of the au-
thor.   London: J. & E. Hodson, 1804.   3 v.
  Set incomplete: v. 2-3 wanting.
  Autograph and notes.

————.   ————.   A new ed., corrected, and enriched by
translations of the numerous classical extracts, by
Democritus Junior [pseud.].   Boston: William
Vlazie, 1859.   3 v.
  Inscription: v. 1, R. W. Emerson with affectionate re-
  gards of E. Channing, Oct. 1860, and notes, v. 1, 3.

BURTON, WARREN.   The scenery-shower, with word paint-
ings of the beautiful, the picturesque, and the grand
in nature.   Boston: W. D. Ticknor, 1844.   119 pp.
  Inscription.

BUSHNELL, HORACE.   Sermons for the new life.   2d ed.
New York: Charles Scribner, 1858.   vi, 456 pp.
  Inscription: To Lydia Emerson by Russell.

————.   Views of Christian nurture, and of subjects ad-
jacent thereto.   Hartford: E. Hunt, 1847.   251 pp.
  Autograph: Hawthorne.

Business.   Edinburgh, 1873.
  Presented to the Concord Free Public library by Ralph
  Waldo Emerson in Feb. 1874. Withdrawn from circulation
  in 1917 (Cameron, III, 866).

BUTLER, DAVID P.   System of physical training.   The
lifting cure: an original, scientific application of the
laws of motion or mechanical action to physical
culture and the cure of disease.   With a discussion
of true and false methods of physical training ...
Boston, 1868.   104 pp.
  Inscription by author.

BUTLER, JOSEPHINE ELIZABETH (GRAY). The new abolitionists, a narrative of a year's work. Being an account of the mission undertaken to the continent of Europe, and of the events subsequent thereupon. Published under the direction of the British, Continental, and General Federation for the Abolition of Government Regulation of Prostitution. London: Dyer Bros., 1876. vii, 237 pp.

BUTLER, SAMUEL. Poetical works ... Boston: Little, Brown, 1853. 2 v.
> Autographs.

——. An atlas of ancient geography. Philadelphia: Lea & Blanchard, 1844. 34 pp.
> Autograph: Ellen T. Emerson, Aug. 21, 1847.

BUXTON, SIR THOMAS FOWELL. Memoirs. With selections from his correspondence. Ed. by his son, Charles Buxton ... London: J. Murray, 1848. xvi, 600 pp.
> Inscription: From W. E. Forster, 15 July 1848.

BYRON, GEORGE GORDON. Childe Harold's pilgrimage.
> Lent by Emerson in 1821 to one of his classmates at Harvard. "Probably a two-volume edition, the second volume of which contained Cantos 3 and 4" (Cameron, III, 856).

——. Heaven and earth. Prelude to an unpublished lyrical drama entitled "Adam and Eve, a new Paradise lost." [London, 18—?] 57 pp.
> Inscription: Ralph Waldo Emerson with reverent admiration of Virginia Vaughn. March 18, 1876. London.

——. The life, letters and journals of Lord Byron, by Thomas Moore ... New and complete ed., with portraits and illus. London: John Murray, 1860. xix, 735 pp.
> Autograph.

——. Works, including the suppressed poems. Also a sketch of his life, by J. W. Lake ... Philadelphia: R. W. Pomeroy and Henry Adams, 1829. 716 pp.
> Autograph, and notes on inside back cover.

C

Cabinetsbibliothek der deutschen Classiker ... Hildburghausen, Neu-York: Bibliographischen Instituts,
1829. [464] pp.
    Each pt. separately paged with special t.p.

_____. Anthologie aus den Werken Jean Paul's. 1.
Bd. Hildburghausen, Neu-York: Bibliographischen
Institut, 1829. 108 pp.
    Autograph: Lydian Jackson.

CABOT, JAMES ELLIOT. Discovery of America by the
Norsemen. 30 pp.
    Ascribed to Cabot by Emerson.
    Inscription.

CADET DE GASSICOURT, CHARLES LOUIS. The tomb of
James Molai; or, The secret of the conspirators.
Tr. by a gentleman of Boston. Addressed to those
who wish to know everything. Boston: Benjamin
Edes, 1797. 22 pp.

CAESAR, JULIUS. Commentaries on the Gallic and civil
wars, with supplementary books attributed to Hirtius,
including the Alexandrian, African, and Spanish
wars. Literally tr. [by W. A. McDevitte and W. S.
Bohn], with notes and a very elaborate index. London: Henry G. Bohn, 1851. 572 pp.
    Signature: W. Emerson.

CAIRD, EDWARD. A critical account of the philosophy
of Kant, with an historical introduction. London,
New York: Macmillan, 1877. xx, 673 pp.

CALMET, AUGUSTIN. Dictionary of the Holy Bible, as published by the late Charles Taylor, with the fragments incorporated. The whole condensed and arranged in alphabetical order. American ed. Rev., with large additions, by Eduard Robinson ... Illus. with maps, and engravings on wood. Boston: Crocker and Brewster; New York; Jonathan Leavitt, 1832. iv, 1000 pp.
Signature: R. Emerson.

CAMERON, JOHN. Phases of thought. London: Simpkin, Marshall, 1870. 208 pp.
Presented to Concord Free Public Library in Feb. 1874 by Ralph Waldo Emerson.
Inscription: To Ralph Waldo Emerson Esq. with affectionate regards from his old friend, Alex Ireland. Inglewood, Bowdon Cheshire England April 19th 1872.

CAMPBELL, JOHN MCLEOD. Responsibility for the gift of eternal life. Comp. by permission of the late John McLeod Campbell, from sermons preached chiefly at Row, in the years 1829-31. London: Macmillan, 1873. viii, 196 pp.
Inscription. Signature: Ellen T. Emerson from Miss Stevenson April 28, 1873.

CAMPBELL, THOMAS. Life of Petrarch. Philadelphia: Carey and Hart, 1841. 444 pp.

_____. Poetical works, including Theodric, and many other pieces not contained in any former ed. Philadelphia: J. Crissy and J. Grigg, 1826. iv, 183 pp.
Notes.

The Canadian guide book, with a map of the province. Montreal: Armour & Ramsay, 1849. 153 pp.
Marginal notes.

CANDOLLE, AUGUSTIN PYRAMUS DE, AND SPRENGEL, K. Elements of the philosophy of plants, containing the principles of scientific botany, nomenclature, theory of classification, phytography, anatomy, chemistry, physiology, geography, and diseases of plants; with a history of the science, and practical illustrations.

Tr. from the German.   Edinburgh: William Blackwood;
London: T. Cadell, 1821.   xxxiii, 486 pp.
Signature: R. W. Emerson, and notes.

CANTON, CHINA.   American citizens.   The centennial
celebration of American independence at Canton,
China, on the 4th July, 1876.   Canton: "Daily advertiser," 1876.   60 pp.
Inscription.

CAREW, THOMAS.   Poems, with a maske [Coelum Britan-
nicum].   The songs were set in musick.   3d ed.
rev. and enl.   London: F. Martin, 1651 .   221 pp.
Masque has also a separate t.p.

CAREY, HENRY CHARLES.   Review of the decade 1857-
67.   Philadelphia: Collins, 1867.   40 pp.

CARLILE, RICHARD.   An exposure of freemasonry; or, A
mason's printed manual, with an introductory keystone to the royal arch of freemasonry.   London,
1831.   87 pp.

CARLYLE, THOMAS.   Collected works.   Library ed. ...
London: Chapman and Hall, 1869-71.   30 v.
Set incomplete: v. 12 wanting.
Inscription: v. 1, 26 Jan. 1869.

_____ .   Critical and miscellaneous essays.   [1st collected ed.]   Boston: James Munroe, 1838-39.   4 v.
Set incomplete: v. 1, 3, 4 wanting.

_____ .   _____ .   Boston: Munroe, 1839.   4 v.
According to Cameron (III, 866), all four vols. were presented to Concord Free Public Library by Ralph Waldo
Emerson in July 1873 and withdrawn from circulation in
1916.   But the library still has v. 3, which is inscribed,
Presented by R. W. Emerson Aug. 1878, and v. 4, which is
inscribed, Presented by R. W. Emerson, Aug. 1873.

_____ .   _____ .   London: James Fraser, 1840.   5 v.
Set incomplete: v. 3 wanting.
Inscription: To Lydia Emerson, Nov. 1840.   Autograph.

_____ .   The diamond necklace.   London: James
Fraser, 1837.   37 pp.
Reprinted from Fraser's magazine, v. 15.

Inscription.   Signature: R. W. Emerson (by T. C.).
Bound with the author's Sartor resartus.   London, 1834.

———.   The French Revolution, a history.   Boston: C.
C. Little and J. Brown, 1839.   3 v.
Given to Concord Free Public Library by Ralph Waldo
Emerson in Aug. 1873.   "Worn out, 1893-1894" (Cameron,
III, 867).

———.   History of Frederich the Second called Fred-
erick the Great.   New York: Harper, 1858.   4v.
Set incomplete: v. 2-4 wanting.
Signature: Emerson.

———.   ———.   2d ed.   London: Chapman and Hall,
1858.   4 v.
Set incomplete: v. 3, 4 wanting.
Notes and autograph.

———.   ———.   Vol. III [-VI].   London: Chapman
and Hall, 1862-1865.   6v.
Set incomplete: v. 1, 2 wanting.
Inscriptions: 6 Dec. 1858, 17 May 1862, 2 Mar. 1864, 15
Feb. 1865, and notes.

———.   Inaugural address at Edinburgh, April 2nd 1866,
on being installed as rector of the University there
...   Edinburgh: Edmonston and Douglas; London:
Chapman and Hall, 1866.   46 pp.
Inscription dated 18 April 1866.

———.   Latter-day pamphlets.   Ed. by Thomas Carlyle.
Boston: Phillips, Sampson, 1850.   [342] pp.
Autograph.

———.   Life and works of Diderot.   (*In* the Foreign
quarterly review.   [London, 183-?]   v. 11, no. 22,
pp. [261-315].)
Bound with the author's Sartor resartus.   London, 1834.

———.   The life of John Sterling.   Boston: Phillips,
Sampson, 1851.   iv, 344 pp.
Inscription: R. W. Emerson.   "Presented by R. W. Emer-
son Aug 1873" to the Concord Free Public Library.

———.   ———.   2d ed.   London: Chapman and Hall,
1852.   vi, 344 pp.
Inscription: January 1852, and notes.

———. ———. London: Chapman and Hall, 1870. vi, 342 pp. (*His* Collected works. Library ed., v. 23.)

———. Memoirs of Mirabeau. From the "London and Westminster review" for January 1837. [London, 1837?] 59 pp.
Inscription and marginal lines.
Bound with the author's Sartor resartus. London, 1834.
Signature: R. Waldo Emerson (by T. C.).

———. On heroes, hero-worship, and the heroic in history. New York, 1859. [218?] pp.
Presented to the Concord Free Public Library by Ralph Waldo Emerson in July 1873 (Cameron, III, 867).

———. Past and present. London: Chapman and Hall, 1843. vi, 399 pp.
Inscription: 24 Apr. 1843.

———. Reminiscences, ed. by James Anthony Froude. New York: C. Scribner's Sons, 1881. x, 536 pp.

———. Sartor resartus. In three books. Reprinted for friends from Fraser's magazine ... London: James Fraser, 1834. 107 pp.
Inscription: Lydian Emerson from Mr. Thomas Carlyle (in R. W. E.'s hand).

———. ———. London: Saunders and Otley, 1838. xii, 310 pp.
Inscription: 15 Nov. 1838.

———. Shooting Niagara; and after? London: Chapman and Hall, 1867. 55 pp.
Inscription: 4 Oct. 1867.

———. The life of Friedrich Schiller, comprehending an examination of his works. Suppl. of 1872. London: Chapman and Hall, 1873. pp. [241]-337.
Inscription: From the Author (not in Carlyle's hand).

———. Translations from the German ... London: Chapman and Hall, 1871. 3 v.

CARMICHAEL, SARAH E. Poems. A brief selection, published by permission of the authoress, for private circulation. San Francisco: Towne and Bacon, 1866. vi, 72 pp.

CARPENTER, LANT. Harmony of the Gospels on the plan proposed by Lant Carpenter. Boston: Gray and Bowen, 1831. xv, 260 pp.
Signature: Emerson (in Ellen's hand). Notes in E. T. E.'s hand.

CARPENTER, MARY. Six months in India. London: Longmans, Green, 1868. 2 v. in 1.
Inscription: To Mr. R. W. Emerson with kind regards of S. S. Forbes.

CARPENTER, WILLIAM BENJAMIN. Principles of mental physiology, with their applications to the training and discipline of the mind, and the study of its morbid conditions. New York: D. Appleton, 1874. xxi, 737 pp.

_____. Principles of physiology, general and comparative. With three hundred and twenty-one wood-engravings. 3d ed. London: J. Churchill, 1851. xxiv, 1098 pp.
Inscription by author.

CARR, SIR JOHN. A northern summer; or, Travels round the Baltick, through Denmark, Sweden, Russia, Prussia, and part of Germany, in the year 1804. 2d Connecticut ed. Hartford: Lincoln & Gleason, Cady & Eells, 1806. x, 330 pp.

Cato redivivus; or, New wine in old bottles. A tragedy born again ... London: Samuel Tinsley, 1879. 150 pp.
Inscription by William Simmons, and note.

CATULLUS, C. VALERIUS, TIBULLIUS, ALBIUS, AND PROPERTIUS, SEXTUS. Opera. Ex optimis editionibus sedula recensione accurata. Londini: Rodwell et Martin, excudit T. Davison, 1822. 126 pp.
Autograph.

CAUGHEY, ANDREW HERVEY. Home, and other poems. New York: Carleton, 1862. 82 pp.

[CECIL, RICHARD.] A friendly visit to the house of mourning ... 4th ed. Boston: Manning & Loring, 1805. 72 pp.

Bound with: Grosvenor, Benjamin. The mourner. Exeter, [N. H., 1795?].

CENTURY ASSOCIATION, NEW YORK. The Bryant festival at "The Century," November 5, M.DCCC. LXIV. New York: D. Appleton, 1865. 88 pp.

CHABOT, CHARLES. The handwriting of Junius professionally investigated. With preface and collateral evidence, by Edward Twisleton ... London: J. Murray, 1871. lxxviii, 136 pp.
Inscription.

CHAIGNET, ANTHELME ÉDOUARD. Pythagore et la philosophie pythagoricienne, contentant les fragments de Philolaüs et d'Archytas, tr. pour la première fois en français. Paris: Didier, 1873. 2 v.

CHAMBERLAIN, MRS. C. A. Poems. Cincinnati: Ward & Taylor, 1853. iv, 209 pp.
Inscription: To E. W. Emerson by the author, Sept. 3 [1853?].

[CHAMBERS, ROBERT.] Explanations: a sequel to "Vestiges of the natural history of creation." New York: Wiley & Putnam, 1846. vii, 142 pp.

[_____.] Vestiges of the natural history of creation. 2d ed., from the 3d London ed., greatly amended by the author. And introduced by George B. Cheever. New York: Wiley and Putnam, 1845. xxviii, 280 pp.
Autograph.

CHANNING, FRANCIS ALLSTON CHANNING, *Baron.* The Greek orators considered as historical authorities. The Arnold prize essay for 1866. Oxford: T. & C. Shrimpton, 1866. 59 pp.
Autograph.

CHANNING, WILLIAM ELLERY. A discourse on the evidences of revealed religion, delivered before the University in Cambridge, at the Dudleian lecture, March 14, 1821. Boston: Cummings and Hilliard, 1821. 36 pp.
Bound with: Webster, Daniel. A discourse delivered at Plymouth, December 22, 1820. Boston, 1821.

————. A discourse, preached at the dedication of the
Second Congregational Unitarian Church, New York,
December 7, 1826. 2d ed. New York: Second Con-
gregational Unitarian Church, 1827. 57 pp.

————. A letter to Henry Clay, on the annexation of
Texas to the United States. Boston: James Munroe,
1837. 72 pp.

————. The perfect life, in twelve discourses. Ed.
from his manuscripts by his nephew William Henry
Channing. Boston: Roberts Bros., 1873. xix,
311 pp.
Inscription: With kind regards of the editor.

————. ————. Copy 2.
Given to Concord Free Public Library by Ralph Waldo
Emerson in Aug. 1873 (Cameron, III, 867).

————. Religion a social principle. A sermon, delivered in the Church in Federal Street, Boston,
December 10, 1820. Boston: Russell & Gardner,
1820. 19 pp.
Autograph.

————. A sermon, delivered at the ordination of Ezra
Stiles Gannett, as colleague pastor of the Church of
Christ, in Federal Street, Boston, June 30, 1824.
Boston: Christian Register Office, 1824. 47 pp.
Bound with: Webster, Daniel. A discourse delivered at
Plymouth, December 22, 1820. Boston, 1821.

————. A sermon delivered at the ordination of Jared
Sparks, to the pastoral care of the First Independent
Church of Baltimore, May 5, 1819. 2d ed. Balti-
more: J. Robinson, 1819. 72 pp.
Bound with: Webster, Daniel. A discourse delivered at
Plymouth, December 22, 1820. Boston, 1821.

————. A sermon delivered at the ordination of John
Codman, to the pastoral care of the Second Church of
Christ in Dorchester, Dec. 7, 1808. 2d ed. Bos-
ton: Joshua Belcher, 1809. 24 pp.
Autograph.

____. A sermon, preached at the annual election, May 26, 1830, before Levi Lincoln, Thomas L. Winthrop, the Honorable Council, and the Legislature of Massachusetts. Boston: Dutton and Wentworth, 1830. 46 pp.
Bound with: Everett, Edward. An oration delivered at Plymouth, December 22, 1824. Boston, 1825.

____. Works. With an introduction. New and complete ed., rearranged. Boston: American Unitarian Association, 1882. iv, 931 pp.

CHANNING, WILLIAM ELLERY, THE YOUNGER. Conversations in Rome, between an artist, a Catholic, and a critic. Boston: Wm. Crosby and H. P. Nicholas, 1847. xiv, 141 pp.

[____.] Near home, a poem. Boston: James Munroe, 1858. 52 pp.
Signature: R. W. Emerson.
Ms. poem inserted at end.

____. Poems. Boston: Charles C. Little and James Brown, 1843. viii, 151 pp.
Autograph. Notes and ms. poem at end.

____. Poems. 2d ser. Boston: James Munroe, 1847. vii, 160 pp.
Note.

____. Thoreau, the poet-naturalist. With memorial verses. Boston: Roberts Bros., 1873. xii, 357 pp.
Autograph and notes. Postcard laid in.

____. The wanderer, a colloquial poem. Boston: J. R. Osgood, 1871. ix, 137 pp.

____. The woodman, and other poems. Boston: James Munroe, 1849. iv, 92 pp.
Inscription on flyleaf: F. B. Sanborn, Concord, April, 1855.
Pencil markings in text.

CHANSON DE ROLAND. The song of Roland. Tr. into English verse by John O'Hagan ... London: C. Kegan, Paul, 1880. 220 pp.
R. W. E.'s notes inserted on slip.

CHAPMAN, FREDERICK WILLIAM.   The Bulkeley family;
   or, The descendants of Rev. Peter Bulkeley, who
   settled at Concord, Mass., in 1636.   Comp. at the
   request of Joseph E. Bulkeley.   Hartford, Conn.:
   Case, Lockwood & Brainard Co., 1875.   vi, 288 pp.

Characteristics of men of genius; a series of biographical, historical, and critical essays, selected ...
   chiefly from the North American review ...   London:
   Chapman Bros., 1846.   2 v.
   Inscriptions.

CHARLES, EMILY (THORNTON).   Hawthorn blossoms.
   Philadelphia: J. B. Lippincott, 1876.   x, 165 pp.

CHARTERHOUSE SCHOOL, GODALMING, ENG.   Charterhouse.
   Examination of the upper school.   London: S.
   Walker, 1843.   [23] pp.

CHATTERTON, THOMAS.   Poetical works.   With notices of
   his life, a history of the Rowley controversy, a selection of his letters, notes critical and explanatory,
   and a glossary ...   Boston: Little, Brown, 1857.
   2 v.
   Autographs and notes.

CHAUCER, GEOFFREY.   Canterbury tales, and other
   poems ...   London: John Cumberland, [182-?-3-?]
   2 v.
   Notes.

_____.   The Canterbury tales.   From the text and with
   the notes and glossary of Thomas Tyrwhitt.   Con-
   densed and arranged under the text.   New ed.
   Illus. by Edward Corbould.   London, New York:
   G. Routledge, 1857.   xxxiv, 586 pp.
   Inscription: Ellen T. Emerson from Father, 1858 (in
   E. T. E.'s hand).

_____.   Legende of goode women.   Ed., with an intro-
   duction, and notes, glossarial and critical, by Hiram
   Corson ...   Philadelphia: F. Leypoldt; New York:
   F. W. Christern, 1864.   xxxviii, 145 pp.
   Inscriptions: Editor-Furness-Emerson.

_____. Poetical works. With an essay on his language and versification, and an introductory discourse; together with notes and a glossary, by Thomas Tyrwhitt. London, New York: George Routledge, 1871. x, lxx, 501 pp.
  Notes. Letter from George B. Emerson laid in at front.

[CHENEY, EDNAH DOW (LITTLEHALE).] Memoir of Seth W. Cheney, artist. Boston: Lee and Shepard, 1881. 144 pp.
  Inscription slip inserted: June 4, 1881.

[CHENEY, MARY A. (BUSHNELL)], *ed.* Life and letters of Horace Bushnell. New York: Harper, 1880. x, 579 pp.

CHESTER, ROBERT. "Loves martyr; or, Rosalins complaint" (1601) with its supplement "Diverse poetical essaies" on the turtle and phoenix, by Shakespeare, Ben Johnson, George Chapman, John Marston, etc. Ed., with introduction, notes and illus., by Alexander G. Grosart ... London: New Shakespeare Society, 1878. lxxxiv, 254 pp.
  Inscription. Letter, 15 May 1879, from editor, inserted.

CHIABRERA, GABRIELLO. Delle opere. In questa ultima impressione tutte in un corpo novellamente unite ... Venizia: Baglioni, 1805. 5 v. in 2.
  Autographs: Oct. 1822.

CHICAGO RELIEF AND AID SOCIETY. Report of disbursement of contributions for the sufferers by the Chicago fire. Chicago, 1874. x, 440 pp.
  Inscription by K. Dexter to R. W. E.

CHILD, FRANCIS JAMES. Observations on the language of Chaucer. Cambridge: Welch, Bigelow, 1862. [445]-502 pp.
  Reprinted from the Memoirs of the American Academy, new ser., v. 8, pt. 2, 1863.

_____. _____. Copy 2.

———, *ed.*   English and Scottish ballads.   Boston:
Little, Brown, 1857-58.   8 v.
> Autographs.   Notes in v. 1, 2, 4 and 5.

[———.]   Four old plays.   Three interludes: Thersytes,
Jack Jugler and Heywood's Pardoner and frere; and
Jocasta, a tragedy by Gascoigne and Kinwelmarsh,
with an introduction and notes.   Cambridge: G.
Nichols, 1848.   xxxiv, 288 pp.

CHILD, LYDIA MARIA (FRANCIS).   The biographies of
Lady Russell, and Madame Guyon. ...   Boston:
Carter, Hendee, 1832.   264 pp.

———.   Looking toward sunset.   From sources old
and new, original and selected.   Boston: Ticknor
and Fields, [1864].   ix, 455 pp.

———.   The progress of religious ideas, through suc-
cessive ages.   New York: C. S. Francis; London:
S. Low, 1855.   3 v.
> Inscription and note.

———, *comp.*   Aspirations of the world.   A chain of
opals.   Collected, with an introduction, by L. Maria
Child ...   Boston: Roberts Bros., 1878.   vi,
276 pp.

The child's gem, for 1845.   Ed. by S. Colman.   Boston: T. H. Carter [1845?].   viii, 95 pp.
> Autograph: Ellen Emerson.   Inscription, Alice to Ellen.

The Christian examiner and theological review.   v. 1-5,
Jan./Feb. 1824-Nov./Dec. 1828.   Boston [etc.]:
Cummings, Hilliard [etc.].   5 v.

Christian hymns for public and private worship.   A collection comp. by a committee of the Cheshire Pastoral Association.   45th ed.   Boston: Crosby,
Nichols, 1855.   xxxii, 530 pp.
> On cover, stamped in gold, Emerson.   Pew 53.
> Signature: Emerson (in Ellen's hand).

The Christian remembrancer, a quarterly review. [v. 40, no. 52], Apr. 1846. London: James Burns. [243]-506 pp.
> Note.

The Christian teacher's manual designed for families and Sunday Schools. v. 1, no. 1-6, [Apr.]-Sept., 1828. Boston: L. C. Bowles. 384 pp.

Christliche Harmonika in einer Auswahl von geistlichen Liedern mit drenstimmigen Melodien. Basel: Felix Schneider, [18—?]. 44 pp.

Chronicles of the crusades: contemporary narratives of the crusade of Richard Coeur de Lion, by Richard of Devizes and Geoffrey de Vinsauf; and of the crusade of Saint Louis, by Lord John de Joinville. With illustrative notes and an index. London: Henry G. Bohn, 1848. v, 562 pp.
> Autograph and notes.

CHURCH OF ENGLAND. The book of common prayer, and administration of the sacraments, and other rites and ceremonies of the church, according to the use of the Church of England; together with the Psalter, or Psalms of David, pointed as they are to be sung or said in churches. Cambridge: J. Archdeacon, 1781.
> Autograph: Ruth Haskins her book 1786. Signature: R. W. Emerson 1879.

CHURCH OF JESUS CHRIST OF LATTER DAY SAINTS. Sacred hymns and spiritual songs. 14th ed. Salt Lake City: George Q. Cannon, 1871. 432 pp,

CICERO, MARCUS TULLIUS. De officiis libri tres. Item, Cato major, sive De senectute; Laelius, sive De amicitia. Paradoxa, Somnium scipionis. Ad optimorum exemplarium fidem recensiti. Londini: J. Roberts, Impensis autem Societatis Stationariorum, 1726. 244 pp.
> Inscription: From C. C. E., and notes.

_____. Epistolae selectae. Ex Reinholdi Klotzii recensione scholarum in usum edidit Rudolfus

Dietsch. Lipsiae: B. G. Teubneri, 1855.
Autograph: Ellen T. Emerson.

———. Epistolarum Libri IV. Cum postremis H.
Stephani & D. Lambini. Editionibus diligenter
collati, & quàm accuratissimè emendati. A Joanne
Sturmio in puerilem educationem confecti. Huic
editioni accesserunt Graeca Latinis expressa.
Londini: A. Wilde, pro Societate Stationariorum,
1759. 92 pp.
Autograph: Charles C. Emerson.

———. Familiar epistles. Englished and conferred
with the French, Italian and other translations.
London: Edwin Griffin, [1640?]. 919 pp.

———. Philosophica ... Tomus 3. Lipsiae: Caroli
Tauchnitii, [182-?]. 432 pp.
Imperfect copy: pp. 353-423 wanting.

Circumstances. [n.p., n.d.] 1 l.
Bound with: Lane, Charles. A classification of science and arts ... London, 1826.

The circumstantial law. [n.p., 18—?] Broadside.
Considers the circumstances most conducive to the
harmonious development of the true practical socialist.
Bound with: Lane, Charles. A classification of science and arts ... London, 1826.

CLARENDON, EDWARD HYDE, *1st Earl of*. The beauties
of Clarendon, consisting of selections from his historical and moral works. By Alfred Howard. London: T. Davison, [n.d.]. 212 pp.
Autograph.

———. The history of the rebellion and civil wars in
England, to which is added An historical view of the
affairs of Ireland. New ed., exhibiting a faithful
collation of the original ms. with all the suppressed
passages; also the unpublished notes of Bishop
Warburton. Boston: Wells and Lilly, 1827. 6 v.
Autographs and notes.

CLARKE, HENRY G.   The Dulwich Gallery, its pictures
and their painters.   A handbook guide for visitors.
London: H. G. Clarke, 1843.   [16] pp.
　Inscription: With Henry Buts' regards.

CLARKE, JAMES FREEMAN.   The Christian doctrine of
prayer, an essay.   Boston: Crosby, Nichols, 1854.
xviii, 224 pp.
　Autograph: M. M. Emerson, June 15, 1855, and marginal
　lines.

_____ .   Orthodoxy: its truths and errors.   Boston:
American Unitarian Association, 1866.   xi, 512 pp.
　Inscription: Mrs. Lydian Emerson, Dec. 1866 from author.

_____ .   Selections from sermons preached to the Church
of the Disciples.   [Boston: John A. Lowell, 18—?]
[40] pp.

CLARKE, MARY COWDEN, *comp.*   The complete concord-
ance to Shakespere: being a verbal index to all the
passages in the dramatic works of the poet.   New
York: Wiley and Putnam, 1846.   vii, 860 pp.
　Inscription: R. W. Emerson from his brother William (in
　Emerson's hand). Author's autograph at end of preface.

The classical journal, and scholars' review.   v. 1, no.
1-2, 7-12; v. 2, no. 1-3, 5-7, 9-10, 12.   Jan.-Feb.,
July-Dec., 1830; Jan.-Mar., May-July, Sept.-Oct.,
Dec., 1831.   Boston.   2 v. in 1.

CLOUGH, ARTHUR HUGH.   A consideration of objections
against the Retrenchment Association ...   Oxford:
Francis Macpherson, 1847.   20 pp.

_____ .   Letters and remains of Arthur Hugh Clough ...
London: Spottiswoode, 1865.   vi, 328 pp.
　Inscription by Mrs. Clough to R. W. E.   Notes inserted.

_____ .   Poems ..., with a memoir.   2d ed.   London:
Macmillan, 1863.   xxxi, 313 pp.
　Inscription to Emerson from E. L. Stanley.

COBDEN, RICHARD.   Political writings.   London: William Ridgway; New York: D. Appleton, 1867.   2 v.

COBDEN CLUB. ... Local government and taxation. Ed. by J. W. Probyn ... London, New York: Cassell, Petter & Galpin, 1875. vi, 454 pp.

———. Local government and taxation in the United Kingdom. A series of essays published under the sanction of the Cobden Club. Ed. by J. W. Probyn ... London, New York: Cassell Petter, Galpin, 1882. vi, 520 pp.

———. Systems of land tenure in various countries. A series of essays published under the sanction of the Cobden Club. Ed. by J. W. Probyn. London: Cassell, Petter & Galpin, [1876]. viii, 418 pp.

———. ———. New ed., rev. and cor. London, New York: Cassell, Petter, Galpin, [1881]. vi, 534 pp.

CODDINGTON, DAVID SMITH. Speeches and addresses, with a biographical sketch. New York: D. Appleton, 1866. xxxii, 177 pp.

COHEN, JOSEPH. The deicides. Analysis of the life of Jesus, and of the several phases of the Christian church in their relation to Judaism. Tr. by Anna Maria Goldsmid. 1st American ed. Baltimore: Deutsch, 1873. xliv, 283 pp.

COLEBROOKE, HENRY THOMAS. Miscellaneous essays. London: W. H. Allen, 1837. 2 v.
　　Inscription: Henry D. Thoreau from Thomas Cholmondeley. Autograph: R. W. Emerson from Henry D. Thoreau.

———, *tr.* Two treatises on the Hindu law of inheritance ... Calcutta: A. H. Hubbard, 1810. xv, 377 pp.
　　Consists of the Dáyabhága of Jímútaváhana and Mitácshará, an inheritance.
　　Inscription: Thomas Cholmondeley to Henry D. Thoreau. Autograph of R. W. Emerson: The bequest of Henry D. Thoreau.

COLERIDGE, HENRY NELSON. Introductions to the study of the Greek classic poets, designed principally for

the use of young persons at school and college.
Part I.   Containing—I. General introduction.
II. Homer.   Philadelphia: Carey and Lea, 1831.
239 pp.
    No more published.
    Autograph.

COLERIDGE, SAMUEL TAYLOR.   Biographia literaria; or,
    Biographical sketches of my literary life and opin-
    ions ...   New York: Leavitt, Lord; Boston: Crocker
    & Brewster, 1834.   2 v. in 1 (351 pp.).
    Autograph, and notes on inside of back cover.

_____.   The friend: a series of essays, in three vol-
    umes, to aid in the formation of fixed principles in
    politics, morals and religion, with literary amuse-
    ments interspersed.   A new ed.   London: Rest
    Fenner, 1818.   3 v.
    Autographs and notes.

_____.   Letters, conversations, and recollections ...
    London: E. Moxon, 1836.   2 v.
    Autograph and notes.

_____.   The literary remains of Samuel Taylor Cole-
    ridge, collected and ed. by Henry Nelson Coleridge
    ...   London: William Pickering, 1836–39.   4 v.
    Autographs and notes.

_____.   _____.   Another set.
    Autograph: R. Waldo Emerson.

_____.   Poetical and dramatic works, with a memoir.
    Boston: Little, Brown, 1854.   3 v.
    Notes in v. 3.

_____.   Specimens of table-talk of the late Samuel
    Taylor Coleridge ...   New York: Harper, 1835.
    2 v. in 1.
    Autograph and notes.

_____.   The statesman's manual; or, The Bible, the
    best guide to political skill and foresight.   A lay
    sermon, addressed to the higher classes of society.
    Burlington: Chauncey Goodrich, 1832.   231 pp.
    Autograph and notes.

COLESWORTHY, DANIEL CLEMENT. School is out. Boston: Barry and Colesworthy, 1876. xxv, 508 pp.
Inscription: Apr. 29, 1876 inscribed by author to R. W. E.

A collection of psalms and hymns for Christian worship ... 18th ed. Boston: Charles J. Hendee, 1836. xxvi, [446] pp.

A collection of psalms and hymns for social and private worship ... 2d ed. New York: A. Paul, 1823. xx, 420 pp.
On cover: Lydia Emerson.

COLLET, SOPHIA DOBSON. "Pantheism, an essay." [London, 1844.] [9] pp.
Clippings from the movement, anti-persecution gazette, no. 67, 1844. Ed. by G. Jacob Holyoake, and Q. Ryall. Mounted on correspondence paper.

COLLINS, H. G., *firm, publishers*. New map of the Black Sea, shewing all the fortifications &c. on an extended scale ... London, [18—?]. col. map.

COLLINS, WILLIAM. Poetical works. With a life of the author and critical observations by Dr. Langhorne. London: Suttaby, Evance and Fox, 1815. 96 pp.
Inscription: C. C. E. from W. E.

———. Poetical works. London: W. Pickering, 1830. lxxii, 150 pp.
Autograph.

COLONNA, VITTORIA, *Marchesa di Pescara.* Rime e lettere. Firenze: G. Barbèra, 1860. xlvi, 462 pp.

COLTON, G. W., AND COLTON, C. B., & Co., *firm, publishers*. Map of the Pacific rail road route from the Mississippi River to the Pacific Ocean. New York, [18—?]. col. map.

———. New Hampshire [map]. New York, 1874. col. map.

———. New sectional map of the State of Nebraska. New York, 1869. col. map.
Eastern half of Nebraska only, with inset map of Nebraska and parts of Dakota, Iowa, Missouri, and Kansas.

———. Railroad & township map of the State of New York, with parts of the adjoining states & Canada. New York, 1878. col. map.

COLTON, JOSEPH HUTCHINS, *firm, publishers.* Map of the United States, the Canadas, &c. showing the rail roads, canals & stage roads with distances from place to place. New York: Johnson & Browning, 1860 [c1855]. col. map.

———. Map of the United States of America, the British provinces, Mexico, the West Indies, and Central America, with part of New Granada and Venezuela. New York: J. H. Colton, 1848. col. map.

COMBE, ANDREW. The principles of physiology applied to the preservation of health, and to the improvement of physical and mental education. With fine wood-cuts. To which is added, Notes and observations by O. S. Fowler ... From the 7th Edinburgh ed., enl. and improved. New York: Fowler and Wells, [1842?]. xii, 320 pp.
Autograph, Ellen T. Emerson, June 1853.

A common place book, upon the plan recommended and practiced by John Locke ... Boston: Cummings and Hilliard, 1821. Blank leaves.
"Book No 4." Ms. notes. Emerson's address list and some poetry.

CONCORD, MASS. Proceedings at the centennial celebration of Concord fight, April 19, 1875 . Concord, Mass.: Pub. by the Town, 1876. 176 pp.
Includes a brief address by Ralph Waldo Emerson. Signature: R. W. Emerson.

———. Reports of the selectmen and other officers. Also, the Report of the School Committee. 1866/67, 1871/72, 1872/73, 1878/79, 1881/82. Concord: Tolman & White, 1867-[84]. 6 v.
Report year ends Feb. 28 or 29.
Vol. for 1866/67 published by Benjamin Tolman.
Vol. for 1866/67 includes also "the marriages, births and deaths in 1866."

———. ———. Copy 2. 1881/82.

CONCORD, MASS. FIRST PARISH. By-laws, Nov. 25, 1881.
Concord, 1881. 1 l.
> Broadside.

[———.] Officers, committees, etc. 1867-68, 1870-
71—1872-73, 1874-75—1881-82. [Concord.]
22 ll.
> Broadsides.

———. ———. Copy 2, 1874-75—1875-76. 4 ll.
> Broadsides.

———. Ordination services of Benjamin Reynolds
Bulkley, as minister of the First Parish at Concord,
Wednesday, July 12th, 1882. [Concord, 1882?]
2 ll. music.
> Includes "Hymn [We love the venerable house]" by R. W.
> Emerson.

CONCORD, MASS. FIRST UNITARIAN CONGREGATIONAL
CHURCH. SUNDAY SCHOOL. ... Floral anniversary,
1880. Sunday, June 20, 1880. [Boston]: Geo. H.
Ellis, 1880. 2 ll.
> Broadside and two poems by Mrs. M. A. Allen and J. W.
> Chadwick inserted.

———. ———. June 19, 1881. [Boston, 1881?]
[1?] l.
> Broadside.

———. SCHOOL COMMITTEE. Reports of the School Committee, and Superintendent of the Schools, with a
notice of an exhibition of the schools in the Town
Hall. 1859/60—1861/62, 1863/64. Concord:
Benjamin Tolman, 1860-64. 4 v.
> Title varies: 1863/64, Report of the School Committee.
> Inscription in vol. for 1859/60; autograph in vol. for
> 1860/61.

CONCORD, N. H. SECOND CONGREGATIONAL (UNITARIAN)
CHURCH AND SOCIETY. Proceedings at the semi-
centennial celebration of the organization in Concord, New Hampshire, together with the historical
address and the poem read on that occasion. Also,

the Proceedings at the dedication of the new chapel, and of the social gathering in the evening, Wednesday, Oct. 1, 1879. Comp. and published by the Committee of Arrangements. Concord: Republican Press Association, 1879. 60 pp.

CONCORD, [N. H.?]. UNITARIAN CHURCH. SUNDAY SCHOOL. Order of exercises at the anniversary of the Unitarian Sunday School, Concord, Sunday, June 15th, 1873. [Concord, 1873.] 3 pp.

CONCORD SCHOOL, CONCORD, MASS. Catalogue of the teachers and pupils, 1859-'60. June, 1860. Concord: Benjamin Tolman, 1860. 14 pp.
Notes, possibly in Emerson's hand.

CONDIVI, ASCANIO. Vita di Michelangelo Buonarroti, pittore, scultore, architetto, e gentiluomo fiorentino. Pubblicata mentre viveva dal suo scolare Ascanio Condivi. 2. ed. cor. ed accresciuta di varie annotazioni col ritratto del medesimo ed altre figure in rame. Firenze: Gaetano Albrizzini, 1746. xxx, 160 pp.
Signature : R. W. Emerson.

CONDORCET, MARIE JEAN ANTOINE NICOLAS CARITAT, *Marquis* DE. Outlines of an historical view of the progress of the human mind: being a posthumous work of the late M. de Condorcet. Tr. from the French. Baltimore: G. Fryer, 1802. vi, 244 pp.
Autograph.

Contentment. [n.p., n.d.] Broadside.
Bound with: Lane, Charles. A classification of science and arts ... London, 1826.

CONWAY, MONCURE DANIEL. Demonology and devil-lore. New York: H. Holt, 1879. 2 v.

———. The earthward pilgrimage. London: J. C. Hotten, 1870. x, 406 pp.
Inscription: To R. W. Emerson, Dec. 3, '70, from author.

———. Emerson at home and abroad. Boston: J. R. Osgood, 1882. 383 pp.

[_____.]   The rejected stone; or, Insurrection vs. re-
surrection in America.   By a native of Virginia.
Boston: Walker, Wise, 1861.   132 pp.
> Inscription.

[_____.]   _____.   2d ed.   Boston: Walker, Wise, 1862.
131 pp.
> Inscription: R. W. Emerson from M. D. C. (in Emerson's
> hand).

_____.   Republican superstitions as illustrated in the
political history of America.   London: H. S. King,
1872.   xii, 130 pp.
> Inscription: 1873.

_____.   Tracts for today.   Cincinnati: Truman &
Spoffard, 1858.   303 pp.
> Inscription: Gift of author to Mrs. R. W. E., Jan. 1858.

CONWELL, RUSSELL HERMAN.   The life, travels, and
literary career of Bayard Taylor ...   Boston: B. B.
Russell; Detroit: R. D. S. Tyler, 1879.   360 pp.
> Inscription.

COOKE, GEORGE WILLIS.   Ralph Waldo Emerson: his life,
writings, and philosophy.   Boston: J. R. Osgood,
1881.   viii, 390 pp.

COOPER, MARY (HANSON).   Memoirs of the late Mary
Cooper, of London; who departed this life, June 22,
1812, in the twenty-sixth year of her age.   Extracted
from her diary and epistolary correspondence, by
Adam Clarke.   From the 4th London ed.   Boston:
Wells and Lilly, 1819.   xi, 276 pp.

COOPER, WILLIAM.   The honours of Christ demanded of
the magistrate.   A sermon preached in the audience
of his excellency the Governour, the Honourable the
Council and Representatives, of the province of the
Massachusetts-Bay, in New-England, May 28, 1740,
the day for the election of His Majesty's Council
there.   Boston, N. E.: J. Draper, 1740.   48 pp.

CORMON, J. L. BARTHÉLÉMY, ET MANNI, VINCENT.   Dictionnaire portatif et de prononciation italien-français

et français-italien, composé sur le Vocabulaire de l'Académie de la Crusca ... et sur les meilleurs dictionnaires français; rédigé d'après un plan absolument neuf ... on y a joint un vocabulaire des mots nouveaux introduits dans la langue française. 2. éd., rev. et corrigée avec soin. Lyon: B. Cormon et Blanc, 1807. 899 pp.

CORNEILLE, PIERRE. Chefs-d'oeuvre ... Éd. stéréotype. Paris: Pierre Didot l'aîné et Firmin Didot, 1800. 4 v.
    Vol. 4 has title Chefs-d'oeuvre de Th. [sic] Corneille. Autograph: E. B. Emerson.

———. Oeuvres diverses. Nouv. éd. augm. Amsterdam: Zacharie Chatelain, 1740. lx, 428 pp.
    Autograph.

———. Le théâtre. Nouv. éd., revue corr. & augm. de ses Oeuvres diverses ... Amsterdam: Zacharie Chatelain, 1740. 5 v. illus.
    Autograph in v. 3.

CORNELL, S. S. Companion atlas to Cornell's high school geography: comprising a complete set of maps, designed for the student to memorize, together with numerous maps for reference, etc. New York: D. Appleton, 1863. [18] l., 8 pp. col. maps.
    Sheet inserted at front: The Census of 1860.

CORSON, JULIET. Cooking school text book, and housekeepers' guide to cookery and kitchen management. An explanation of the principles of domestic economy taught in the New York Cooking School. 3d ed. New York: O. Judd Co., 1879. xii, 240 pp.

COUSIN, VICTOR. Cours de l'histoire de la philosophie ... Histoire de la philosophie du XVIIIe siècle ... Paris: Pichon et Didier, 1829. 2 v.
    Autographs. Notes in v. 2.

———. Cours de philosophie ... Introduction à l'histoire de philosophie. Paris: Pichon et Didier, 1828. xvi, [515] pp.
    Autograph and notes.

————. Introduction to the history of philosophy ...
Tr. from the French by Henning Gotfried Linberg.
Boston: Hilliard, Gray, Little, and Wilkins, 1832.
viii, 458 pp.
    Autograph.

————. Jacqueline Pascal. Premières études sur les
femmes illustres et la société du xviie siècle. 7^e
éd. Paris: Didier, 1869. 465 pp.
    Autograph: Ellen T. Emerson.

————. Report on the state of public instruction in
Prussia; addressed to the Count de Montalivet ...
With plans of school houses. Tr. by Sarah Austin.
New York: Wiley & Long, 1835. lii, 333 pp.
    Autograph and notes.

COWPER, WILLIAM. The minor poems. London: John
Sharpe, 1818. 2 v. in 1.
    Notes.

————. Table talk, and other poems. London: John
Sharpe, 1822. 204 pp.
    Autograph.

————. The task. London: John Sharpe, 1812.
220 pp.
    Autograph.

COX, SAMUEL SULLIVAN. Why we laugh. New York:
Harper, 1876. 387 pp.

CRAIK, DINAH MARIA (MULOCK). A woman's thoughts
about women. Philadelphia: T. B. Peterson,
[1866?]. v, 309 pp.
    Autograph. Signature: Ellen T. Emerson.

CRAIK, GEORGE LILLIE. A compendious history of Eng-
lish literature, and of the English language, from the
Norman conquest. With numerous specimens. New
York: C. Scribner, 1863. 2 v.
    Inscription: v. 2, Ellen T. Emerson from Mr. Cabot, and
    note, v. 1.

[————.] ... The pursuit of knowledge under difficul-
ties; illustrated by anecdotes. London: Charles

Knight; Longman, Rees, Orme, Brown & Green, 1830.
viii, 419 pp.
> Autograph.

CRANCH, CHRISTOPHER PEARSE. Satan, a libretto. Boston: Roberts Bros., 1874. 36 pp.
> Inscription: Apr. 1874.

CRAWFORD, W. N. The new Biblical epoch caused by the restoration of the ancient science of freemasonry. Essay on the work called "Veritas," solving Biblical, historical, and social problems ... London: A. Hall, [1873]. 20 pp.
> Inscription.

CRAWSHAY, GEORGE. Speech delivered at a meeting in Gateshead, Monday, May 26, 1845; containing a vindication of the conduct of the Gateshead Free Trade Society; and a warning to the free trade party in this country generally. Also, a note on the debate on Mr. Villiers's motion ... Newcastle-upon-Tyne: John and James Selkink, 1845. 19 pp.

The credentials of conscience. A few reasons for the popularity of "Ecce Homo": and a few words about Christianity ... London: Longmans, Green, Reader & Dyer, 1868. iv, 392 pp.
> Inscription: From John Castle.

[CROGHAN, JOHN.] Rambles in the Mammoth Cave, during the year 1844, by a visitor. Louisville, Ky.: Morton & Griswold, 1845. xii, 101 pp.
> Autograph.

CROMWELL, OLIVER. Letters and speeches. With elucidations, by Thomas Carlyle ... 1st ed. Suppl. London: Chapman and Hall, 1846. xii, 224 pp.

_____. _____. 2d ed., enl. London: Chapman and Hall, 1846. 3 v.
> Inscription: 20 June 1846.

CRONISE, TITUS FEY. The natural wealth of California; comprising early history; geography, topography, and

scenery; climate; agriculture and commercial products; geology, zoology, and botany; mineralogy,
mines, and mining processes; manufactures; steamship lines, railroads, and commerce; immigration,
population and society; educational institutions and
literature; together with a detailed description of
each county ... San Francisco: H. H. Bancroft,
1868. xvi, 696 pp.
  Inscription from publisher, and notes by R. W. E.

CRUCHLEY, GEORGE FREDERICK. New map of the British
Isles; shewing the principal roads and rivers, with
all the boroughs & market towns, & the principal
villages; comp. from the latest surveys. London,
1832.

CUDWORTH, RALPH. The true intellectual system of the
universe: wherein all the reason and philosophy of
atheism is confuted, and its impossibility demon-
strated. With a discourse concerning the true notion
of the Lord's supper; and two sermons, on I John II:
3, 4 and I Cor. XV: 57. A new ed.; with references
to the several quotations in The intellectual system;
and an account of the life and writings of the author,
by Thomas Birch. London: J. F. Dane, Priestley,
1820. 4 v.
  Notes, v. 1-2.

CULLIS, CHARLES. More faith cures; or, Answers to
prayer in the healing of the sick. Boston: Willard
Tract Repository, [ᶜ1881]. 105 pp.

CUMMINGS, ASA. A memoir of Edward Payson, late
pastor of the Second Church in Portland. 3d ed.
Boston: Crocker and Brewster, 1830. viii, 400 pp.
  Presented to the Religious Library of the First Parish
  Church of Concord. Now in the Concord Free Public
  Library.
  Autograph: R. W. Emerson.
  On spine: 2d ed.

[CUMMINGS, JACOB ABBOTT.] School atlas to Cummings'
ancient and modern geography. Boston, [n.d.].
maps (part col.).

Emerson's copy was sold by the American Art Association at the Bernheim-Barker sale on Jan. 14-15, 1926.

CURTIS, GEORGE WILLIAM. The life, character and writings of William Cullen Bryant. A commemorative address delivered before the New York Historical Society, at the Academy of Music, December 30, 1878. New York: Charles Scribner's Sons, [c1879]. 64 pp.
  Inscription.

_____. Nile notes of a Howadji. New York: Harper, 1851. xii, 320 pp.
  Inscription: March 1851—to George Bradford from author.

CUTLER, ELBRIDGE JEFFERSON. Poems. New York, [Baker & Godwin], 1859. 36 pp.

CUVIER, GEORGES, *Baron*. A discourse on the revolutions of the surface of the globe, and the changes thereby produced in the animal kingdom. Tr. from the French with illus. and a glossary. Philadelphia: Carey & Lea, 1831. iv, 252 pp.
  Autograph and notes.

D

DABNEY, JOHATHAN PEELE.   Annotations on the New
Testament.   Comp. from the best critical authorities,
and designed for popular use.   Part I.   The historical books.   Cambridge: Hilliard and Brown, 1829.
x, 560 pp.

DALL, CAROLINE WELLS (HEALEY).   The college, the
market, and the court; or, Woman's relation to education, labor, and law.   Boston: Lee and Shepard,
1867.   xxxv, 498 pp.
 Inscription: To Ralph W. Emerson by the author, May
1867.

———— . Egypt's place in history, a presentation.   Boston: Lee and Shepard, 1868.   xv, 108 pp.
 Signature: R. W. Emerson.

———— .   The romance of the Association; or, One last
glimpse of Charlotte Temple and Eliza Wharton.   A
curiosity of literature and life.   Cambridge, [Mass.]:
J. Wilson, 1875.   xii, 102 pp.
 Inscription to Mrs. E.: With the love of C. W. D.

———— .   The "romance of the Association" for the last
time.   [n.p., 1875?]   pp. 103-114.
 A supplement, paged continuously with the preceding.
 Notes.   Author's ms. notes.

DALZEL, ANDREW.   Ἀνάλεκτα Ἑλληνικὰ Μείσονα,
sive Collectanea Graeca majora, ad usum academicae
juventutis accommodata: cum notis philologicis,
quas partim collegit, partim scripsit Andreas Dalzel

... Tomus I.   Complectens excerpta ex variis
orationis salvtae scriptoribus.   Ed. 4. Americana,
ex auctoribus connecta, prioribus emendatior, cum
notis aliquot interjectis.   Boston: Hilliard, Gray;
Philadelphia: Kimber & Sharpless, 1833.   xvi,
364 pp.
    Autograph: C. Emerson.

DANTE ALIGHIERI.   The ante-purgatorio.   Tr. by T. W.
Parsons.   London: Hatchards, 1876.   62 pp.
    The first 9 cantos of the Purgatorio.

_____.   Dante con l'espositioni di Christoforo Landino
et d'Alessandro Vellvtello, sopra la sua comedia
dell'Inferno, del Purgatorie, & del Paradiso.   Con
tauole, argomenti & allegorie; & riformato, riueduto
& ridotto alla sua vera lettura per Francesco
Sansovino Fiorentino ...   Venetia: Gio. Battista,
& Gio. Bernardo Sessa, 1596.   392 l.
    Inscription: From J. A. Carlyle, 10 July 1848.

_____.   Divine comedy: The Inferno.   A literal prose
translation with the text of the original collated from
the best editions, and explanatory notes, by John A.
Carlyle ...   New York: Harper, 1849.   xxxiv,
375 pp.
    Autograph.

_____.   La divina commedia., Corretta, spiegata, e
difesa dal P. Baldassarre Lombardi.   Ed. terza
romana.   Si aggiungono le note de migliori commendatore co'riscontri di famosi mss. non ancora
osservati ...   Roma: Stamperia de Romanis, 1820-
22.   3 v.
    Autographs.

_____.   La divina commedia ...   Con privilegio ...
Firenze: Domenico Manzoni, 1595.   493 pp.

_____.   The first canticle, Inferno, of the Divine comedy
of Dante Alighieri. *tr.* by Thomas William Parsons.
Boston: De Vries, Ibarra, 1867.   216 pp.
    Inscription: August 1867.

____. New life, an essay. With translations, by
Charles Eliot Norton. Cambridge: Riverside Press,
1859. 109 pp.
"One hundred copies printed. No. 44."
Inscription: Xmas 1859.

____. ____. Boston: Ticknor and Fields, 1867.
149 pp.
Inscription: R. W. E. with affectionate regards C. E.
Norton. Sept. 25, 1867, and notes.

____. Seventeen cantos of the Inferno. [Tr. by
Thomas William Parsons.] Boston: John Wilson,
1865. xi, 104 pp.

____. ____. Copy 2.

____. The vision; or Hell, Purgatory, and Paradise.
Tr. by Henry Francis Carey. Philadelphia: Samuel
F. Bradford, 1822. 2 v.
Autographs.

____. Vita nuova. 2. ed. Firenze: Felice le
Monnier, 1856. 75 pp.

____. ____. Con XV. canzione del medesimo. E
la vita di esso Dante scritta da Giovanni Boccaccio
... Firenze: Bartolomeo Sermartelli, 1576. 116,
80 pp.
Given to Emerson by George Bancroft. Given by Emer-
son to Samuel Gray Ward in 1857. Presented to Harvard
College Library by Mrs. Charles B. Perkins. Inscription:
S. G. Ward from R. W. E. (See J. Chesley Mathews,
"Emerson's Translation of Dante's *Vita Nuova*," *Harvard
Library Bulletin*, XI [1957], 211.)

DASENT, GEORGE WEBBE. The story of Gisli the outlaw,
from the Icelandic. With illus. by C. E. St. John
Mildmay ... Edinburgh: Edmonston and Douglas,
1866. xxxv, 123 pp.
Inscription: 24 Apr. 1873.

[DAVIS, JOHN BRAZER.] A letter to the Senate and
House of Representatives of the United States upon
the expediency of an uniform system of bankruptcy
... Boston, 1821. 31 pp.

[_____.]   A letter to William H. Crawford, secretary of
the Treasury of the United States, on the establishment of a uniform system of bankruptcy.   By a
citizen of Massachusetts.   Boston: Wells and Lilly,
1821.   41 pp.

DAVY, SIR HUMPHRY, *Bart.*   Elements of chemical philosophy.   Part I., vol. I.   London: J. Johnson,
1812.   xiv, 511 pp.
  No more published.
  Notes and autograph.

DEARBORN, NATHANIEL, *firm, publisher.*   New map of
Massachusetts comp. from the latest and best authorities and corrected by permission from the survey
ordered by the legislation in 1830.   Carefully revised and additions made in 1845.   3d ed.   Boston, [1845?].   col. map.

Declaration of the modern Free-Masons.   [n. p., 18—?]
Broadside.
  Bound with: Lane, Charles.   A classification of
  science and arts ...   London, 1826.

DE FOREST, JOHN WILLIAM.   European acquaintance:
being sketches of people in Europe.   New York:
Harper, 1858.   iv, 276 pp.
  Inscription: To R. W. E. by author.

_____.   Oriental acquaintance; or, Letters from Syria.
New York: Dix, Edwards, 1856.   v, 285 pp.
  Inscription: To Emerson from Chipham Shepard.

DEKAY, CHARLES.   Hesperus, and other poems.   New
York: C. Scribner's Sons, 1880.   276 pp.
  Inscription.

_____.   The vision of Nimrod.   New York: D. Apple-
ton, 1881.   261 pp.

DELZELL, SIR JOHN GRAHAM.   Rare and remarkable
animals of Scotland represented from living subjects.
v. 1.   London, 1847.
  Reprinted from the British and foreign medico-
  chirurgical review, no. 1, Jan. 1848.
  Inscription.

DEMOSTHENES. Orations. Tr. by Thomas Leland ...
New York: Harper, 1844. 2 v.
Autographs and notes.

DENNYS, EDWARD NICHOLS. The alpha, a revelation,
but no mystery. Stereotyped ed., rev. and enl.
London: C. H. Clarke, [1855].
Inscription: From author to R. W. E.

The Desâtîr or sacred writings of the ancient Persian
prophets, in the original tongue; together with the
ancient Persian version and commentary of the fifth
sasan; carefully published by Mulla Firuz bin Kaus,
who has subjoined a copious glossary of the obso-
lete and technical Persian terms: to which is added
an English translation of the Desâtîr and commentary. Bombay: Courier press, 1818. 2 v.
Set incomplete: v. 1 wanting.
Includes Sanscrit text, numbered in Sanscrit (v. 2, 83
pp. at end).
Autograph and marginal notes.

DESCARTES, RENÉ. Discours de la méthode pour bien
conduire sa raison et chercher la vérité dans les
sciences. Paris: Bureaux de la publication, 1867.
iv, 127 pp.

A description and history of vegetable substances, used
in the arts, and in domestic economy. London:
Charles Knight, 1829-33. 3 v.
Set incomplete: v. 2, 3 wanting.
Autograph.

_____. Timber trees: fruits. Illus. with wood en-
gravings. Boston: Wells and Lilly, 1830. 422 pp.

[DESOR, EDOUARD.] The ocean and its meaning in na-
ture. [n.p., n.d.] 18 pp.
Penciled changes in the text by the author.
Inscription.

DE VERE, AUBREY [THOMAS]. Alexander the Great, a
dramatic poem. London: Henry S. King; Dublin:
McGlashan & Gill, 1874. xxiv, 231 pp.
Inscription.

———. The infant bridal, and other poems.   London:
Macmillan, 1864.   iv, 356 pp.

DEWEY, ORVILLE.   An oration delivered at Cambridge
before the Society of Phi Beta Kappa, August 26,
1830.   Boston: Gray and Bowen, 1830.   32 pp.
Bound with: Webster, Daniel.   Speech ... on the 14th
January, 1814.   Alexandria, 1814.

———. The problem of human destiny; or, The end of
providence in the world of man.   New York, 1864.
Given to Concord Free Public Library by Ralph Waldo
Emerson in Feb. 1874 (Cameron, III, 867).

The dial; a magazine for literature, philosophy, and
religion.   v. 1-4; July 1840-Apr. 1844.   Boston:
Weeks, Jordan; London: Wiley and Putnam, 1841-
1844.   4 v.
Autograph.   Notes assigning authors to many articles.

———. Copy 2,   July 1843, Jan. 1844.   Oct. 1840;
Jan., April 1841; Oct. 1842; April, July 1843; Jan.,
April 1844.
Inscription: Miss M. M. Emerson, South Waterford, Maine.

———. "Ethnical scriptures."   (In the dial.   Boston.
v. 3, July 1842, Jan., Apr., July 1843; v. 4, Oct.
1843, Jan., April 1844.)

———. ———. Copy 2.
Autograph.

The dial; a monthly magazine for literature, philosophy
and religion.   M. D. Conway, editor.   v. 1, no. 1 to
12, Jan. to Dec., 1860.   Cincinnati, 1860.   1 v.
No more published.
Emerson's set sold at the Swann Sale on March 22,
1960, at the Parke-Bernet Galleries in New York City.
The set is described as autographed by him, "Evening
transcript" on no. 1, "Transcript" on no. 2 and 9, and
"Prof. H. W. Longfellow" on no. 8.

Dialogue between two friends, in a pleasant parlor, with
a bright christmas fire.   [n.p., 18—?]   4 pp.
Bound with: Lane, Charles.   A classification of science and arts ...   London, 1826.

DICKENS, CHARLES.   Bleak house.   With illus. by H. K.
Browne.   New York: Harper, 1853.   20 pts. in 1 v.
    Copy imperfect: pts. 1, 7–13 wanting.
    Signature: Emerson.

DICKSON, SAMUEL.   The unity of disease analytically
and synthetically proved, with facts and cases sub-
versive of the received practice of physic.   London:
Simkin and Marshall, 1838.   xxiii, 200 pp.

DIDOT, AMBROISE FIRMIN.   ... Catalogue des éstampes
et ouvrages a graveurs de la chalcographie romaine.
Paris: Firmin Didot frères, 1841.   36 pp.

DIGBY, SIR KENELM.   Private memoirs ... written by
himself ...   With an introductory memoir [by Sir
Nicholas Harris Nicolas].   London: Saunders and
Otley, 1827.   lxxxvi, 328 pp.
    Notes.

DIMAN, JEREMIAH LEWIS.   The alienation of the educated class from politics.   An oration before the
Phi Beta Kappa Society at Cambridge, June 29,
1876.   Providence: Sidney S. Rider, 1876.   37 pp.

The disciples' hymn book; a collection of hymns for public and private devotion ...   3d ed. with additions
and alterations.   Boston: Crosby, Nichols, 1857.
iv, 476 pp.
    Bound with: Book of worship for the congregation and
    the home.   8th ed.   Boston, 1858.

DISRAELI, ISAAC.   Amenities of literature, consisting of
sketches and characters of English literature.   A
new ed., ed. by his son B. Disraeli ...   New York:
Hurd & Houghton; Boston: William Veazie, 1864.
2 v.

DOANE, WILLIAM HOWARD.   The silver spray; a new and
choice collection of popular Sabbath-school music
consisting of duets, quartets, chants, choruses,
&c., adapted for anniversary meetings, sabbath-
school and temperance celebrations, home and so-

cial circle, etc.   Cincinnati: John Church, Jr.,
1868.   138 pp.

———.   ———.   Copy 2.

The documentary history of the State of New-York; arranged under direction of Christopher Morgan, Secretary of State, by E. B. O'Callaghan.   Albany: Weed,
Parsons, 1850–51.   4 v.
   Inscription: 1853 (in R. W. E's hand).

DODGE, MARY (MAPES).   Hans Brinker; or, The silver
skates, a story of life in Holland.   London: Sampson
Low, Son, & Marston, [18—?].   xii, 303 pp.

DODSLEY, ROBERT, *supposed author*.   The duties of
human life; tr. from a Sanscrit manuscript, written by
an ancient Brahmin.   To which is prefixed a letter,
giving an account of the manner in which the manuscript was found, from an English gentleman residing
in China, to the Earl of K******.   Ed. by Joshua
Perkins.   New York: James Miller, 1861.   xx,
128 pp.

DONIZETTI, GAETANO.   L'elisir d'amore, melodramma
giocoso in due atti da rappresentarsi nell'I. R.
teatro alla canobbiana la primavera dell'anno 1832.
Milano: Gaspare Truffi, [18—?].   42 pp.

DONNE, JOHN.   Devotions.   With two sermons.   I. On
the decease of Lady Danvers, mother of George
Herbert.   II. Deaths duel—his own funeral sermon.
To which is prefixed his life, by Izaak Walton.
London: William Pickering, 1840.   cviii, 227 pp.
   Autograph.

———.   Poems on several occasions.   With elegies on
the author's death.   To this edition is added, some
account of the life of the author.   London: Jacob
Tonson, 1719.   365 pp.
   Autographs and notes, some on slips inserted.

DONNELL, E. J.,   Chronological and statistical history
of cotton.   New York: James Sutton, 1872.   xviii,
650 pp.

    Presented to Concord Free Public Library in Aug. 1873
by Ralph Waldo Emerson.
    Autograph: R. W. Emerson.

DORGAN, JOHN AYLMER. Studies. 2d ed. Philadelphia: C. H. Marot, 1864. viii, 223 pp.

——. ——. Copy 2.

DORR, BENJAMIN. An affectionate invitation to the holy communion, being selections from the works of eminent English divines. Philadelphia: R. S. H. George, 1843. iv, 144 pp.

DORR, JULIA CAROLINE (RIPLEY). Friar Anselmo, and other poems. New York: C. Scribner's Sons, 1879. v, 178 pp.
    Inscription: R. W. E. from author, 20 Sept. 1879.

[——.] In memoriam. Cyrus M. and Mary Ripley Fisher, lost on the Steamship Atlantic, April 1st, 1873. [n.p., 1873.] 2 l.
    Autograph of authoress.

——. Poems. Philadelphia: J. B. Lippincott, 1872. ix, 192 pp.
    Inscription by author to R. W. E.

DOVE, PATRICK EDWARD. The theory of human progression, and natural probability of a reign of justice ... Boston: Benjamin B. Mussey, 1851. 528 pp.
    Signature: R. W. Emerson, and notes.

DOWNING, ANDREW JACKSON. The fruits and fruit trees of America; or, The culture, propagation, and management, in the garden and orchard, of fruit trees generally; with descriptions of all the finest varieties of fruit, native and foreign, cultivated in this country. New York: Wiley and Putnam, 1846. xiv, 590 pp.
    Autograph.

DRAKE, DANIEL. A systematic treatise, historical, etiological and practical, on the principal diseases of the interior valley of North America, as they appear in the Caucasian, African, Indian, and Esqui-

maux varieties of its population.   Cincinnati: W. B.
Smith; New York: Mason & Law, 1850.   xvi, 878 pp.

DRIPPS, MATHEW, *firm, publisher*.   New York [City] and
vicinity.   New York, 1865.   col. map.

DRUMMOND, WILLIAM.   Poems.   London: J. Jeffery,
1790.   viii, 326 pp.
  Inscription: To R. W. Emerson from A. Bronson Alcott,
  and note.

DRYDEN, JOHN.   Poetical works.   Boston: Little,
Brown, 1859.   5 v.
  Autographs, and notes on inside back cover (v.1. 5).

_____ .   Poetical works.   Containing original poems,
tales and translations; with notes by Joseph Wharton,
John Warton, and others.   London, New York:
George Routledge, 1873.   lx, 455 pp.

The Dublin review.   no. 51, April 1849.   London:
Thomas Richardson, [1849].   272 pp.

DUFIEF, NICHOLAS GOUIN.   Nature displayed in her mode
of teaching language to man; or, A new and infallible
method of acquiring a language, in the shortest time
possible, deduced from the analysis of the human
mind, and consequently suited to every capacity.
Adapted to the French.   3d ed., highly improved and
much enl.   v.1. containing the French language, and
Le lecteur français, première partie.   Philadelphia:
T. & G. Palmer, 1810.   xl, 433 pp.
  Autograph: L. C. and L. Jackson, and notes.

_____ .   A universal, pronouncing, and critical French-
English dictionary, upon an entirely new plan; con-
taining above 30,000 terms, names, acceptations,
phrases, modes of expression, and new words ...
To which is added, A dictionary of French and
English sea terms and phrases, for the use of the
British and American navies.   London: J. & C.
Allard, 1833.   xii, 577 pp.
  Inscription: from author to Mr. Charles Lane, Nov. 23,
  1833.

DUMAS, ALEXANDRE. Le demi-monde, comédie en cinq actes, en prose. 2me éd. Paris: Michel Lévy, 1855. 162 pp.

DUNHAM, SAMUEL ASTLEY. History of Spain and Portugal from B.C. 1000 to A.D. 1814. London: Baldwin and Cradock, 1833. xvi, 364 pp.

DUNLAP, SAMUEL FALES. Sod, the mysteries of Adoni. London: Williams and Norgate, 1861. xvii, 216 pp.
Inscription: to Emerson by the author, and notes.

———. Sod, the son of the man. London: Williams and Norgate, 1861. xxii, 152 pp.
Inscription: R. W. E. from author, and notes.

———. Vestiges of the spirit-history of man. New York: D. A. Appleton, 1858. vi, 404 pp.
Inscription.

DUNN, DANIEL. Common good society; or, Economical union to reciprocate good. [London, 1834]. 4 pp.
Bound with: Lane, Charles. A classification of science and arts ... London, 1826.

———. ———. Copy 2.

DUPPA, RICHARD, AND QUATREMÈRE DE QUINCY, ANTOINE CHRYSOSTOME. The lives and works of Michael Angelo and Raphael. Illus. with fifteen highly finished engravings. London: H. G. Bohn, 1855. 474 pp.
Signature: R. W. E.

DUTT, KEDAR NATH. [A book written in Sanscrit. n.p., n.d.]

DUTTON, E. P., & COMPANY. A new and complete map of the City of Boston, with part of Charlestown, Cambridge, Brookline, Dorchester &c. Boston, 1868, [c1867]. col. map.

DWIGHT, MARY ANN. Grecian and Roman mythology. With an introductory notice by Tayler Lewis ... 2d ed. New York: George P. Putnam, 1849. 451 pp.
Autograph: Ellen T. Emerson at Mrs. Sedgwick's School, June 3, 1858, and notes.

E

EATON, AMOS. Manual of botany, for North America:
containing generic and specific descriptions of the
indigeneous plants and common cultivated exotics,
growing north of the Gulf of Mexico.   5th ed., rev.,
cor., and much extended.   Albany: Websters and
Skinners, 1829.   451 pp.

EBERS, GEORGE MORTIZ.   An Egyptian princess.   From
the German, by Eleanor Grove.   Authorized ed.
Leipzig: Bernhard Tauchnitz, 1870-71.   2 v.

ECKERMANN, JOHANN PETER.   Conservations with Goethe
in the last years of his life.   Tr. from the German of
Eckermann, by S. M. Fuller.   Boston: Hilliard, Gray,
1839.   xxvi, 414 pp.

   Inscription: From S. M. Fuller (in R. W. E.'s hand), and
   notes.

EDDA SAEMUNDAR.   Die Edda, die ältere und jüngere
nebst den mythischen Erzählungen der Skalda, übers.
Und mit Erläuterungen begleitet von Karl Simrock.
2. verm. und verb. Aufl.   Stuttgart: J. G. Cotta,
1855.   vii, 490 pp.

   Signature: R. W. Emerson.

———— .   Icelandic poetry; or, The Edda of Saemund, tr.
into English verse, by A. S. Cottle.   Bristol:
N. Biggs, 1797.   xlii, 318 pp.

EDDA SNORRA STURLUSONAR.   The prose or younger Edda
commonly ascribed to Snorri Sturluson, tr. from the

Old Norse by George Webbe Dasent.   Stockholm:
Norstedt; London: William Pickering, 1842.   viii,
115 pp.
  Autograph.

EDGEWORTH, MARIA.   Moral tales for young people . . .
Lessons without books, by Mrs. E. Sedgewick
[pseud.].   Boston: Crosby & Nichols, 1845.
216 pp.
  Inscription: To Eddie Emerson from L. J. Whiting.

_____ .   The parent's assistant; or, Stories for children.
Philadelphia: J. B. Lippincott, 1880.   535 pp.

EDGEWORTH, RICHARD LOVELL.   Memoirs, begun by him-
self and concluded by his daughter, Maria Edgeworth.
Boston: Wells and Lilly, 1821.   2 v. in 1.
  Signature: R. W. Emerson.

The Edinburgh review, or critical journal.   v. 35-36
(no. 70-71), July-Oct. 1821; v. 46 (no. 81-82), Oct.
1824—Jan. 1825; v. 48 (no. 95-96), Sept.—Dec.
1828; v. 50 (no. 99-100), Oct. 1829—Jan. 1830.
Boston: Wells and Lilly.   5 v.
  Signatures: R. W. Emerson (omitted in v. 48).   Notes in
  v. 48.

EDWARDS, JONATHAN.   The treatise on religious affec-
tions.   Somewhat abridged, by the removal of the
principal tautologies of the original; and by an attempt to render the language throughout more perspic-
uous and energetic.   To which is now added a copious index of subjects . . .   Loring's 2d ed.   Boston:
James Loring, 1824.   xii, 315 pp.

[EDWARDS, JOSEPH, *of Bristol*?]   Modern Christianity
and the first millennium, a poem by "Outis" [pseud.
n.p.], Priv. Print., 1877.   19 pp.
  Inscription giving author's name.

EHRENFRIED, JOSEPH.   Colloquial phrases and dialogues
in German and English, on every topic necessary to
maintain conversation; with directions for pronunciation.   Ehrenfried's Gespräche und Redensarten, über

jeden Gegenstand gesellschaftlicher Unterhaltung.
Nebst Anleitung zur Aussprache der englischen Buch-
staben.   Philadelphia: Hogan & Thompson, 1841.
228 pp.
  Autograph: Miss E. T. Emerson.

EICHORN, JOHANN GOTTFRIED.   Einleitung ins Alte Test-
ament.   Leipzig, 1780.   3 v.
  Apparently presented to Miss Elizabeth Palmer Peabody
  (Cameron, III, 857).
  Sold at the Wakeman Sale (New York: American Art As-
  sociation, 1924), Lot #257.

———.   Die hebraischen Propheten.   Göttingen, 1816.
3 v.
  Apparently presented to Miss Elizabeth Palmer Peabody
  (Cameron, III, 857).   Sold at the Wakeman Sale (New
  York: American Art Association, 1924), Lot #258.

ELDER, WILLIAM.   Biography of Elisha Kent Kane.
Philadelphia: Childs & Peterson; Boston: Phillips,
Sampson, 1858.   416 pp.
  Inscription: Author to R. W. E.

Electro-magnetism.   [Cheltenham: E. G. Wells, 18—?]
8 pp.
  Bound with: Lane, Charles.   A classification of science
  and arts ...   Boston, 1826.

ELIOT, ANDREW.   A sermon preached at the ordination of
John Eliot, to the pastoral care of the New-North
Church in Boston, November 3, 1779.   Boston: John
Boyle, 1780.   35 pp.
  Signatures: R. W. Emerson, Rev. M. Ripley.

ELIOT, GEORGE, pseud., i.e. MARIAN EVANS.   The legend
of Jubal, and other poems, old and new.   Edinburgh:
William Blackwood, [18—?].   vi, 303 pp.
  Autograph: Ellen T. Emerson.

ELIOT, SAMUEL.   Address before the American Social
Science Association, at the fifth general meeting,
New York, November 19, 1867 ... to which are added
lists of papers, members, etc. December, 1867.
Boston: Wright & Potter, 1867.   267 pp.

_____ , ed.   Poetry for children.   Authorized for use in
the Boston public schools.   Boston: Lee and Shepard; New York: C. T. Dillingham, 1880.   xii, 327 pp.

ELLIS, GEORGE EDWARD.   History of the Battle of Bunker's Hill, on June 17, 1775, from authentic sources in
print and manuscript.   Boston: Lockwood, Brooks,
1875.   144 pp.

_____ .   Memoir of Charles Wentworth Upham.   Cambridge, [Mass.]: J. Wilson, 1877.   43 pp.
   Inscription.

ELLIS, SIR HENRY.   The British Museum.   The Townley
Gallery.   London: Charles Knight, 1836.   2 v.

EMERSON, GEORGE BARRELL.   Education in Massachu-
setts: early legislation and history.   A lecture of a
course by members of the Massachusetts Historical
Society, delivered before the Lowell Institute,
Feb. 16, 1869.   Boston: J. Wilson, 1869.   36 pp.
   Inscription: From the author.

———.   ———.   Copy 2.
   Inscription: From the author.

_____ .   Reminiscences of an old teacher.   Boston:
A. Mudge, 1878.   154 pp.

———.   ———.   Copy 2.
   Inscription: 18 July 1878.

_____ .   A report on the trees and shrubs growing naturally in the forests of Massachusetts.   Originally
published agreeably to an order of the Legislature by
the Commissioners on the Zoological and Botanical
survey of the State.   2d ed.   Boston: Little, Brown,
1875.   2 v.
   Inscription: 9 Sept 1875, and notes.

EMERSON, GOUVERNEUR.   On the causes operative in
determining the proportions of the sexes at birth.
(In the Boston medical and surgical journal.   Boston.   v. 31, no. 6, July 1846, pp. 78–85.)
   Signature consists of pp. 77–92.

EMERSON, RALPH.   A sermon preached at Narfold, Connecticut, May 16, 1816, the first Sabbath after his
ordination.   Hartford: George Godwin, 1817.   31 pp.
    Month corrected, in pencil, to read "June."
    Inscriptions: Daniel Emerson, Esq. from his dutiful son
R. E., when you have read this return it to Wm. Emerson.

EMERSON, RALPH WALDO.   Address.   [n.p., 186-?]
60 pp.
    Running title: Soldiers' monument.

——— .   Books, art, eloquence.   Boston: James R. Osgood, 1877.   104 pp.

——— .   ——— .   Copy 2.

——— .   Complete works.   [Boston]: James R. Osgood,
[1876-78].   9 v.
    Incomplete set: v. 7 (Society and solitude), v. 9 (Poems)
wanting.
    "Little classic" edition.

——— .   The conduct of life.   Boston: Ticknor and
Fields, 1861.   288 pp.
    Errata ms. slip inserted at front.
    Signature: Emerson (in Ellen's hand).   Notes in R. W.
E's hand.

——— .   ——— .   Boston: James R. Osgood, 1873.
288 pp.

——— .   ——— .   Boston: Houghton, Mifflin, 1881.
288 pp.
    Marginal notes, and notes at end.

——— .   English traits.   Boston: Phillips, Sampson,
1856.   312 pp.
    R. W. E.'s notes.

——— .   ——— .   Boston: James R. Osgood, 1872.
312 pp.

——— .   Essays.   Boston: James Munroe, 1841.
303 pp.
    Inscription: Abel Adams from his friend R. W. E.,
19 Mar. 1841, and notes.

——— .   ——— .   Copy 2.
    Inscription and autograph.

Marginal notes, and notes inside back cover.   Ms. notes on leaf inserted at p. 133.

_____ .   _____ .   With preface by Thomas Carlyle.   London: James Fraser, 1841.   xvi, 371 pp.
Inscription on leaf tipped in at front: To Lydian Emerson from Carlyle, 21 Aug. 1841.

_____ .   _____ .   1st series.   Boston: James R. Osgood, 1873.   vi, 333 pp.
Note.

_____ .   _____ .   Boston: Houghton, Mifflin, 1881.   vi, 333 pp.

_____ .   _____ .   2d series.   Boston: James Munroe, 1844.   313 pp.
Inscription: To my mother with the affectionate respect of her son Waldo, Concord, 15 Oct. 1844.

_____ .   _____ .   Boston: James R. Osgood, 1873. 274 pp.

_____ .   _____ .   Boston: Houghton, Osgood, 1880. 274 pp.

_____ .   Fortune of the Republic.   Lecture delivered at the Old South Church, March 30, 1878.   Boston: Houghton, Osgood, 1879.   44 pp.

_____ .   _____ .   Copy 2.

_____ .   Historical discourse, delivered before the citizens of Concord, 12th September, 1835, on the second centennial anniversary of the incorporation of the town.   Concord: G. F. Bemis, 1835.   32 pp.

_____ .   Index to the Journals of Ralph Waldo Emerson. [n.p., n.d.]   5 v.
Manuscripts.   "Vol. I" only numbered.
First vol. called "vol. I."   Also lettered vol. A^1, A^2, B, C, and D.
Binder's title: Record.

_____ .   Letters and social aims.   Boston: James R. Osgood, 1876.   314 pp.
Autograph: Ellen T. Emerson, Dec. 1875 (in R. W. E's hand).

——— . ——— . Copy 2.
Manuscript note on flyleaf: For correction.   Notes at front and back, in text and inside back cover.

——— . ——— . Copy 3.
Autograph: Lydian Emerson (in R. W. E's hand).

——— . ——— . Copy 4.
Given to Concord Free Public Library in Dec. 1875 [*sic*] by Ralph Waldo Emerson (Cameron, III, 867).

——— . Love, friendship, domestic life.   Boston: James R. Osgood, 1877.   93 pp.

——— . [Ms. digest of R. W. Emerson's lectures, 1843-63.]   [n.p., n.d.]   361 pp.
On cover: Morning journal & New York Inquirer, 1843. Tribune 1852, 1853, 1863.
Red paper notebook, written in pencil on one side of leaf only, by J. E. Cabot, with a list of Emerson's lectures.

——— . [Ms. digest of R. W. Emerson's lectures, 1850-63.]   [n.p., n.d.] 321 pp.
On cover: Herald 1850, 1863.
Buff paper notebook, written in pencil on one side of leaf only, by J. E. Cabot.

——— . May-day, and other pieces.   Boston: Ticknor and Fields, 1867.   iv, 205 pp.
Inscription: For Mrs. E. from J. T. F(ields).   The first copy bound of this lovely Spring volume.

——— . ——— . Copy 2.
Notes.

——— . ——— . Copy 3.
Marginal notes.

——— . ——— . Boston: James R. Osgood, 1871.   iv, 205 pp.

——— . ——— . Boston: Houghton, Mifflin, 1881.   iv, 205 pp.

——— . Miscellanies; embracing Nature, addresses, and lectures. Boston: Fields, Osgood, 1870. vi, 383 pp.

——— . Nature.   Boston: James R. Osgood, 1876. 93 pp.

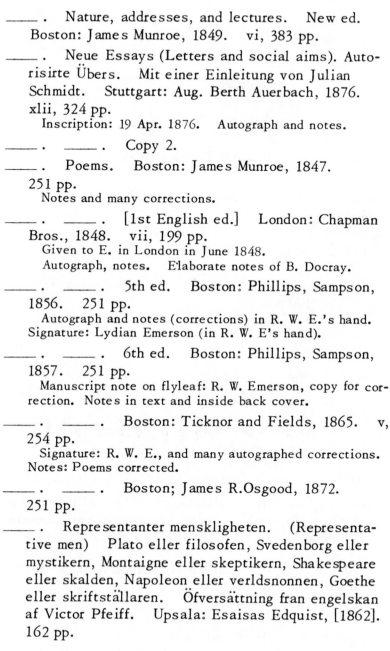

———. Nature, addresses, and lectures. New ed. Boston: James Munroe, 1849. vi, 383 pp.

———. Neue Essays (Letters and social aims). Autorisirte Übers. Mit einer Einleitung von Julian Schmidt. Stuttgart: Aug. Berth Auerbach, 1876. xlii, 324 pp.
 Inscription: 19 Apr. 1876. Autograph and notes.

———. ———. Copy 2.

———. Poems. Boston: James Munroe, 1847. 251 pp.
 Notes and many corrections.

———. ———. [1st English ed.] London: Chapman Bros., 1848. vii, 199 pp.
 Given to E. in London in June 1848.
 Autograph, notes. Elaborate notes of B. Docray.

———. ———. 5th ed. Boston: Phillips, Sampson, 1856. 251 pp.
 Autograph and notes (corrections) in R. W. E.'s hand.
 Signature: Lydian Emerson (in R. W. E's hand).

———. ———. 6th ed. Boston: Phillips, Sampson, 1857. 251 pp.
 Manuscript note on flyleaf: R. W. Emerson, copy for correction. Notes in text and inside back cover.

———. ———. Boston: Ticknor and Fields, 1865. v, 254 pp.
 Signature: R. W. E., and many autographed corrections.
 Notes: Poems corrected.

———. ———. Boston; James R. Osgood, 1872. 251 pp.

———. Representanter menskligheten. (Representative men) Plato eller filosofen, Svedenborg eller mystikern, Montaigne eller skeptikern, Shakespeare eller skalden, Napoleon eller verldsnonnen, Goethe eller skriftställaren. Öfversättning fran engelskan af Victor Pfeiff. Upsala: Esaisas Edquist, [1862]. 162 pp.

_____. Representative men, seven lectures.   Boston:
Phillips, Sampson, 1850.   285 pp.
   Autograph: Lydian Emerson, 30 Dec. 1849 (in R. W. E's
   hand).

_____. _____. Copy 2.
   On flyleaf; R. W. E. copy for correction.   Notes.

_____. _____. Authorized ed.   Leipzig: Alphons
Dürr, 1856.   214 pp.

_____. _____. Boston: James R. Osgood, 1873.
285 pp.

_____. _____. Boston: Houghton, Mifflin, 1881.
285 pp.

_____. Selected poems.   New and rev. ed.   Boston:
J. R. Osgood, 1876.   218 pp.
   Notes.

_____. Society and solitude.   Boston: Fields, Osgood,
1870.   300 pp.
   On verso of flyleaf: Copy for correction.   Notes,
   changes marked for printer in text.

_____. _____. 1872.   300 pp.

_____. Versuche.   (Essays)   Aus dem Englischen
von G. Fabricius ...   Hannover: Carl Meyer, 1858.
vi, 448 pp.

_____, ed.   Parnassus.   Boston: Osgood, 1875.
534 pp.
   Presented to Concord Free Public Library by Ralph
   Waldo Emerson on December 22, 1874 (Cameron, III, 867).

EMERSON, WILLIAM.   A discourse, delivered before the
   Roxbury Charitable Society, at their annual meeting,
   September 15, 1800.   Boston: Samuel Hall, 1800.
   23 pp.
   Bound with the author's Piety and arms.   Boston, 1799.

_____. _____. Copy 2.

_____. An historical sketch of the First Church in
   Boston, from its formation to the present period.   To
   which are added two sermons, one on leaving the

old, and the other on entering the new house of worship.   Boston: Munroe & Francis, 1812.   256 pp.
Signature: R. Emerson.

_____.   Oration pronounced July 5, 1802, at the request of the inhabitants of the town of Boston, in commemoration of the anniversary of American independence.   Boston: Manning & Loring, [1802?].
23 pp.
Bound with the author's Piety and arms.   Boston, 1799.
CONTENTS:—Vote of the town.—Oration.—Ode for the anniversary of American independence, July 4th, 1802, by a citizen of Boston.

_____.   Piety and arms.   A sermon preached at the request of the Ancient and Honourable Artillery Company in Boston, June 3, 1799; the anniversary of the election of officers.   Boston: Manning & Loring, 1799.   23 pp.

_____.   _____.   Copy 2.
Signature: R. W. E. from Edward Jarvis.   Inscriptions.

_____.   A selection of psalms and hymns, embracing all the varieties of subject and metre, suitable for private devotion, and the worship of churches.   Boston: Munroe, Francis & Parker, 1808.   iv, 150 pp.
Autograph: Hannah Stevenson.   Signature on wrapper: E. W. Emerson.

_____.   A sermon, deliverd in Brattlestreet Church, Boston, on the Sunday after the interment of Madam Elizabeth Bowdoin, relict of the late Honourable James Bowdoin, who departed life May 5, 1803, in the seventy second year of her age.   Boston: David Carlisle, 1803.   20 pp.
Signature: R. W. Emerson.
Bound with the author's Piety and arms.   Boston, 1799.

_____.   _____.   Copy 2.

_____.   A sermon, delivered March 2, 1803, at the ordination of Thomas Beede, to the care of the Church of

Christ in Wilton.   Amherst, N. H.: Joseph Cushing,
1803.   32 pp.
  Signature: R. W. E.
  Bound with the author's Piety and arms.   Boston, 1799.

——.   A sermon, on the decease of Peter Thacher,
pronounced Dec. 31, 1802, in Brattle-street Church,
Boston.   Boston: Young and Minns, 1803.   40 pp.

——.   ——.   Copy 2.

——.   A sermon, preached at the ordination of Robin-
son Smiley, to the pastoral care of the Christian
Church and Society in Springfield, State of Vermont,
September 23, 1801.   Windsor, Printed by Nahum
Mower for the Society, 1801.   24 pp.
  Bound with the author's Piety and arms.   Boston, 1799.

EMERY, GEORGE EDWIN.   Body of the Zeni map of the
North Sea and lands, 1380, exhibiting an original
identification of Frisland, Islanda, Crolandia,
Podanda, Monaco, Icaria, Neome, Grislada and the
Seven Islands (Mimant, etc.), also the Islande of the
Zeni Narrative and the Lost colony of East Green-
land.   Lynn, Mass., 1877.   facs. map.

——.   Map of the North Sea and lands delineated upon
a chart in the 14th century by Antonio Zeno, and as
printed at Venice in 1558 to accompany the Narrative
of the Northern voyages of the brothers Nicolo and
Antonio Zeno to Iceland, Greenland, Spitzbergen,
Franz Joseph Land, etc., etc., 1830 and after.
Lynn, Mass., 1877.   fasc. map.

Encyclopaedia Americana; a popular dictionary of arts,
sciences, literature, history, politics and biography,
brought down to the present time; including a copious
collection of original articles in American biography;
on the basis of the 7th ed. of the German Conversa-
tions-lexicon.   Ed. by Francis Lieber, assisted by
E. Wigglesworth.   Philadelphia: Carey, Lea &
Carey, 1829-33.   13 v.
  Autograph.

EPICTETUS. Selections. Boston: Roberts Bros., 1877. x, 150 pp.

——. Works. Consisting of his discourses, in four books, the Enchiridion, and fragments. A translation from the Greek based on that of Elizabeth Carter, by Thomas Wentworth Higginson. Boston: Little, Brown, 1865. xvi, 437 pp.
Inscription: From T. W. H., 20 Sept. 1865.

ERASMUS, DESIDERII. Colloquia familiaria et encomium moriae. Ad optimorum editionum fidem diligenter emendata cum succincta difficiliorum explanatione ... Editio stereotypa. Lipsiae: Car Tauchnitii, 1829. 2 v. in 1.
Autograph.

ERCKMANN, ÉMILE. Histoire du plebiscite racontrée par un des 7,500,000 oui. 2. éd. Paris: J. Hetzel, 1872. 341 pp.
Inscription: Ellen T. Emerson from C. E., Nov. 20, 1872, in her hand.

ERNESTI, JOHANN AUGUST. Clavis Ciceroniana; siv, Indices rerum et verborum philologico-critici in opera Ciceronis accedvnt Graeca Ciceronis necessariis observationibvs illvstrata. Editio seconda longe avctior. Halae: Impensis Orphanotrophei, 1757. [824] pp.
Inscription: From N. L. Frothingham.

ERSKINE, THOMAS. Letters of Thomas Erskine of Linlathen from 1840 till 1870. Ed. by William Hanna. Edinburgh: David Douglas, 1877. x, 419 pp.
Inscription: From Alexander Ireland, 14 Dec. 1877, and notes. Notes also on blue slip laid in at p. 211.

An essay on woman ... Reprinted from "The Sunbeam." London: J. W. Southgate, 1839. 2 v.
Bound with: Lane, Charles. A classification of science and arts. London, 1826.

EUCLIDES. Elements of geometry, containing the first six books of Euclid, with a supplement on the prop-

erties of the circle, the intersections of planes, and
the geometry of solids, by John Playfair ... 2d
American ed., with improvements. Boston: T. B.
Wait, 1814. xxviii, 315 pp.
> Autographs: R. W. Emerson, Cambridge July 11, 1818,
> W. E. to R. W. E. July 1818, Ralph W. Emerson. Notes.

EURIPIDES. Τραγωδιαι. Euripides tragoediae. Nova
editio accurata in usum praelectionum academicarum
et scholarum. Ex nova recognitione Aug. Matthiae.
Oxonii: J. Parker, et R. Bliss, 1821. 2 v.
> Inscription: To E. B. Emerson from Joshua T. Kirkland.

――. Tragedies. Literally tr. or rev., with critical
and explanatory notes, by Theodore Alois Buckley.
London: Bell & Daldy, 1868-70. 2 v.

EVANS, WARREN FELT. Mental medicine; a theoretical
and practical treatise on medical psychology. 5th
ed. Boston: Colby and Rich, 1875. x, 216 pp.

EVANS, SIR WILLIAM DAVID. A letter to Sir Samuel
Romilly, knight, on the revision of the bankrupt
laws. [n.p., n.d.] [171]-233 pp.
> "Originally published in 1810."

EVANSVILLE, IND. CHURCH OF THE UNITY. Foundation
stones of the Church of the Unity, Evansville,
Indiana. Evansville, Ind.: George C. Smith, 1878.
95 pp.

EVELYN, JOHN. Acetaria; a discourse of sallets. 2d
ed. By J. E., S.R.S. London: B. Tooke, 1706.
192 pp.
> Bound with the author's Kalendarium hortense. 10th
> ed. London, 1706.

――. Kalehdarium hortense; or, The gard'ner's almanac, directing what he is to do monthly throughout
the year; and what fruits and flowers are in prime.
10th ed., with many useful additions. London: Rob.
Scot, Ric. Chiswell, George Sawbridge, and Emj.
Took, 1706. ix, 170 pp.
> Inscription: From A. B. Alcott, and notes. Note also
> on slip inserted at p. 82.

_____. Memoirs; comprising his diary, from 1641 to
1705-6, and a selection of his familiar letters.   Ed.
by William Bray.   London: Frederick Warne; New
York: Scribner, Welford, [1871].   xvi, 783 pp.

EVELYN, WILLIAM GLANVILLE.   Memoir and letters of
Captain W. Glanville Evelyn, of the 4th regiment,
("King's own") from North America, 1774-1776.
Ed. and annotated by G. D. Scull.   Oxford: J.
Parker, 1879.   x, 140 pp.
   Inscription.

Evening school for boys [in School House, Hare street,
Bethnal Green.   London, 1828.]
   Broadside.
   Bound with: Lane, Charles.   A classification of sci-
ence and arts.   London, 1826.

EVERETT, CHARLES CARROLL.   The science of thought, a
system of logic.   Boston: Nichols and Hall, 1870.
xii, 424 pp.
   Inscription.

EVERETT, EDWARD.   An address delivered as the introduction to the Franklin lectures, in Boston, November 14, 1831.   Boston: Gray and Bowen, 1832.
24 pp.
   Bound with: Webster, Daniel.   Speech ... on the 14th
January, 1814.   Alexandria, 1814.

_____. An address delivered at Charlestown, August 1,
1826, in commemoration of John Adams and Thomas
Jefferson.   Boston: William L. Lewis, 1826.   36 pp.
   Bound with: Webster, Daniel.   A discourse, delivered
at Plymouth, September 22, 1820.   Boston, 1826.

_____. An address delivered on the 28th of June, 1830,
the anniversary of the arrival of Governor Winthrop at
Charlestown.   Delivered and published at the request of the Charlestown Lyceum.   Charlestown:
William W. Wheildon; Boston: Carter and Hendee,
1830.   51 pp.
   Bound with the author's An oration delivered at Plymouth, December 22, 1824.   Boston, 1825.

————. An address, pronounced, October twenty-first, at the funeral of John Lovejoy Abbot, pastor of the First Church of Christ in Boston. Boston: Munroe, Francis and Parker, 1814. 20 pp.
Autograph.

————. An oration delivered at Cambridge on the fiftieth anniversary of the declaration of the independence of the United States of America. Boston: Cummings, Hilliard, 1826. 51 pp.
Bound with: Webster, Daniel. A discourse, delivered at Plymouth, December 22, 1820. Boston, 1826.

————. ————. Copy 2.
Bound with the author's An oration delivered at Plymouth, December 22, 1824. Boston, 1825.

————. An oration delivered at Concord, April the nineteenth, 1825. Boston: Cummings, Hilliard, 1825. 59 pp.
Bound with the author's Speech ... March 9, 1826. Washington, 1826.

————. ————. Copy 2.
Bound with: Webster, Daniel. A discourse, delivered at Plymouth, December 22, 1820. Washington, 1826.

————. An oration delivered at Plymouth, December 22, 1824. Boston: Cummings, Hilliard, 1825. 73 pp.
Autograph.

————. ————. Copy 2.
Bound with: Webster, Daniel. A discourse, delivered at Plymouth, December 22, 1820. Boston, 1826.

————. An oration pronounced at Cambridge before the Society of Phi Beta Kappa, August 26, 1824. Published by request. Boston: Oliver Everett, 1824. 67 pp.
Bound with: Webster, Daniel. A discourse, delivered at Plymouth, December 22, 1820. Boston, 1826.

————. ————. Copy 2.
Signature: R. W. Emerson.
Bound with: Webster, Daniel. A discourse delivered at Plymouth, December 22, 1820. Boston, 1821.

_____. A sermon, preached at the dedication of the
First Congregational Church in New York, Jan. 20,
1821. Published at the request of the Society. 2d
ed. Boston: Cummings and Hilliard, and Oliver
Everett, 1821. 23 pp.
    Signature: R. W. Emerson.
    Bound with: Webster, Daniel. A discourse delivered at
Plymouth, December 22, 1820. Boston, 1821.

_____. Speech of Mr. Everett, of Massachusetts, on the
bill for removing the Indians from the East to the
West side of the Mississippi. Delivered in the
House of Representatives, on the 19th of May, 1830.
Boston: Daily Advertiser, 1830. 46 pp.
    Bound with the author's An oration delivered at Plym-
outh, December 22, 1824. Boston, 1825.

_____. Speech of Mr. Everett, on the proposition to
amend the Constitution of the United States. Delivered in the House of Representatives, March 9,
1826. Washington: P. Thompsom, 1826. 51 pp.
    Autograph.

_____. Speech of the Hon. Edward Everett, in the
House of Representatives of the United States, March
9, 1826, in committee, on the proposition to amend
the Constitution. Boston: Dutton and Wentworth,
1826. 38 pp.
    Autograph.
    Bound with: Webster, Daniel. A discourse, delivered at
Plymouth, December 22, 1820. Boston, 1826.

_____. Synopsis of a course of lectures on the history
of Greek literature. [n.p., 182-?] 84 pp.
    Notes by E. B. E. or R. W. E.
    Bound with the author's Speech ... March 9, 1826.
Washington, 1826.

EWING, GREVILLE. A Greek and English lexicon: originally a scripture lexicon; and now adapted to the
Greek classics; with a Greek grammar prefixed. 3d
ed. Glasgow: University Press; London: James
Duncan, 1827. x, 899 pp.
    Autograph.

F

FABER, FREDERICK WILLIAM. Hymns, with a sketch of
his life. New York: E. P. Dutton, 1881. xii,
253 pp.
  Inscription: Ellen T. Emerson from A. H. B. Ward, 1881
Xmas, and note.

FALL RIVER LITHOGRAPH COMPANY. The spirit of young
America. Fall River, Mass.: Fall River Litho. Co.;
Boston: G. W. Cottrell, [18—?] 13 l.

FARNHAM, ELIZA WOODSON (BURHANS) "Mrs. T. J. Farnham." Woman and her era. New York: A. J.
Davis, 1864. 2 v.

FARRAR, ELIZA WARE (ROTCH) "Mrs. John Farrar." The
young lady's friend, by a lady. Improved stereotype ed. Boston: American Stationers' Co., John B.
Russell, 1836. xi, 432 pp.

FAURE, D. P. "Modern theology." Sixteen discourses
held in the Mutual Hall, Cape Town. Cape Town:
Van de Sandt de Villiers, 1869. x, 241 pp.

FAURIEL, CLAUDE CHARLES. History of Provençal poetry. Tr. from the French, with occasional notes
and references to the authorities cited or alluded to
in the volume, specimens of verse in the original and
an introd. on the literature of the history of Provençal poetry, by G. J. Alder. New York: Derby &
Jackson, 1860. xl, 496 pp.
  Inscription and notes.

FAWCETT, EDGAR.   Fantasy and passion.   Boston:
Roberts Brothers, 1878.   xi, 191 pp.
Inscription: R. W. E. by author.

FAY, THEODORE SEDGWICK.   Atlas to Fay's great outline
of geography for high schools and families, with a
text-book.   New York: G. P. Putnam, [ᶜ1867].

――――.   Great outline of geography for high schools and
families; text-book to accompany the universal atlas.
New York: G. P. Putnam, 1867.   viii, 238 pp.

FELLER, FRIEDRICH ERNST.   A new pocket dictionary:
English, German, and French ...   16th ed.
Leipzig: B. G. Teubner, 1870.   3 v.
Autograph.

――――.   ――――.   21st ed.   Leipzig: B. G. Teubner,
1877.   3 v.

FELTHAM, OWEN.   Resolves, divine, moral and political.
With some account of the author and his writings.
Cambridge: Hilliard and Brown, 1832.   xx, 316 pp.
Autograph.

FÉNELON, FRANÇOIS DE SALIGNAC DE LA MOTHE, *Abp. de
Cambrai.*   Abrégé de la vie des plus illustres philosophes de l'antiquité, avec leurs dogmes, leurs
systèmes, leur morale et leurs plus belles maximes,
attribué à F. de Salignac de la Motte de Fénelon ...
auquel on a ajouté un Abrégé de la vie des femmes
philosophes de l'antiquité; orné de portraits d'après
les pierres gravées antiques, par F.-A. David ...
Ouvrage destiné à l'éducation de la jeunesse. Nouv.
éd.   Paris: F. A. David, 1822.   vi, 353 pp.

――――.   Les aventures de Télémaque.   2 v.
In 1821 Emerson lent this to a Harvard classmate.
(Cameron, III, 856).

――――.   Dialogues of the dead, ancient and modern ...
Tr. into English from the best Paris edition.
Cooke's ed.   London: Cooke, [1797].   iv, 176 pp.

———. Leçons, contenant ses fables; ses histoires, y compris les aventures d'Aristonoüs; ses dialogues des morts . Avec des notes et explications par M. de Lévizac.   Paris: J. E. Gabriel Dufour, 1804. xvi, 242 pp.

———. Selections.   Boston: Roberts Bros., 1881. xxxv, 194 pp.
   Autograph: Ellen T. Emerson, 12 July 1882.

———. Selections from the writings.   With a memoir of his life, by a Lady.   3d ed., rev. and enl.   Boston: Hilliard, Gray, Little, and Wilkins, 1831.   304 pp.
   Inscriptions, and autograph: Ellen T. Emerson.

———. ———. With a memoir of his life, by Mrs. Follen.   4th ed. rev. and enl.   Boston: S. G. Simpkins, 1841.   xiii, 304 pp.
   Autograph: Ellen T. Emerson.

———. Thoughts on spiritual subjects, tr. from the writings of Fénelon.   Boston: Samuel G. Simpkins, 1843.   viii, 148 pp.
   Autograph on outside of wrapper: Ellen T. Emerson. Inscription: R. W. Emerson for his friend George P. Bradford 1843.

FERGUSON, ROBERT.   The Teutonic name-system applied to the family names of France, England, & Germany. London: Williams & Norgate, 1864.   xv, 606 pp.
   Inscription: Dec. 1864.

FERGUSON, WALTER.   My early days.   2d ed.   Boston: Bowles & Dearborn, 1827.
   Given to the Concord Free Public Library by Ralph Waldo Emerson in Feb. 1874; discarded as worn out in 1910 (Cameron, III, 867).

FERGUSSON, JAMES.   The illustrated handbook of architecture; being a concise and popular account of the different styles of architecture prevailing in all ages and countries.   London: J. Murray, 1855.   2 v.
   Autograph.

FERNALD, WOODBURY M.   God in his providence; a comprehensive view of the principles and particulars of

an active divine providence over man; his fortunes, changes, trials, entire discipline as a spiritual being, from birth to eternity. Boston: O. Clapp; New York: D. Appleton, 1859. xv, 437 pp.
  Autograph: Ellen T. Emerson.

FEUERBACH, LUDWIG ANDREAS. The essence of Christianity. Tr. from the 2d German ed., by Marian Evans. New York: C. Blanchard, 1855. 442 pp.

FICHTE, JOHANN GOTTLIEB. On the nature of the scholar, and its manifestations. Tr. from the German, with a memoir of the author, by William Smith. London: John Chapman, 1845. vii, 220 pp.

FIELD, HORACE. Heroism; or, God our Father, omnipotent, omniscient, omnipresent. London: Longmans, Green, Reader, & Dyer, 1867. xix, 113 pp.

——. A home for the homeless; or, Union with God. London, [Printed], 1869.
  Presented to the Concord Free Public Library by Ralph Waldo Emerson in Feb. 1874; withdrawn in 1921 (Cameron, III, 867).

FIELDS, JAMES THOMAS. Yesterdays with authors. Boston: James R. Osgood, 1872. 352 pp.
  Inscription: For Mrs. Emerson with cordial regards of J. T. Fields.

FINLEY, ANTHONY, *firm, publisher.* Map of Louisiana, Mississippi and Alabama constructed from the latest authorities. Philadelphia, 1826. col. map.

FISHER, SIDNEY GEORGE. Winter studies in the country. Philadelphia: Parry and McMillan, 1856. 43 pp.

Fleets pocket almanack for the year of our Lord 1790. Being the second after leap year and fourteenth of American Independence, calculated chiefly for the use of the Commonwealth of Massachusetts, Boston, the metropolis ... to which is annexed the Massachusetts Register, etc. Boston: T. & J. Fleet, [1789?]. 24, 130 pp.
  Notes by W. Emerson.

FLORENCE.   Plan de la ville de Florence [avec in-
dications utiles pour les touristes].   [Florence]:
Ottavio Pieri, [18—?].   map.

FLORIAN, JEAN PIERRE CLARIS DE.   Éliezer et
Nephthali, poème traduit de l'Hébreu par Florian.
Paris: A. A. Renouard, 1812.   90 pp.
   Bound with the author's Guillaume Tell.   Paris, 1812.

———.   Guillaume Tell; ou, La Suisse libre, ouvrage
posthume.   Paris: A. A. Renouard, 1812.   100 pp.
   Autograph.

The flower people.   By a lady.   Hartford: Tyler &
Porter; Boston: E. P. Peabody, 1842.   228 pp.

FLÜGEL, JOHANN GOTTFRIED.   A complete dictionary of
the English and German and German & English lan-
guages containing all the words in general use.
London: Black, Young, and Young, 1830.   2 v.
   Set incomplete: v. 2, German and English, wanting.
   Signature: R. W. Emerson.

[———.]   Vollstandiges englisch-deutsches und
deutsch-englisches Wortenbuch, enthaltend Alle in
beiden Sprachen allgemein gebräuchliche Wörter.
Nach den anerkannt besten Schriftestellern, insbe-
sondere nach Heinsius grossem, volksthümlichen
Wörterbuche der deutschen Sprache bearbeitet von
Johann Sporschil.   Leipzig: A. G. Liebeskind, 1830.
2 v.
   Set incomplete: v. 1, Englisch und Deutsch, wanting.
   Signature: R. W. Emerson.

FOA, EUGÉNIE (RODRIGUES-GRADIS).   Le petit Robinson
de Paris.   Avec vocabulaire.   Boston: S. R.
Urbino; New York: Leypoldt & Holt, 1867.   166 pp.

FOLLEN, CHARLES THEODORE CHRISTIAN.   A practical
grammar of the German language.   Boston: Hilliard,
Gray, Little, and Wilkins, 1828.   xix, 282 pp.
   Clipping laid in at p. 129.

Food for the heart.   [London? 18—?]   1 l.
  Broadside.
  Bound with: Lane, Charles.   A classification of sci-
  ence and arts.   London, 1826.

FORBES, JOHN MURRAY.   The currency, Remarks and examination of John M. Forbes, of Boston, before the
  committee of the House of Representatives of the
  United States on banking and currency, January 20,
  1874.   Washington: S. & R. O. Polkinhorn, 1874.
  18 pp.

FORBES, ROBERT BENNET.   Personal reminiscences.
  Boston: Little, Brown, 1878.   vii, 382 pp.

FORD, JOHN.   Dramatic works. With an introduction,
  and notes critical and explanatory.   London: John
  Murray, 1831.   2 v.
  Autograph: Nathaniel Hawthorne. Inscription: To R. W.
  Emerson (in Emerson's hand).

FORMAN, JACOB GILBERT, *comp.*   The soldier's manual
  of devotion; or, Book of common prayer; containing a
  form of public worship, with responses, additional
  prayers, a psalter, scripture lessons, articles of
  religion, and a collection of hymns and national
  songs. ...   For the use of chaplains and soldiers
  in the army.   2d ed. stereotyped.   Alton, Ill., 1863.
  vi, 224 pp.
  Autograph: E. Emerson.

FORSTER, JOHN.   Walter Savage Landor, a biography.
  London: Chapman and Hall, 1869.   2 v.
  Notes.

FORSTER, WILLIAM EDWARD.   William Penn and Thomas
  B. Macaulay; being brief observations on the charges
  made in Mr. Macaulay's History of England against
  the character of William Penn.   London: Charles
  Gilpin, 1849.   54 pp.
  Inscription.   Manuscript corrections by the author.

Fort Monroe and vicinity, showing entrance to Chesa-
peake Bay, Norfolk, Portsmouth, Gosport Navy Yard
&c. [Boston]: E. P. Dutton, [186—?].
  Inserted in: Tanner, H. S.   New universal atlas.
  Philadelphia, 1845.

FOSTER, JOHN.   Essays in a series of letters.   9th ed.,
cor.   London: Holdsworth and Ball, 1830.   xx,
456 pp.
  Underlined.

FOURIER, FRANÇOIS MARIE CHARLES.   The passions of
the human soul.   Tr. from the French, by John
Reynell Morell.   With critical annotations, a biography of Fourier, and a general introduction, by
Hugh Doherty.   London, New York: H. Bailliere,
1851.   2 v.

[FOURNET, JOSEPH JEAN BAPTISTE XAVIER.]   Notice bio-
graphique, Madame Anniette Grote.   Poitiers: Oudin
frères, 1879.   22 pp.
  Inscription.

FOX, WILLIAM JOHNSON.   Christ and Christianity.   Sermons on the mission, character, and doctrine of
Jesus of Nazareth.   Boston: Leonard C. Bowles,
1833.   2 v.
  Set incomplete: v. 2 wanting.

FOXCROFT, THOMAS.   The day of a godly man's death,
better than the day of his birth.   Shewed in a sermon, preach'd Feb. 25, 1722.   Boston: B. Greene,
1722.   ii, 196 pp.
  Autograph deleted.

FRANCE. MINISTÈRE DE L'INTÉRIEUR.   Statistique de
l'Egypte.   Année 1873 (1290 de l'Hégire).   Le
Caire: Française Mourès, 1873.   lxxxvi, 315 pp.

FRANCIS, CONVERS.   Life of John Eliot, the apostle to
the Indians.   Boston: Hilliard, Gray; London: Richard James Kennett, 1836.   xii, 357 pp.
  Inscription and notes.

FRANCKE, H. Outlines of a new theory of disease, applied to hydropathy, showing that water is the only true remedy. With observations on the errors committed in the practice of hydropathy; notes on the cure of cholera by cold water; and a critique on Priessnitz's mode of treatment. Intended for popular use. Tr. from the German, by Robert Baikie. New York: John Wiley, 1867. viii, 271 pp.

FRANÇOIS DE SALES, *Saint.* A selection from the spiritual letters ... Tr. by the author of "Life of S. Francis de Sales," "A Dominican artist," etc., etc. ... London: Rivingtons, 1871. x, 362 pp. Autograph: Ellen T. Emerson.

FRASER, SIR WILLIAM AUGUSTUS. Coila's whispers. 2d ed. London: F. Harvey, 1872. vi, 160 pp. Inscription: From the author (in Emerson's hand).

FREEMASONS. CONCORD, MASS. CORINTHIAN LODGE. Bylaws ... To which is added an historical sketch of Masonry, by Louis A. Surrette. Concord: B. Tolman, 1859. 191 pp.

FROISSART, JEAN. Chronicles of England, France, Spain and the adjoining countries, from the latter part of the reign of Edward II, to the coronation of Henry IV. Tr. from the French, with variations and additions, from many celebrated mss., by Thomas Johnes. To which are prefixed a life of the author, an essay on his works, and a criticism on his history. With an original introductory essay on the character and society of the middle ages, by John Lord. [1st American ed.] New York: J. Winchester, [1843?]. xv, 634 pp. Autograph. Notes on slip inserted at p. 283.

FROST, BARZILLAI. Two sermons on the death of Ezra Ripley. One preached at the funeral, by Barzillai Frost, of Concord; the other on the following Sabbath, by Convers Francis, of Watertown. Boston: James Munroe, 1841. 46 pp.

FROTHINGHAM, EPHRAIM LANGDON, AND FROTHINGHAM, ARTHUR LINCOLN. Philosophy as absolute science, founded in the universal laws of being, and including ontology, theology, and psychology made one, as spirit, soul and body. v. 1. Boston: Walker, Wise, 1864. xxxiv, 453 pp.
No more published.

FROTHINGHAM, NATHANIEL LANGDON. Farewell. A sermon preached to the First Church, on resigning its pastoral charge, Sunday, March 10, 1850. Printed by request. Boston: John Wilson, 1850. 26 pp.
Inscription: To Mrs. William Emerson.

————. Metrical pieces, translated and original. Boston: Crosby, Nichols, 1855. x, 362 pp.
Inscription.

————. ————. Copy 2.
Inscription: To Miss Edith Emerson by author.

————. ————. Part second. Boston: Roberts Bros., 1870, viii, 276 pp.
Inscription: From R. W. Emerson to I. Haven Emerson, April, 1870.

————. [The prophet and the honorable man taken away.] ... A sermon preached to the First Church, on Sunday morning, 10th April, after the funerals of Dr. Harris, and Daniel Sargent. Not published. Boston: J. T. Buckingham, 1842. 15 pp.

————. A sermon, delivered before the Ancient and Honourable Artillery Company, June 6th, 1825, being the 187th anniversary. Boston: E. G. House, 1825. 21 pp.
Inscription: R. W. Emerson from Mr. Frothingham (in R. W. E.'s hand).

————. A sermon preached to the First Church by its minister, on the twentieth anniversary of his ordination, March 15, 1835. Boston: Munroe and Francis, 1835. 16 pp.
Bound with: Webster, Daniel. Speech ... on the 14th January, 1814. Alexandria, 1814.

FROTHINGHAM, OCTAVIUS BROOKS. Transcendentalism in New England; a history. New York: G. P. Putnam's Sons, 1876. ix, 395 pp.
Inscription.

FROTHINGHAM, RICHARD. The rise of the Republic of the United States. 2d ed. Boston: Little, Brown, 1873. xxii, 640 pp.
Inscription: Jan. 1874.

FROUDE, JAMES ANTHONY. The nemesis of faith. London: J. Chapman, 1849. 227 pp.
Autograph.

_____. Short studies on great subjects. [1st series.] New York: C. Scribner, 1872. 534 pp.
Bookplate of Samuel Moody Haskins.

Fruit aliment. [Cheltenham: Harper, Free Press Office, 1840?] 2 pp.
Letter signed: F. P. B.
Bound with: Lane, Charles. A classification of science and arts. London, 1826.

_____. _____. Another issue.
Text with additions set in line border.

FULLER, RICHARD FREDERICK. Visions in verse; or, Dreams of creation and redemption. Boston: Lee and Shepard, 1864. 282 pp.
Inscription: 14 July 1864.

FULLER, THOMAS. The holy and profane states. With some account of the author and his writings. Cambridge: Hilliard and Brown, 1831. xxxix, 293 pp.
Autograph.

_____. _____. Copy 2.
Now in Concord Free Public Library. Apparently given first to the Religious Library of the First Parish Church, and labeled (not in Emerson's handwriting): R. W. Emerson.

FURNESS, WILLIAM HENRY. Discourses ... Philadelphia: G. Collins; Boston: Crosby, Nichols, 1855. vii, 308 pp.
Inscription: From publisher.

_____. _____. Copy 2.
Inscription: From publisher.

——. Gems of German verse. A new ed. rev. and enl. Philadelphia: Willis P. Hazard, 1860. 158 pp.

——. Jesus. Philadelphia: J. B. Lippincott, 1871. iii, 223 pp.
Inscription: Ellen Emerson from her father's oldest friend, May '76 (the author).

——. Jesus, the heart of Christianity. Priv. Print. Philadelphia: J. B. Lippincott, 1879. 84 pp.
Inscription: From author, Oct. 1879.

——. The power of spirit manifest in Jesus of Nazareth. Philadelphia: J. B. Lippincott, 1877. 208 pp.
Inscription: R. W. Emerson from his oldest friend, June 1877.

——. Thoughts on the life and character of Jesus of Nazareth. Boston: Phillips, Sampson, 1859. 311 pp.

——. The veil partly lifted and Jesus becoming visible. Boston: Ticknor and Fields, 1864. 301 pp.
Signature: R. W. Emerson. Inscription slip inserted: From author.

FUSTEL DE COULANGES, NUMA DENIS. La cité antique; étude sur le culte, le droit, les institutions de la Grèce et de Rome. 3. éd. Paris: L. Hachette, 1870. 496 pp.
Autograph.

G

GAGANI, GUGLIELMO. The Roman exile. Boston: J. P. Jewett; New York: Sheldon, Blakeman 1856. vi, 450 pp.
> Inscription: To R. W. E. by author.

GALLAUDET, THOMAS HOPKINS. The child's book on the soul ... 5th ed., with questions. Hartford: Belknap & Hamersley, 1836. 2 v. in 1.
> Autograph: Ellen Emerson.

GANNETT, WILLIAM CHANNING. Ezra Stiles Gannett, Unitarian minister in Boston, 1824-1871. A memoir, by his son. Boston: Roberts Bros., 1875. xv, 572 pp.

——. A year of miracle, a poem in four sermons. Boston: Geo. H. Ellis, 1882. 106 pp.

GARBETT, EDWARD LACY. Rudimentary treatise on the principles of design in architecture as deducible from nature and exemplified in the works of the Greek and Gothic architects. London: John Weale, 1850. viii, 264 pp.
> Autograph and notes.

GARDNER, ANNA. Harvest gleanings in prose and verse. With an introduction by Phebe A. Hanaford. New York: Fowler & Wells, 1881. viii, 200 pp.

[GARRISON, WILLIAM LLOYD.] Helen Eliza Garrison, a memorial. Cambridge: Riverside Press, 1876. 70 pp.

GASPARIN, AGÉNOR ÉTIENNE, *Comte de.*   La conscience.
5 éd.   Paris: Calmann Lévy, 1877.   346 pp.

_____ .   L'Égalité.   4. éd.   Paris: Calmann Lévy,
1876.   vii, 409 pp.
   Printed presentation slip.

_____ .   L'ennemi de la famille.   4. éd.   Paris: Michel
Lévy 1875.   367 pp.

_____ .   Les États-Unis en 1861; un grand peuple qui se
relève.   4. éd. rev. et cor.   Paris: Michel Lévy,
1873.   viii, 414 pp.

_____ .   Luther et la réforme au xvie siècle.   4. éd.
Paris: Michel Lévy frères, 1875.   455 pp.
   Notes.

GAUTIER, THÉOPHILE.   Le roman de la momie.   Paris:
L. Hachette, 1858.   302 pp.

GENLIS, STÉPHANIE FÉLICITÉ DUCREST DE SAINT-AUBIN,
Comtesse de.   Le siége de La Rochelle.   Nouv.
éd., rev. et cor.   New York: R. Lockwood; Paris:
Didier, 1855.   307 pp.
   Autograph: Edith Emerson. 1855.

GENTRY, THOMAS GEORGE.   Life-histories of the birds of
eastern Pennsylvania.   Philadelphia: Pub. by the
Author, 1876-77,   2 v.
   Set incomplete: v. 2 wanting.

GENTZ, FRIEDRICH VON.   Tagebucher.   Mit einem Vor-
und Nachwort von K. A. Varnhagen von Ense.   Leipzig: F. A. Brockhaus, 1861.   xi, 369 pp.

GÉRANDO, JOSEPH MARIE DE, *Baron.*   Histoire comparée
des systèmes de philosophie, considérés relativement
aux principes des connaissances humaines.   2. éd.,
rev., cor. et augm.   Paris: A. Eymery, 1822-23.
4 v.
   Autographs.   Notes in v. 1.

_____ .   Self-education; or, The means and art of moral
progress.   [Tr. from the French by E. P. Peabody.]
Boston: Carter and Hendee, 1830.
   Given to the Sunday School Library in Concord by Ralph
Waldo Emerson, sometime after 1835 (Cameron, III, 857).

———. ———. Copy 2.
Given to the Religious Library of the First Parish in
Concord by Emerson. Sold at the Wakeman Sale (New
York: American Art Association, 1924), Lot #260.

AL-GHAZZĀLĪ. The alchemy of happiness, by Mohammed
al-Ghazzali, the Mohammedan philosopher. Tr. from
the Turkish, by Henry A. Homes ... Albany, N. Y.:
J. Munsell, 1873. 120 pp.
Printed inscription tipped in.

GIBBON, EDWARD. History of the decline and fall of the
Roman Empire. New ed. London: Printed for
W. Allason; [by] B. Whitrow, 1821. 12 v.

———. Miscellaneous works. With memoirs of his life
and writings, composed by himself, illustrated from
his letters. With occasional notes and narrative, by
John, Lord Sheffield. Complete in one volume.
London: B. Blake, 1837. xv, 848 pp.
Autograph and notes.

GIBBS, JOSIAH WILLARD. Hebrew and English lexicon of
the Old Testament, including the Biblical Chaldee.
From the German works of W. Gesenius. Andover:
Codman Press, 1824. v, 715 pp.
Signature: R. W. Emerson.

GILBERT, HOWARD WORCESTER. Aldornere, a Pennsylvania idyll. Illus. with nine original etchings, by
Lloyd Mifflin, Jr. Philadelphia: John Penington,
1872. 27 pp.

GILCHRIST, JOHN. A collection of ancient and modern
Scottish ballads, tales and songs, with explanatory
notes and observations. Edinburgh: William Black-
wood; London: Baldwin, Cradock, & Joy, 1815. 2 v.
Set incomplete: v. 2 wanting.
Signature: R. W. Emerson.

GILES, JOHN ALLEN, *comp.* Scriptores Graeci minores,
quorum reliquias, fere omnium milioris notae, ex
editionibus variis excerpsit. Oxon: D. A. Talboys,
1831. 2 v. in 1.
Inscription: R. W. Emerson from W. E. C., and note.

_____ , *ed.*, Six old English chronicles, of which two are
now first tr. from the monkish Latin originals.
Ethelwerd's Chronicle.   Asser's Life of Alfred.
Geoffrey of Monmouth's British history.   Gildas.
Nenius.   And Richard of Cirencester.   Ed., with il-
lustrative notes, by J. A. Giles.   London: Henry G.
Bohn, 1848.   xx, 512 pp.
   Notes.

GILL, THOMAS HORNBLOWER.   The anniversaries.
Poems in commemoration of great men and great
events.   Cambridge: Macmillan, 1858.   viii, 193 pp.
   Signature: R. W. Emerson (in Ellen's hand).   Inscription: Fr. the author (by author).

_____ .   The papal drama; a historical essay.   London:
Longmans, Green, 1866.   xvi, 483 pp.

GILL, WILLIAM FEARING.   The life of Edgar Allan Poe.
4th ed., rev. and enl.   New York: W. J. Widdleton;
London: Chatto and Windus, 1878.   xiv, 347 pp.

[GILMAN, ARTHUR], *ed.*   Theatrum majorum.   The Cambridge of 1776: wherein is set forth an account of the
town, and of the events it witnessed: with which is
incorporated the diary of Dorothy Dudley, now first
publish'd; together with an historicall sketch; sever-
all appropriate poems; numerous anecdotes ...
Done by divers eminent hands, and ed. for the Ladies
Centennial Committee by A. G.   [2d ed.]   Boston:
Lockwood, Brooks, 1876.   v, 123 pp.

Glimpses of the wonderful.   1847.   New York: Wiley
and Putnam, 1847.   175 pp.
   At head of title: Christmas annual.
   Inscription: Ellen from Edith, 4 Feb. 1852.

GOETHE, JOHANN WOLFGANG VON.   Auto-biography.   Truth
and poetry: from my own life ...   London: H. G.
Bohn, 1848-49.   2 v.
   Autograph.   Note in v.l.

_____ .   Characteristics of Goethe.   From the German
of Falk, von Müller, &c., with notes, original and

translated, illustrative of German literature, by Sarah
Austin. London: Effingham Wilson, 1833. 3 v.
  Autographs.

_____ . Conversations of Goethe with Eckermann and
Soret. Tr. from the German by John Oxenford.
London: Smith, Elder, 1850. 2 v.
  Autograph in v.2.

_____ . _____ . New ed. London: G. Bell, 1875.
xxvii, 583 pp.

_____ . Essays on art. Tr. by Samuel Gray Ward.
Boston: James Munroe, 1845. vi, 263 pp.
  Inscription: From translator.

_____ . Faust; a dramatic poem. Tr. into English
prose, with notes, etc., by A. Hayward. 1st American from the 3d London ed. Lowell: Daniel Bixby:
New York: D. Appleton, 1840. xxxi, 17 pp.
  Signature: R. W. E.

_____ . Faust; a tragedy. Tr. from the German with
notes by Charles T. Brooks. Boston: Ticknor and
Fields, 1856. 234 pp.
  Signature: R. W. E.

_____ . _____ . Tr., in the original metres, by Bayard
Taylor. Boston: Fields, Osgood, 1871. 2 v.
  Inscriptions: v. 1, 14 Dec. 1870; v. 2, 25 Mar. 1871.

_____ . _____ . Part II. Tr. from the German, partly
in the metres of the original and partly in prose.
With other poems, original and translated, by Leopold
J. Bernays. London: Sampson Low, 1839. xx,
268 pp.
  Inscription: S. G. Ward Esq. Sam and Anne's gift to
Waldo.

_____ . Lettres inédites ... Publiées par Kestner.
Tr. par L. Poley. Paris: E. Glaeser, 1855. vi,
24 pp.

_____ . Roman elegies. Tr. into English verse, in the
original metre, by L. Noa. Boston: Schoenhof &
Moeller, [18—?]. 39 pp.
  Inscription: From translator.

———. Sämmtliche werke ... Vollständige, neugeor-
dnete ausgabe. Stuttgart: J. G. Cotta, 1840.
Set incomplete: v. 15, 24, 36 only.
Autographs.

———. ———. Mit Einleitungen von Karl Goedeke.
Stuttgart: J. G. Cotta, 1872. 15 v.

———. Sprüche in Prosa. Zum ersten Mal erlautert und
auf ihre Quellen zurückgefuhrt von G. von Loeper.
Berlin: Gustav Hempel, 1870. 259 pp.
Inscription: From Hon. George Bancroft, Jan. 1, 1871 (in
R. W. E.'s hand).

———. Sprüche in Reim und Prosa. [n.p., 18—?]
350 pp.
Notes and autograph.

———. Unterhaltungen mit dem Kanzler Friedrich v.
Müller. Hrsg. von C. A. H. Burkhardt. Stuttgart:
J. G. Cotta, 1870. xii, 170 pp.
Inscription: R. W. Emerson the gift of Herman Grimm,
February (in Emerson's hand). Note.

———. Werke. Vollstandige ausg. letzter Hand.
Stuttgart: J. G. Cotta, 1828–33. 55 v.
Notes. Ms. poetry and notes in v. 50.

———. West-Easterly divan. Tr., with introduction
and notes, by John Weiss. Boston: Roberts Bros.,
1877. xxxi, 264 pp.

———. Wilhelm Meister's apprenticeship, a novel.
From the German of Goethe. Boston: Wells and
Lilly, 1828. 3 v.
Presented by Miss Sophia Thoreau to Parker Pillsbury,
June 17, 1862. Now in the John L. Cooley Collection of
the Pierpont Morgan Library in New York City.
Signatures: v. 1–3, R. W. Emerson, Parker Pillsbury;
v. 1–2, Henry D. Thoreau.

———. Wilhelm Meister's apprenticeship and travels.
From the German of Goethe ... New ed. rev. Lon-
don: James Fraser, 1839. 3 v.
Inscription: R. W. Emerson, T. C. London, Dec. 1839.
Autographs in v. 2 and 3.

GOLDSMITH, OLIVER. The history of Rome, from the foundation of the city of Rome, to the destruction of the Western Empire. New ed., complete in one vol. London: Charles Wood; and Edinburgh: H. S. Baynes, 1823. x, 564 pp.

Good stories by De Quincy, Hawthorne, Thackeray, Zschökke, Winthrop, Hood, Moenish, Lee, and others. Illus. by Nast, Hennessy, Happin, Meadows, Perkins, Ehninger, Eytinge, Jr., Lumley, Davenport, and others. Boston: De Wolfe, Fiske, [18—?]. 421 pp.

GOODWIN, THOMAS. Latin-English dictionary compiled from the best authorities, for use in schools and colleges. London: Strahan, 1870. [246] pp.
Signature: R. W. Emerson.

GOODWIN, WILLIAM WATSON. De potentiae veterum gentium maritimae epochis apud Eusebium. Dissertatio inauguralis quam amplissimi philosophorum ordinis consensu et auctoritate in academia Georgia Augusta ad summas in philosophia honores vite impetrandos scripsit Guilelm. Watson Goodwin, Gottingae: Dieterichiana, 1855. 70 pp.
Bound with: Everett, Edward. Speech ... March 9, 1826. Washington, 1826.

GOODY TWO SHOES. The history of goody two shoes. London: J. L. Marks, [18—?]. 8 ll. col. illus.

GOSTWICK, JOSEPH, AND HARRISON, ROBERT. Outlines of German literature. London: Williams and Norgate, 1873. xii, 588 pp.
Inscription: To Emerson from the author, April 1873.

[GOTAMA, *called* AKSAPĀDA.] The aphorisms of the Nyaya philosophy, by Gautama, with illustrative extracts from the commentary by Viswanátha in Sanscrit and English. Tr. by J. R. Ballantyne. Printed for the use of the Benares College by order of Gov't. N. W. P. Allahabad: Presbyterian Mission Press, 1850–54.

Inscriptions: Henry D. Thoreau from Thomas Cholmondeley (in H. D. T.'s hand), R. W. Emerson by the bequest of Henry D. Thoreau (in R. W. E.'s hand). Autograph: R. W. Emerson by the bequest of Henry D. Thoreau. Marginal notes in bk. 1.

GOUGH, JOHN BARTHOLOMEW. Sunlight and shadow; or, Gleanings from my life work. Comprising personal experiences and opinions, anecdotes, incidents, and reminiscences, gathered from thirty-seven years' experience on the platform and among the people, at home and abroad. Hartford, Conn: A. D. Worthington, 1882. xxii, 542 pp. port., plates.

GOULD, THOMAS RIDGEWAY. The tragedian; an essay on the histrionic genius of Junius Brutus Booth. New York: Hurd and Houghton; Cambridge, [Mass.]: Riverside Press, 1868. 189 pp.
Inscription: To R. W. E. from author.

A Grammar of the Greek language. Boston: Thomas, 1800.
Sold at the Chicago Book & Art Auctions, Inc., on April 1, 1931.
Four autograph signatures of Emerson on flyleaves.

Grandmamma Easy's new story about Little Jack Horner and his mince pie. Albany, N. Y.: Steele & Durrie, [184—?].
Autograph: Edward Emerson.

[GRATET DUPLESSIS, PIERRE ALEXANDRE.] Petite encyclopédie des proverbes français recueillis, annotés et publiés par Hilaire le Gai [pseud.] Paris: Passard, 1852. 504 pp.

GRAVES, ALFRED PERCEVAL. Songs of Killarney. London: Bradbury, Agnew, 1873. viii, 174 pp.
Inscription: From Sarah Forbes, 15 Mar. 1876.

GRIMM, HERMAN FRIEDRICH. Arnim, ein Drama in fünf Auszügen. Leipzig: Weidmann, 1851. 153 pp.

———. Aus dem September—Heft der Preussischen Jahrbücher, 1870. [Berlin: G. Reimer, 1870?] 7 pp.
Caption title.

————. Bettina von Arnim. Frankfurt a/M: Rütten &
Loening, 1880. 16 pp.
    "Sonder-Abdruck aus dem Goethe-Jahrbuch, 1. Bd.,
1880."

————. Cornelius und die ersten funfzig Jahre nach
1800. [Abdruck aus dem 35. Bde. der Preussischen
Jahrbücher. Berlin: G. Reimer, 1875?] 83 pp.
    Inscription: Berlin 1875 (in R. W. E.'s hand).

————. Engel und Liebesgotter. Gelegentlich eines
unedirten Briefes aus der Schule Raphaels. <Ab-
druck aus dem 34. Bde. der Preussischen Jahrbücher.> [Berlin: G. Reimer, 1874.] 35 pp.

————. Essays. Hannover: Carl Rumpler, 1859.
353 pp.
    Autograph.

————. Goethe in Italien. Vorlesung gehalten zum
Besten des Goethedenkmals in Berlin. Berlin: Wilhelm Hertz, 1861. 32 pp.
    Signature: R. W. Emerson.

————. Goethe und Luise Seidler. <Erinnerungen und
Leben der Malerin Luise Seidler. Aus dem Hand-
schriftl. Nachlasse zusammengestellt und bearbeitet von Hermann Uhde.> Berlin: Wilh. Hertz,
1874. Abdruck aus dem 33. Bde. der Preussischen
Jahrbücher. Berlin: Reimer, [1873?]. 17 pp.
    Title written in E.'s hand on wrapper.

————. Goethe und Suleika. Zur erinnerung an Mari-
anne von Willemer. Abdruck aus dem 24. Bde. der
Preussischen Jahrbücher. Berlin: G. Reimer,
[1869]. 21 pp.

[————.] Hamlet. [Abdruck aus dem 35. Bde. der
Preussischen Jahrbücher. Berlin: G. Reimer, 1875?]
21 pp.
    Signature: R. W. Emerson.

————. Leben Michangelo's. Hannover: Carl Rumpler,
1863. 2 v.
    Set incomplete: 1. Th. wanting.
    Autograph.

———. ———. 2. durchgearbeitete Aufl. Hannover:
Carl Rumpler, 1864. 742 pp.

———. Das Leben Raphaels, von Urbino Italiänischer
Text von Vasari Übersetzung und Commentar von
Herman Grimm. 1. Th.: Bis zur Vollendung der
Disputa und Schule von Athen. Berlin: Ferd. Dum-
mler (Haarwitz und Gossmann), 1872. lxxix, 403 pp.
  Autograph and notes.

———. The life and times of Goethe. Tr. by Sarah
Holland Adams. Boston: Little, Brown, 1880.
viii, 559 pp.

———. ———. Copy 2.

———. Über Künstler und Kunstwerke ... Berlin:
Ferd. Dümmler (Haarwitz und Gossmann); New York:
L. W. Schmidt, 1865. 24 pp.

———. Unüberwindliche Mächte, Roman. Berlin: Wilhelm Hertz, 1867. 3 v.
  Inscription in v.1.

———. Die Venus von Milo. Raphael und Michel
Angelo. Zwei Essays. Boston: DeVries, Ibarra,
[n.d.]. 139 pp.

———. Voltair und Frankreich, ein Versuch. [Abdruck
aus dem 27. Bde. der Preussischen Jahrbücher.
Berlin: George Reimer, 1870?] 25 pp.
  Inscription.

———. Voltaire und Frankreich, ein Versuch.
<Schluss.> 7 [–14. Abdruck aus dem 27. Bde. der
Preussischen Jahrbücher. Berlin: George Reimer,
1871?]. 74 pp.
  Inscription: An Ralph Waldo Emerson, Herman Grimm,
  Berlin, 12 May 1871.

GRIMM, JAKOB LUDWIG KARL, UND GRIMM, WILHELM KARL.
Deutsches Worterbuch. Leipzig: S. Hirzel, 1854–
[19—]. 15 v.
  Set incomplete: 6.–15. Bd. wanting.

GROSVENOR, BENJAMIN. The mourner; or, The afflicted
. relieved. Exeter, [N. H.]: H. Ranlet, [1795?].
139 pp.

[GROUT, HENRY MARTYN], *ed.* The gospel invitation:
sermons related to the Boston revival of 1877. Boston: Lockwood, Brooks, 1877. 332 pp.

GUÉRIN, EUGÉNIE DE. Journal. Ed. by G. S. Trebutien.
London, New York: Alexander Strahan, 1866.
423 pp.

GUNNISON, ELISHA NORMAN. One summer's dream, an
idyl of the vineyard; and other poems. York, Penna:
H. Young, 1875. vi, 176 pp.

GUYON, JEANNE=MARIE (BOUVIÈRES DE LA MOTTE). [Opus-
cules spirituels. Cologne: J. de La Pierre, 1712.]
1 v. (various pagings).

GUYOT, ARNOLD HENRY. The earth and man: lectures on
comparative physical geography, in its relation to the
history of mankind. Tr. from the French, by C. C.
Felton ... 3d ed., rev. Boston: Gould and Lincoln, 1851. 334 pp.
Signature: R. W. Emerson.

Gymnasium for National Education, established at the
London Gymnasium, Pentonville. [London, 1827.]
1 l.
Broadside.
Bound with: Lane, Charles. A classification of science
and arts. London, 1826.

H

HAFIZ. Der Diwan von Mohammed Schemsed-din Hafis. Aus dem Persischen sum erstenmal Ganz übersetzt von Joseph v. Hammer. Stüttgart: J. G. Cotta, 1812–13. 2 v.
> Autograph and notes; several laid in.

———. Hafiz of Shiraz: selections from his poems. Tr. from the Persian by Herman Bicknell. London: Trübner, 1875. xix, 384 pp.
> Bookplate of Henry Bicknell with inscription: Dr. Rt. Lty. Collier with every good wish.

HAGEMAN, SAMUEL MILLER. Silence. New York: Dodd, Mead, 1877 [ᶜ1876]. 107 pp.
> Inscription: R. W. E. by author.

HAKLUYT, RICHARD. A discourse concerning western planting, written in the year 1584; now first printed from a contemporary manuscript, with a preface and an introduction, by Leonard Woods ... Ed., with notes in the appendix, by Charles Deane. Cambridge, [Mass.]: J. Wilson, 1877. lxi, 253 pp.
> Inscription by editor to R. W. E.

HALE, EDWARD EVERETT. What career? Ten papers on the choice of a vocation and the use of time. Boston: Roberts Bros., 1878. 271 pp.
> Inscription.

HALL, DAVID. A mite into the treasury; or, Some serious remarks on that solemn and indispensable duty of

duly attending assemblies for divine worship.   London: Printed; Philadelphia: Re-printed by B. Franklin and D. Hall, 1758.   53 pp.
Given to the Sunday School Library in Concord by Ralph Waldo Emerson, after 1835 (Cameron, III, 856–57).   Sold at the Wakeman Sale (New York: American Art Association, 1924), Lot #256.

HALL, EDWARD BROOKS.   Memoir of Mary L. Ware, wife of Henry Ware, Jr.   11th thousand.   Boston: American Unitarian Association, 1867.   vii, 434 pp.

HALL, EUGENE J.   Lyrics of home-land.   Chicago: S. C. Griggs, 1882.   xii, 160 pp.

HALLAM, HENRY.   Introduction to the literature of Europe in the fifteenth, sixteenth, and seventeenth centuries. Paris: Baudry's European Library, 1839.   4 v.

HAMILTON, ALEXANDER.   Letter from Alexander Hamilton concerning the public conduct and character of John Adams, President of the United States, written in the year 1800.   New ed., with a preface.   Boston: E. G. House, 1809.   56 pp.
Autograph: D. B. Ripley.

HAMMER-PURGSTALL, JOSEPH, *Freiherr* VON.   Geschichte der schönen redekünste Persiens, mit einer Blüthen-lese aus zweyhundert persischen Dichtern.   Mit dem Porträt des Verfassers, einem Notenblatte und einem Sachregister.   Wien: Heubner und Volke, 1818.   xii, 432 pp.
Autographs and notes.

HARBOUGH, H.   The birds of the Bible.   Philadelphia: Lindsay & Blakiston, 1854.   xi, 300 pp.

HARDENBERG, FRIEDRICH LEOPOLD, *Freiherr* VON.   Henry of Ofterdingen, a romance.   From the German of Novalis.   Cambridge, [Mass.]: J. Owen, 1842.   xvii, 236 pp.
Inscription to R. W. Emerson and notes by R. W. E.

HARRIS, JAMES. Philosophical arrangements. London: John Novrse, 1775. xiv, 485 pp.

HARRISON, JAMES ALBERT. A group of poets and their haunts. New York: Hurd and Houghton; Boston: H. O. Houghton, 1875. vi, 319 pp.

HARTE, BRET. East and West, poems. Boston: James R. Osgood, 1871. 171 pp.

The Harvard advocate. Verses from the Harvard Advocate ... New York: Hurd and Houghton, 1876. xiii, 254 pp.

—— . —— . Copy 2.

HARVARD UNIVERSITY. Catalogus senatus academici Collegii Harvardiana, et eorum qui muneribus et officiis praefuerant, quique honoribus academicis donati sunt, in universitate quae est Cantabrigiae in civitate Massachusettensium. Cantabrigiae: Carolo—Guilielmo Sev[er], 1875. xxxii, 119 pp.
Autograph.

—— . Reports of the president and treasurer of Harvard College. 1872–73, 1876–77. Cambridge: Welch, Bigelow. 2 v.
Publisher varies: 1876–77, John Wilson.
Autograph in report for 1872–73.

—— . BOARD OF OVERSEERS. Report of the committee to visit the academical departments in 1876–1877. [Cambridge, 1877?] 20 pp.

—— . Rules and by-laws of the Board of Overseers of Harvard College. To which is appended the College Charter, with sundry acts and instruments relating to the powers and duties of the Overseers. Boston: Rockwell and Rollins, 1866. 60 pp.
Laid in at end: Amendments to the Rules and by-laws.

—— . —— . Boston: J. E. Farwell, 1869. 60 pp.

—— . CHAPEL. A service-book for public worship. Prepared especially for use in the Chapel of Harvard University. Cambridge: John Bartlett, 1858. viii, 308 pp.

HASKINS, DAVID GREENE. Biographical sketches of Ebenezer Davis, and his son, Charles Stewart Daveis [sic], of Portland, Maine, members of the Massachusetts Society of the Cincinnati. Cambridge; John Wilson, 1873. 17 pp.
  Inscription: 28 June 1873.

HASKINS, THOMAS W. The Lord's supper, the frequency of its celebration and the rights of children to be partakers of the bread and wine, considered in a series of conferences and four sermons delivered at Trinity Church, Newtown, Conn. Claremont, N. H.: Claremont Manufacturing Co., 1880. 129 pp.
  Inscription: To R. W. Emerson with love of the compiler and author, June 1880. Letter from author inserted.

HASTINGS, WILLIAM SODEN. Remarks made in the Senate upon the manufacturing bill, by Messrs. Hastings & Pickering. [n.p., 1830] 20 pp.
  Imprint date supplied by Emerson.

HATHAWAY, BENJAMIN. Art-life, and other poems. Boston: H. H. Carter, 1877. viii, 225 pp.

—— . —— . Copy 2.
  Letter from author, 16 Sept. 1877, inserted.

[HAVEN, ALICE (BRADLEY).] "All's not gold that glitters"; or, The young Californian, by Cousin Alice [pseud.]. New York: D. Appleton, 1873. 214 pp.
  Bookplate: No. 202. Sunday-school Library of the First Parish in Concord.

—— . Contentment better than wealth, by Alice B. Neal (Cousin Alice) [pseud.]. New York: D. Appleton, 1853. viii, 188 pp.
  Autograph: Ellen Emerson.

HAVERGAL, FRANCES RIDLEY. Loyal responses; or, Daily melodies for the king's minstrels. New York: Fleming H. Revell, [18—?]. 96 pp.

HAWEIS, HUGH REGINALD. Thoughts for the times. 4th ed. London: Henry S. King, 1873. xv, 383 pp.

HAWTHORNE, NATHANIEL.   The Blithedale romance.
Boston: Ticknor, Reed, and Fields, 1852.   288 pp.
Inscription.

——— .   The house of the seven gables, a romance.
Boston: Ticknor, Reed, and Fields, 1851.   vi,
344 pp.
Inscription.

——— .   The marble faun; or, The romance of Monte
Beni.   Boston: Ticknor and Fields, 1860.   2 v.

——— .   Mosses from an old manse.   New York: Wiley
and Putnam, 1846.   2 v.
Inscriptions on paper covers: R. W. Emerson from the
author.

——— .   ——— .   New ed., carefully rev. by the author.
Boston: Ticknor and Fields, 1864.   2 v.
Set incomplete: v. 2 wanting.

——— .   Our old home, a series of English sketches.
Boston: Ticknor and Fields, 1863.   xi, 398 pp.
Inscription.

——— .   Passages from the English note-books.   Boston: Fields, Osgood, 1870.   2 v.
Autograph: R. W. E.

——— .   The scarlet letter, a romance.   Boston: Ticknor, Reed, and Fields, 1850.   iv, 322 pp.

HAY, DAVID RAMSAY.   The laws of harmonious colouring,
adapted to interior decorations, with observations on
the practice of house painting.   6th ed.   Edinburgh:
W. Blackwood, 1847.   ix, 198 pp.
Autograph.

HAYDN, JOSEPH TIMOTHY.   Dictionary of dates, relating
to all ages and nations, for universal reference, by
Benjamin Vincent ...   Authorized American ed.,
with supplement relating chiefly to American topics,
and a copious biographical index, by G. P. Putnam.
New York: G. P. Putnam, 1867.   833 pp.
Autograph.

HAYDON, BENJAMIN ROBERT. Life of Benjamin Robert Haydon, historical painter, from his autobiography and journals. Ed. and comp. by Tom Taylor. London: Longman, Brown, Green, and Longmans, 1853. 3 v.
Inscription: 1 Dec. 1853. Autograph and notes.

HAYES, JOHN LORD. Protection a boon to consumers; an address delivered before the National Association of Knit Goods Manufacturers, at the second annual meeting in New-York City, May 1, 1867. Boston: Wilson and Son, 1867. 55 pp.

[HAYWARD, EDWARD FARWELL.] Willoughby. Boston: W. B. Clarke, 1879. 130 pp.

HAZARD, ROWLAND GIBSON. Essay on language, and other papers. Ed. by E. P. Peabody. Boston: Phillips, Sampson, 1857. 348 pp.

———. Two letters on causation and freedom in willing, addressed to John Stuart Mill. With an appendix, on the existence of matter, and our notions of infinite space. Boston: Lee and Shepard, 1869. 300 pp.

HAZLITT, WILLIAM. Select British poets; or, New elegant extracts from Chaucer to the present time, with critical remarks. Embellished with seven ornamental portraits, after a design by T. Stothard. London: Wm. C. Hall, 1824. xxii, 822 pp.
Autograph and notes. Note and addressed envelope laid in.

HEAVYSEGE, CHARLES. Count Filippo; or, The unequal marriage. A drama in five acts. Montreal: The Author, 1860. 153 pp.

———. Saul: a drama in three parts. 2d ed., carefully rev. and amended. Montreal: John Lovell, 1859. 328 pp.
Inscription.

Hebrew.

> In his Pocket Diary (1820–1847) Emerson wrote that he
> lent a book, which he describes only with this one word,
> in Feb. 1829. He does not name the borrower. It is pos-
> sible that he is referring to one of several volumes al-
> ready in this list.

HEDGE, FREDERIC HENRY. The primeval world of Hebrew tradition. Boston: Roberts Bros., 1870.
283 pp.
> Inscription.

——. Reason in religion. Boston: Walker, Fuller,
1865. iv, 458 pp.
> Inscription: From author to R. W. E.

——. Ways of the spirit, and other essays. Boston:
Roberts Bros., 1877. 367 pp.
> Inscription by author to R. W. E.

——, ed. Recent inquiries in theology, by eminent
English churchmen; being "Essays and reviews."
Reprinted from the 2d London ed. Ed. with an introduction. Boston: Walker, Wise, 1860. xii,
480 pp.

—— AND HUNTINGTON, FREDERICK C., eds. Hymns for
the Church of Christ. 11th thousand. Boston:
Walker, Wise, 1865. xxx, 646 pp.
> Inscription: Ellen T. Emerson from Alicia M. Keyes,
> Feb. 24, 1866. Notes.

HEEREN, ARNOLD HERMANN LUDWIG. History of the
political system of Europe, and its colonies, from
the discovery of America to the independence of the
American continent. From the German ... [Tr. by
George Bancroft.] Northhampton, Mass: S. Butler,
1829. 2 v.
> Autographs.

——. Reflections on the politics of ancient Greece.
Tr. from the German, by George Bancroft. Boston:
Cummings, Hilliard, 1824. x, 350 pp.
> Autograph and notes.

HEGEL, GEORG WILHELM FRIEDRICH. The philosophy of art: being the second part of Hegel's Aesthetik, in which are unfolded historically the three great fundamental phases of the art-activity of the world. Tr. and accompanied with an introductory essay giving an outline of the entire "Aesthetik," by Wm. M. Bryant. New York: D. Appleton, [ᶜ1879]. liv, 194 pp.
> Letter from translator, 11 Jan. 1880, laid in.

_____. Vorlesungen uber die Aesthetic. Hrsg. von H. G. Hotho ... Z. Aufl. ... Berlin: Duncker und Humbolt, 1842-43. 3 v.

HEINE, HEINRICH. Letters auxiliary to the history of modern polite literature in Germany. Tr. from the German, by G. W. Haven. Boston: J. Munroe, 1836. vi, 172 pp.
> Inscription: From W. E.

Helen of the glen, a tale for youth. New York: Orville A. Roorbach, 1827. 142 pp.

HELPS, SIR ARTHUR. Companions of my solitude. London: William Pickering, 1851. 275 pp.
> Given to the Concord Free Public Library by Ralph Waldo Emerson in Feb. 1874. Withdrawn from circulation in 1917 (Cameron, III, 867).

[_____.] The conquerors of the New world and their bondsmen; being a narrative of the principal events which led to Negro slavery in the West Indies and America ... London: W. Pickering, 1848-52. 2 v.
> Inscription in R. W. E.'s hand.

[_____.] Conversations on war and general culture. London: Smith, Elder, 1871. 306 pp.
> Inscription: 18 April 1871.

[_____.] Friends in council: a series of readings and discourse thereon ... London: William Pickering, 1847-49. 2 v.
> Autograph.

———. The Spanish conquest in America and its relation to the history of slavery and to the government of colonies. London: J. W. Parker, 1855-61.
4 v.
Inscriptions: 2 July 1855, 6 March 1857.

———. Thoughts upon government. London: Bell and
Daldy, 1872. viii, 245 pp.
Inscription: 16 December 1871.

HEMANS, FELICIA DOROTHEA (BROWNE). Complete works.
Reprinted entire from the last English ed. Ed. by
her sister. New York: D. Appleton, 1856. 2 v.

———. The forest sanctuary, and other poems. Boston: Hilliard, Gray, Little, and Wilkins, 1827. ii,
231 pp.

———. The league of the Alps, The siege of Valencia,
The Vespers of Palermo, and other poems. Boston:
Hilliard, Gray, Little, and Wilkins, 1826. iii,
480 pp.

———. Records of women, with other poems. Boston:
Hilliard, Gray, Little, and Wilkins, 1829. vi,
253 pp.
Bound with the author's: The forest sanctuary. Boston, 1827.

HENWELL, SARAH SOPHIA. Thoughts in aid of faith,
gathered chiefly from recent works in theology and
philosophy. London: George Manwaring, 1860.
vii, 413 pp.
Inscription by author: May 22, 1860.

[HEPWORTH, ADALINE A. (DRURY).] The little gentleman
in green, a fairy tale, by Una Savin [pseud.]. Boston: Loring, 1865. 103 pp.

HEPWORTH, GEORGE HUGHES. The whip, hoe, and sword;
or, The Gulf-Department in '63. Boston: Walker,
Wise, 1864. vi, 298 pp.
Inscription: To Ellen T. Emerson by author.

HERAUD, JOHN ABRAHAM. Education in connection with
an experimental normal school. <Reprinted from the

Monthly magazine for April, 1840.>   London: Sherwood, Gilbert, and Piper, 1840.   15 pp.
   Bound with: Lane, Charles.   A classification of science and arts.   London, 1826.

_____ .   Substance of a lecture on poetic genius as a
moral power; delivered 2nd October, 1837, at the
Milton Institution, (Cripplegate) to which is added,
an ode.   London: James Fraser, 1837.   55 pp.
   Notes.
   Bound with: Lane, Charles.   A classification of science and arts.   London, 1826.

HERBERT.   In his Pocket Diary (1820–47) Emerson wrote
that he lent a book, which he describes only with
this one word, in Feb. 1829.   He does not name the
borrower.   He is probably referring to a work by
George Herbert, but it would of course have to be an
earlier volume than either of the two listed below.

HERBERT, GEORGE.   Poetical works.   With a memoir of
the author, by Robert Aris Willmott.   Boston: Little,
Brown, 1866.   xxxiii, 308 pp.
   Autograph: Ellen T. Emerson.

_____ .   The temple: sacred poems and private ejecula-
tions.   With the Priest to the temple; or, The country parson.   Philadelphia: W. P. Hazard, 1855.   iv,
384 pp.

HÉRISSON, EUSTACHE.   Carte d'Allemagne divisée
d'après le traité de paix fait à Vienne le 20 Novembre
1815.   On le trouvent le Royaume de Prusse,
l'empire d'Autriche, la Confédération germanique,
les roy^me des Pays-Bas, de Hanoune, de Bovière, de
Wurtemberg, et de Lombard-Venitien.   Dressée par
Hérisson, Elève de Mr. Bonne.   Revue et augm. en
1871.   Paris: Basset, [1871?].   col. map.

HERMES TRISMEGISTUS.   The Divine Pymander in XVII
Books.   Tr. formerly out of the Arabick into Greek,
and thence into Latine, and Dutch, and now out of

the original into English, by that learned divine Doctor Everard.   London: Robert White, 1650.   215 pp.
    Inscription: Bronson Alcott Association, 1842.   Notes,
    1844.   Many underlinings in text.

HERNDON, WILLIAM LEWIS.   Exploration of the valley of
the Amazon, made under direction of the Navy Department, by Wm. Lewis Herndon and Lardner Gibbon.
Washington: R. Armstrong, Public Printer, 1853-54.
2 v.
    Signature: v. 1, R. W. Emerson.

HERODOTUS.   Herodotus.   Tr. by William Beloe.   London: A. J. Valpy, 1830.   3 v.
    Autographs.

HERRICK, ROBERT.   Chrysomela; a selection from the
lyrical poems.   Arranged with notes by Francis
Turner Palgrave.   London: Macmillan, 1877.
xxviii, 199 pp.

——.   Poetical works.   London: William Pickering,
1825.   2 v.
    Picture laid in, v. 1, p. 178.
    Autograph.

HERSCHEL, SIR JOHN FREDERICK WILLIAM.   Familiar lectures on scientific subjects.   London, New York:
Alexander Strahan, 1867.   viii, 507 pp.
    Autograph.

——.   Outlines of astronomy.   New ed.   Philadelphia: Blanchard & Lea, 1857.   xvi, 557 pp.
illus.

——.   A preliminary discourse on the study of natural
philosophy.   London: Longman, Rees, Orme, Brown
and Green, 1831.   vii, 372 pp.
    Autograph.   Notes on inside back cover.

——.   A treatise on astronomy.   London: Longman,
Rees, Orme, Brown, Green & Longman, 1833.   viii,
422 pp.
    Notes.

HEYWOOD, JOSEPH CONVERSE.   Salome, the daughter of
Herodias.   A dramatic poem.   New York: Putnam,
1862.   251 pp.
Inscription: From W. Emerson.

HILL, ADAMS SHERMANN.   Stories for children by eleven
sophomores.   Boston: Roberts Bros., 1875.
118 pp.

HILL, THOMAS.   Geometry and faith, a fragmentary supplement to the Ninth Bridgewater treatise.   New
York: C. S. Francis; Boston: J. H. Francis, 1849.
48 pp.
Signature: R. W. Emerson.

HINTON, JAMES.   Man and his dwelling place; an essay
towards the interpretation of nature.   London: John
W. Parker, 1859.   viii, 416 pp.
Inscription.

———.   ———.   2d ed.   London: Smith, Elder, 1861.
xxiv, 416 pp.
Inscription: Ralph Waldo Emerson with J. Hinton's best
regards.
Presented to Concord Free Public Library in Feb. 1874
by Ralph Waldo Emerson (Cameron, III, 867).

Hints for thinking.   [London? 182-?]   1 l.
Broadside.
Bound with: Lane, Charles.   A classification of sci-
ence and arts.   London, 1826.

HITCHCOCK, EDWARD.   The religion of geology and its
connected sciences.   10th thousand.   Boston:
Phillips, Sampson, 1855.   xvi, 511 pp.

HITCHCOCK, ETHAN ALLEN.   Christ the spirit: being an
attempt to state the primitive view of Christianity
...   2d ed., enl.   New York: C. S. Francis, 1861.
xxxix, 465 pp.

[———.]   ———.   Part second.   New York: James
Miller, 1861.   xxviii, 452 pp.

HOAR, GEORGE FRISBIE.   Eulogy upon the life, character
and public services of James Abram Garfield, late
President of the United States, delivered by George
F. Hoar, at the invitation of the City Council of the
city of Worcester, Mass., in Mechanics Hall, on Fri-
day evening, December 30, 1881.   Printed by order
of the City Council.   Worcester, Mass.: Charles
Hamilton, 1882.   27 pp.

———.   James Abram Garfield.   Boston: Houghton,
Mifflin, 1882.   44 pp.
     Autograph: Ellen T. Emerson.

HOBART, NOAH.   A serious address to the members of
the episcopal separation in New-England ...   Boston: J. Bushell and J. Green, 1748.   139 pp.
     Signature: R. W. E.

HOBBY, WILLIAM.   A vindication of the protest against
the result of the Northampton-Council.   In answer to
a letter published by Robert Breck, Joseph Ashley,
Timothy Woodbridge, Chester Williams, intitled, An
account of the condition of the Council which dis-
missed Mr. Edwards ...   Boston: S. Kneeland,
[1750].   37 pp.
     Notes.   Unsigned letters [?] on last page.

HODGMAN, EDWIN RUTHVEN.   A brief memoir of Joseph
Bancroft Hill, who died in the service of U. S.
Christian Commission, at Chattanooga, Tenn., June
16, 1864.   Boston: A. Mudge, 1868.   126 pp.

———.   ———.   Copy 2.
     Inscription.

HODGSON, WILLIAM BALLANTYNE.   The education of girls,
and The employment of women of the upper classes
educationally considered: two lectures.   London:
Trubner, 1869.   xiii, 114 pp.

[HOFLAND, BARBARA.]   Matilda; or, The Barbadoes girl:
a tale for young people.   Philadelphia: M. Carey,
1817.   175 pp.

HOGG, JAMES.   The queen's wake; a legendary poem.
Boston: Wells and Lilly, 1815.   vi, 257 pp.
   Inscription: From Mrs. Alcott, 1845 (in R. W. E.'s hand).

HOLCOMBE, WILLIAM HENRY.   Poems.   New York:
Mason Bros., 1860.   x, 360 pp.

HOLLAND, FREDERIC MAY.   The reign of the Stoics: history; religion; maxims of self-control, self-culture,
benevolence, justice; philosophy.   With citations of
authors quoted from on each page.   New York: C. P.
Somerby, 1879.   viii, 248 pp.
   Inscription: To R. W. E. by author, May 25, '79.

HOLLAND, JOSIAH GILBERT.   The mistress of the manse.
New York: Scribner, Armstrong, 1874.   245 pp.

[HOLLAND, MRS. ROBERT.]   Channing, sa vie et ses
oeuvres, avec une préface de Charles de Remusat.
Paris: Didier, 1857.   xviii, 404 pp.

HOLMES, OLIVER WENDELL.   Astraea: the balance of il-
lusions.   A poem delivered before the Phi Beta
Kappa Society of Yale College, August 14, 1850.
Boston: Ticknor, Reed, and Fields, 1850.   39 pp.
   Inscription: 1850.

_____.   The autocrat of the breakfast-table.   Every
man his own Boswell.   Boston: Phillips, Sampson,
1859.   viii, 373 pp.
   Large paper copy.
   Inscription: R. W. Emerson from O. W. Holmes.

_____.   Border lines of knowledge in some provinces of
medical science.   An introductory lecture, delivered
before the medical class of Harvard University,
November 6th, 1861.   Boston: Ticknor and Fields,
1862.   80 pp.
   Inscription: R. W. Emerson from his friend O. W.
Holmes, and notes.

_____.   Elsie Venner, a romance of destiny.   Boston:
Ticknor and Fields, 1861.   2 v.
   Inscription: v. 2, R. W. Emerson with the regards of
O. W. Holmes.

———. The guardian angel. Boston: Ticknor and Fields, 1867. xii, 420 pp.

———. The iron gate, and other poems. Boston: Houghton, Mifflin, 1880. 82 pp.
Inscription: Ralph Waldo Emerson with the love and honor of Oliver Wendell Holmes (in O. W. H.'s hand).

———. John Lothrop Motley, a memoir. Boston: Houghton, Osgood, 1879. vii, 278 pp.
Presentation copy. Inscription: Ralph Waldo Emerson with the kindest regards and best respects of Oliver Wendell Holmes, Dec. 25, 1878.

———. Mechanism in thought and morals. An address delivered before the Phi Beta Kappa Society of Harvard University, June 29, 1870. With notes and after-thoughts. Boston: J. R. Osgood, 1871. 101 pp.
Inscription.

———. Poems. New and enl. ed. Boston: William D. Ticknor, 1849. x, 272 pp.
Inscription and notes.

———. Poetical works. Boston: Houghton, Mifflin, 1882. 2 v.
Set incomplete: v. 1 wanting.

———. Songs in many keys. [1st ed.] Boston: Ticknor and Fields, 1862. 308 pp.
Inscription.

———. Songs of many seasons. 1862-1874. Boston: J. R. Osgood, 1875. xii, 216 pp.
Inscription: 25 Nov. 1874.

———. Soundings from the Atlantic. Boston: Ticknor and Fields, 1864. 468 pp.
Inscription.

[HOMERUS. *The Iliad. Greek or Greek and Latin.* Tῆς Ὁμήρου Ἰλιάδος. n.p., n.d.] 227-479 pp.
Greek text with Latin translation and Latin notes, consisting of lib. 5, line 814, through lib. 12, line 471.

———. Ilias, Graece et Latine. Annotationes in usum serenissimi principis Gulielmi Augusti, ducis de

Cumberland, &c. regio jussu scripsit atque edidet Samuel Clarke ... Ed. 2ª ... Londini: Jacobi, Johannis & Pauli Knapton, 1735. 2 v.
> Autograph.

——. 'Ιλιάς. [Oxonii: J. H. & J. Parker, 18—?] xii, 508 pp.
> Autograph: Ellen T. Emerson, Oxford 1894, and notes.

——. 'Ιλιάς. From the text of Wolf. With English notes and Flaxman's illustrative designs, ed. by C. C. Felton. Boston: Hilliard, Gray; Cambridge: Brown, Shattuck, 1833. xii, 478 pp.
> Inscription: To C. C. E. by Felton, 1 May 1833.

——. *English.* The Iliad. Tr. from the Greek by Alexander Pope. Boston: Edward Cotton, 1806. 2 v.
> Autograph: v. 1, Charles C. Emerson.

——. ——. Literally tr., with explanatory notes, by Theodore Alois Buckley. London: Henry G. Bohn, 1854. 466 pp.
> Autograph.

——. The Iliads. Never before in any language truly tr., with a comment on some of his chief places. Done according to the Greek by George Chapman, with introduction and notes, by Richard Hooper ... 2d ed. London: John Russell Smith, 1865. 2 v.
> Inscription: T. C., 24 May 1870.

——. *The Odyssey. Greek and Latin.* Odyssea, Graece et Latine; iuxta edit. Sam Clarke. Glasg[ow], 1799. Editio quarta ... Aberdoniae: J. & D. Chalmers, 1806. 2 v. in 1.

——. *English.* The Odyssey. Tr. by Alexander Pope. To which is added The battle of the frogs and mice. London: J. Walker, F. C. and J. Rivington 1818. 426 pp.
> Inscription: From Julia Gorham, Jan. 1824, (in R. W. E.'s hand).

——. ——. With the Hymns, Epigrams, and Battle of the frogs and mice. Literally tr., with explana-

tory notes, by Theodore Alois Buckley.   London:
Henry G. Bohn, 1855.   xxii, 432 pp.
   Autograph.

HOPKINS, LOUISA PAYSON.   The guiding star; or, The
   Bible, God's message.   Boston: Gould and Lincoln,
   1852.   xi, 260 pp.

——.   Henry Langdon, a tale.   6th ed.   New York:
   Gates & Stedman, 1849.   144 pp.

HOPPS, JOHN PAGE.   Sermons of sympathy.   London:
   Williams & Norgate, [18—?].   101 pp.

Horae poeticae.   Part I.   The spiritual application of
   the classics.   Part II.   A paraphrase of the
   Proserpine of Claudian.   Part III.   Lyrics on various subjects.   To which is appended, A popular
   epistle on the utility of the classics ...   London:
   Priv. Print. 1841.   xvii, 225 pp.
   Autograph.

HORATIUS FLACCUS, QUINTUS.   Horace.   Tr. by Philip
   Francis, and rev. by H. J. Pye.   London: W. Suttaby,
   B. Crosby, 1806.   xxxiv, 453 pp.
   Bookplate and autograph of William Emerson; also
   autograph of R. W. E.

——.   Opera.   Accedunt clavis metrica et notae
   Anglicae juventuti accommodatae Cura B. A. Gould.
   Bostoniae: Hilliard, Gray, 1835.   iv, 340 pp.

——.   Opera omnia, ex recensione A. J. Macleane.
   New York: Harper, 1864.   vii, 211 pp.
   Notes and autograph.

——.   Q. Horatii Flacei, ex ed. Bipontina II, ad
   optimas lectiones mss. et edd. nova editio recensita,
   brevibus notis critic, et interp. subjunctis, necnon
   Horatiano indice; cum adnotata Horatii vita, et
   notitia litteraria, de hujus edd. comment. et vers.
   amplissima.   Parisiis: Treuttel et Wurtz, 1827.
   cxvi, 438 pp.

HORNE, GEORGE.   A commentary on the book of Psalms
   ..., by George, Lord Bishop of Norwich ...   To

which is prefixed a memoir of the life of the author. Philadelphia: Alexander Towar, 1822. 632 pp.
Inscription: From Melish S. Motte.

The horticulturist, and journal of rural art and rural taste. Devoted to horticulture, landscape gardening, rural architecture, botany, pomology, entomology, rural economy, &c. Ed. by A. J. Downing. v. 1-2, 1846/47—1847/48. Albany, [N. Y.]: Luther Tucker: Boston: Joseph Breck. 2 v.

HOSMER, BURR GRISWOLD. Poems. Cambridge, [Mass.]: Riverside Press, 1868. vi, 171 pp.

HOSSFELD, C. New German-English dictionary. Neuestes deutsch-englisches-Worterbuch ... Liverpool: C. Hossfeld; London: Trübner, [18—?]. 397 pp.

HOUSSAYE, ARSÈNE. Les femmes commes elles sont ... Paris: Michel Levy frères, 1857. xii, 308 pp.

_____. Sous la régence et sous la terreur. Talons rouges et bonnets rouges. Paris: Eugene Didier, 1853. xi, 300 pp.

HOWARD, CHARLES F. Olympus. London: Simkin, Marshall, 1855. 321 pp.
Inscription: From the author. Ms. note on t.p.: By the author of "Perseus and his philosophies."

[_____.] Perseus and his philosophies. London: Saunders and Otley, 1852. 267 pp.
Inscription: From W. W. F. Synge, 8 Mar. 1852. Author's name rewritten on t.p. in same hand as inscription.

HOWE, JULIA (WARD). From the oak to the olive, a plain record of a pleasant journey. Boston: Lee and Shepard, 1868. vi, 304 pp.
Inscription: R. W. E. from the author.

[_____.] Words for the hour. Boston: Ticknor and Fields, 1857. iv, 165 pp.
Inscription: 1 Jan. 1856 (?).

_____. The world's own. Boston: Ticknor and Fields, 1857. 141 pp.
Inscription: 9 Apr. 1857.

HOWE, NATHANAEL. A century sermon on Lord's day, December 24, 1815 ... 2d ed., rev. and cor. Andover: Flagg and Gould, 1817. 31 pp.

HOWELL, JAMES. Δενδρολογία. Dodona's grove; or, The vocall forrest. 3d ed., more exact and perfect than the former; with the addition of two other tracts: viz. Englands tears for the present wars, and The pre-eminence of parlements. Cambridge: Humphrey Moseley, 1645. 150, [171]-191, 23 pp.
  Autograph and notes.

HOWELLS, WILLIAM DEAN. Poems. Boston: J. R. Osgood, 1873. ii, 172 pp.

———. Sketch of the life and character of Rutherford B. Hayes. Also a biographical sketch of William A. Wheeler. New York: Hurd and Houghton; Boston: H. O. Houghton, 1876. vi, 195 pp.

HOWITT, MARY (BOTHAM). Birds and flowers, and other country things. 2d ed. Boston: William D. Ticknor, 1843. viii, 208 pp.
  Inscription: Emerson (in Ellen's hand).

———. The picture book for the young. With twenty illus. by Bryon & Peirce. Philadelphia: J. B. Lippincott, 1856. 56 pp.

HOWITT, WILLIAM. The book of the seasons; or, The calendar of nature. Philadelphia: Carey & Lea, 1831. xxi, 312 pp.

———. Jack of the mill, a fireside story. With forty illus. by G. F. Sargent. London, New York: George Routledge, [1871]. xvi, 368 pp.

HOYT, JEHIEL KEELER, AND WARD, ANNA L., comps. The cyclopaedia of practical quotations, English and Latin, with an appendix containing proverbs from the Latin and modern foreign languages; law and ecclesiastical terms and significations; names, dates and nationality of quoted authors, etc., with copious indexes. New York: I. K. Funk, 1882. ii, 899 pp.
  Inscription by Anna L. Ward, Dec. 1881.

Hubbard's newspaper and bank directory of the world
(with gazetteer and atlas combined). Containing the
names and descriptions of over thirty-three thousand
newspapers and fifteen thousand banks ... New
Haven: H. P. Hubbard, 1882. 2 v.
  Inscription of author, v. 1. Letter from author inserted, v. 2.

HUC, ÉVARISTE RÉGIS. A journey through the Chinese
Empire. New York: Harper, 1855. 2 v.
  Autograph.

HUDSON, HANNAH REBA. Poems. Boston: J. R. Osgood, 1874. iv, 214 pp.

———. ———. Copy 2.

HUDSON, JOHN, *ed.* A complete guide to the lakes, comprising minute directions for the tourist, with Mr.
Wordsworth's description of the scenery of the country, &c., and Four letters of the geology of the Lake
District, by Professor Sedgwick. 3d ed., ed. by the
publisher. Kendal: J. Hudson; London: Longman,
1846. ix, 245 pp.
  Autograph.

HUGHES, THOMAS. The manliness of Christ. Boston:
Houghton, Mifflin, 1880. viii, 160 pp.
  Autograph: Ellen T. Emerson.

———. School days at Rugby, by an old boy. Boston:
James R. Osgood, 1872. viii, 405 pp.
  Autograph: Ellen T. Emerson.

———. Tom Brown at Oxford; a sequel to School days
at Rugby. New York: Harper, 1860-61. 2 v.
  Portrait clipping inserted, v. 1.
  Autograph: Ellen T. Emerson.

HUMBOLDT, ALEXANDER, FREIHERR VON. Aspects of nature, in different lands and different climates; with
scientific elucidations. Tr. by Mrs. Sabine.
Philadelphia: Lea and Blanchard, 1849. ix, 475 pp.
  Autograph.

———. Cosmos: sketch of a physical description of the
universe. Tr. under the superintendence of E.

Sabine [by Mrs. Sabine].   London: Longman, Brown, Green, and Longmans [etc.], 1847–[5–?]   4 v.
>Set incomplete: v. 2, pt. 2; v. 3; v. 4, pt. 1 wanting.
>   Vol. 1: 2d ed.; v. 2, pt. 1: Authorized English transla-tion.
>Only pt. 1 of v. 4 published.

——.   The travels and researches of Alexander von Humboldt; being a condensed narrative of his jour-neys in the equinoctial regions of America, and in Asiatic Russia:–together with analyses of his more important investigations, by W. Macgillivray ... With a map of the Orinoco, and engravings.   New York: J. & J. Harper, 1833.   367 pp.
>Notes and autograph.

HUMBOLDT, WILHELM, FREIHERR VON.   Religious thoughts and opinions.   Boston: W. Crosby and H. P. Nichols, 1851.   171 pp.
>Inscription: From M. M. E. to Rev. Charles Cleveland.

The hundred greatest men; portraits of the one hundred greatest men of history reproduced from fine and rare engravings.   London: Sampson Low, Marston, Searle, and Rivington, 1879–80.   8 v.
>Set incomplete: v. 1, 3–8 wanting.
>Includes a general introduction by R. W. Emerson.

HUNT, LEIGH.   The descent of liberty: a mask.   New ed.   London: Gale and Fenner, 1816.   lix, 82 pp.

——, AND LEE, S. ADAMS, *eds.*   The book of the son-net.   Boston: Roberts Bros., 1867.   2 v.
>Set incomplete: v. 2 wanting.

HUNT, THOMAS STERRY.   A century's progress in theo-retical chemistry.   An address delivered on the occasion of the celebration of the Centennial of Chemistry, at Northumberland, Pa., July 31, 1874. Philadelphia: Collins, 1874.   15 pp.
>Inscription.

——.   Contributions to lithology.   I. Theoretical notions.   II. Classification and nomenclature.

III. On some eruptive rocks.   IV. Local metamor-
phism.   Montreal, 1864.   51 pp.

_____.   History of the names Cambrian and Siberian in
geology.   From the Canadian Naturalist for April
and July, 1872.   Montreal: Mitchell & Wilson, 1872.
64 pp.
Inscription.

_____.   On the chemical and mineralogical relations of
metamorphic rocks.   Montreal: John Lovell, 1863.
16 pp.

HUTCHINSON, LUCY (APSLEY).   Memoirs of the life of
Colonel Hutchinson, governor of Nottingham Castle
and Town, representative of the County of Nottingham in the Long Parliament, and of the Town of
Nottingham in the first Parliament of Charles II,
etc., with original anecdotes of many of the most
distinguished of his contemporaries, and a summary
review of public affairs.   Written by his widow Lucy
...   From the original manuscript by Julius Hutchinson.   To which is prefixed The life of Mrs. Hutchinson, written by herself.—A fragment ...   4th ed.
London: Longman, Hurst, Rees, Orme, and Brown,
1822.   2 v.
Signature: Emerson.

The hyacinth ...   New York: J. C. Riker, 1831.
240 pp.
A collection of reprints.

Hymns ancient and modern for use in the services of the
church, with accompanying tunes, comp. and arranged under the musical editorship of William Henry
Monk ...   Appendix ...   London: William Clowes,
[18—?].   xii, [295] pp.
Autograph: Ellen T. Emerson, and her notes.

Hymns for Sabbath school use.   Boston: N. P. Kemp,
[18—?].   38 pp.

I

ISVARA KRISHNA. The Sánkhya kárika; or, Memorial verses on the Sánkhya, philosophy ... Tr. from the Sanscrit by Henry Thomas Colebrooke ... Also The Bhashya; or, Commentary of Gaurapada; tr. and illus. by an original comment by Horace Hayman Wilson ... Oxford: Oriental Translation Fund of Great Britain and Ireland, 1837. xiv, 194 pp.
  Autograph. Inscription: Henry D. Thoreau from Thomas Cholmondeley.

Illustrated family news. Panoramic view of the river Thames, from Westminster, to Greenwich, presented gratis, with no. 1 of the Illustrated family news. London, [18—?].
  Broadside.

Important inquiries. [London? 182-?] 4 ll.
  Bound with: Lane, Charles. A classification of science and arts. London, 1826.

Important questions. [London? 182-?] 1 l.
  Broadside.
  Questions related to the work of the church.
  Bound with: Lane, Charles. A classification of science and arts. London, 1826.

Improved day school for boys ... no. 18, Helmet Row, on the West side of St. Luck's Churchyard. [London? 182-?] 1 l.
  Bound with: Lane, Charles. A classification of science and arts. London, 1826.

Improver. [London? 182-?] 1 l.
  Broadside.
  Bound with: Lane, Charles. A classification of science and arts. London, 1826.

In memoriam. Philadelphia, Sunday, March 17, 1867.
  [Philadelphia, 1867.] 10 pp.
  Inscription: R. W. Emerson, Concord, from W. G. G.

INCONNU, *pseud.* Cathara Clyde, a novel. New York: C. Scribner, 1860. 377 pp.

Infant's magazine. no. 75-76, 78, March, April, June, 1872. London: Seeley, Jackson, & Halliday. 1 v.

INGELOW, JEAN. Off the Skeligs, a novel. Boston: Roberts Bros., 1872. 666 pp.

_____. Poems. Boston: Roberts Bros., 1863. 256 pp.
  Autograph and notes.

_____. A story of doom, and other poems. Boston: Roberts Bros., 1867. vi, 290 pp.

Inward guide. [London? 182-?] 1 l.
  Broadside.
  Bound with: Lane, Charles. A classification of science and arts. London, 1826.

IRELAND, ALEXANDER. List of the writings of William Hazlitt and Leigh Hunt, chronologically arranged; with notes, descriptive, critical, and explanatory; and a selection of opinions regarding their genius and characteristics, by distinguished contemporaries and friends, as well as by subsequent critics; preceded by a review of, and extracts from, Barry Cornwall's "Memorials of Charles Lamb"; with a few words on William Hazlitt and his writings, and a chronological list of the works of Charles Lamb. London: J. R. Smith, 1868. xxiii, 233 pp.
  Inscription: July 24, 1868, by Ireland to R. W. E.

IRVING, WASHINGTON. The sketch book of Geoffrey Crayon, gent. No. V. New York: C. S. Van Winkle, 1819. 443 pp.

IRWIN, MRS. JAMES P.   The hermit of Petraea, a tale, written with the hope of throwing a charm around the out-of-door life so necessary to invalids.   Charlotte, N. C.: Hill & Irwin, 1871.   60 pp.

ISLER, ARNOLD HENRY.   Wild thoughts in rhyme.   Columbus: Smythe, 1873.   viii, 120 pp.
   Inscription: Oct. 1873.

ISOCRATES.   Panegyricus. From the text of Bremi. With English notes, by C. C. Felton ...   2d ed. Cambridge: John Bartlett, 1854.   xvi, 123 pp.
   Autographs and notes.   Signature: Charles Emerson.

J

[JACKSON, HELEN MARIA (FISKE) HUNT.] Bits of talk
about home matters, by H. H. [pseud.]. Boston:
Roberts Bros., 1873. viii, 239 pp.
  Photograph laid in at p. 13. Autograph. Inscription: 25
Sept. 1878.

[_____.] A century of dishonor; a sketch of the United
States government's dealings with some of the Indian
tribes; by H. H. New York: Harper, 1881. x,
457 pp.

[_____.] Mammy Tittleback and her family, a true story
of seventeen cats, by H. H. ... With illus. by
Addie Ledyard. Boston: Roberts Bros., 1881.
101 pp.

[_____.] _____. Copy 2.

[_____.] Verses, by H. H. Boston: Roberts Bros.,
1874. viii, 191 pp.
  Inscription: R. W. Emerson from the author (in Emerson's hand).

[_____.] _____. Copy 2.
  Autograph: R. W. Emerson, over which Ellen Emerson
has written her signature. Notes.

[JACKSON, JAMES.] Memoir of James Jackson, Jr.,
written by his father with extracts from his letters,
and reminiscences of him by a fellow student, for
the Warren Street Chapel. Boston: Hilliard, Gray,
1836. xi, 228 pp.
  Inscription from Teachers of the W. Street Chapel.

————. ————. Copy 2.
Inscription: From Teachers of the Warren Street Chapel.

JACKSON, ROBERT MONTGOMERY SMITH. The mountain.
Philadelphia: J. B. Lippincott, 1860. xii, 632 pp.
Inscription: To R. W. E. from author, and notes.

JACKSON, WILLIAM. Positivism. A lecture delivered
in connection with the Christian Evidence Society,
May 5, 1871. London: Hodder and Stoughton, 1871.
81-137, 531-537 pp.
Inscription: To R. W. E. by author.

————. Right and wrong. A sermon [on Rom. 1:20 and
2:15] upon the question under what conditions is a
science of natural theology possible? Oxford:
[Printed], 1870.
Presented to the Concord Free Public Library by Ralph
Waldo Emerson in Feb. 1874. Withdrawn from circulation,
1921 (Cameron, III, 868).

JAHR, GOTTLICH HEINRICH GEORG. New manual of
homoeopathic practice. Ed. with annotations, by A.
Gerald Hull. 2d American, from the 3d or Paris, ed.
New York: William Raddle, 1841-42. 2 v.

JAIMINI. The aphorisms of the Mimansa philosophy,
with extracts from the commentaries in Sanscrit and
English. Printed for the use of the Benares College
by order of the Gov't. N. W. P. Allahabad: Presbyterian Mission Press, 1851. 36 pp.
Autograph. Inscription: Henry D. Thoreau from Thomas
Cholmondeley.

JAMBLICHUS, OF CHALCIS. De mysteriis Egyptiorvm,
nunc primum ad uerbum de greco expressus. Nicolao
Scvtellio ... interprete. Adiecti de uita & secta
Pythagorae flosculi, ab eodem Scutellio ex ipso
Iamblicho collecti. Romae: Antonivm Bladum,
1556. 148 pp.
Autograph: From C. E. Norton (in R. W. E.'s hand).

————. Iamblichus on the mysteries of the Egyptians,
Chaldeans, and Assyrians. Tr. from the Greek by

Thomas Taylor ... Chiswick: C. Whittingham, 1821. xxiv, 365 pp.
Autographs and markings; notes on inside of back cover.

JAMES, HENRY. Substance and shadow; or, Morality and religion in their relation to life: an essay upon the physics of creation. Boston: Ticknor and Fields, 1863. x, 539 pp.
Inscription and notes.

James Talbot, a tale. Boston: Christian Register Office, 1824. 35 pp.
Bound with: The classical journal, v. 1-2, 1830-31. Boston.

JAMESON, ANNA BROWNELL (MURPHY). Memoirs of the early Italian painters. From the 10th English ed. Boston: Ticknor and Fields, 1859. vi, 352 pp.
Autograph: Ellen T. Emerson.

JĀMĪ. Analysis and specimens of the Joseph and Zulaikha, a historical-romantic poem. London: Williams and Norgate, [1873]. viii, 168 pp.

JANSON, KRISTOFER NAGEL. The spell-bound fiddler, a Norse romance. Tr. from the original by Auber Forestier [pseud.] ... With an introduction by Rasmus B. Anderson. Chicago: S. C. Griggs, 1880. 161 pp.

JARVES, JAMES JACKSON. Art-hints: architecture, sculpture and painting. London: Sampson, Low, 1855. xv, 398 pp.
Inscription: To R. W. E. from the author, Dec. 30, 1857.

JENCKES, THOMAS ALLEN. Speech of Thomas A. Jenckes, of Rhode Island, on the bill to regulate the civil service of the United States and to promote the efficiency thereof; delivered in the House of Representatives, January 29, 1867. Washington: Congressional Globe Office, 1867. 14 pp.
Bound with: U.S. Congress. Joint Select Committee on Retrenchment. The civil service ... Washington, 1868.

_____ . Speech of Thomas A. Jenckes, of Rhode Island, on the bill to regulate the civil service of the United States and promote the efficiency thereof; delivered in the House of Representatives, May 14, 1868. Washington: F. & J. Rives, & Geo. L. Bailey, 1868. 15 pp.
Bound with: U.S. Congress. Joint Select Committee on Retrenchment. The civil service ... Washington, 1868.

JEWETT, SARAH ORNE. Play days, a book of stories for children. Boston: Houghton, Osgood, 1878. 213 pp.
Autograph: Ellen T. Emerson.

[JEWRY, MARY.] Warne's model cookery and house-keeping book, containing complete instructions in household management. London: Frederick Warne; New York: Scribner Welford, 1868. 156 pp.

JOANNE, ADOLPHE LAURENT. Paris-diamant. 8e éd., augmentée d'une liste alphabétique des vues de Paris. Paris: Hachette, 1876. lxxx, 162 pp.

JOHNSON, ALVIN JEWETT. New illustrated family atlas of the world, was awarded the first prize medal at the Universal exposition of 1867, in Paris, with physical geography, and with descriptions, geographical, statistical and historical, including the latest federal census, and the existing religious denominations in the world ... New York: A. J. Johnson, 1869, ^{c}1867. 102, 113, 32 pp.

JOHNSON, G. B. Poems and sonnets. London: Simpkin, Marshall; Manchester: Palmer & House, 1874. xi, 210 pp.
Inscription: April 13, 74, presented by author.

JOHNSON, SAMUEL. The history of Rasselas, Prince of Abyssinia, a tale. London: John Sharpe, 1818. viii, 184 pp.
Autograph.

_____. The lives of the English poets. London:
F. C. and J. Rivington, 1820. 2 v.
    Autograph in v. 2.

_____. Works. New ed. With an essay on his life
and genius, by Arthur Murphy. London: Luke Han-
ford, 1806. 12 v.
    Autographs and notes.

JOHNSTON, W. & A. K., *Ltd., publishers*. A map of
Canada compiled from the latest authorities by Ed-
ward Staveley. Edin[burgh]; Montreal: Armour and
Ramsay, 1848. map.
    Consists of Western Nova Scotia and Gaspé to Lake
Huron.

JONES, CHARLES COLCOCK. The dead towns of Georgia.
Savannah: Morning News Steam Printing House,
1878. 263 pp.
    Inscription: To R. W. E., 25 Jan. 1879, by author.

JONES, H. Lecture on the combinative principle as applicable to modes of collegiate life, addressed to the
settlers of Sarnia, and adjoining townships, in the
Western District of Upper Canada. [n.p., 1835.]
12 pp.
    Notes.
    Bound with: Lane, Charles. A classification of sci-
ence and arts. London, 1826.

[JONES, J.] "Una and her paupers": memorials of
Agnes Elizabeth Jones, by her sister. With an introduction by Florence Nightingale. 2d American
from the 5th London ed. With an introductory preface by Henry Ward Beecher, and a supplementary
chapter on hospital nursing and training in the United
States, by the author of "Woman's work in the Civil
War." New York: George Routledge, 1872. xlvi,
497 pp.
    Inscription: Ellen Emerson from Bessie Greene.

JONES, JUDSON.   The alphabet of orthoëpy and its application to monosyllables.   Saint Paul: Press
Printing Co., 1870.   v, 96 pp.
> Inscription of author.

JONSON, BEN.   Works.   London: J. Walthoe, M. Wotton,
J. Nicholson, 1717.   6 v.
> Set incomplete: v. 2 wanting.
> Autographs and notes.

——.   ——.   With a biographical memoir, by William
Gifford.   New ed. London, New York: George
Routledge, 1873.   viii, 819 pp.
> Notes.

JOSEPHUS, FLAVIUS.   Works ...   Containing twenty
books of the Jewish antiquities, seven books of the
Jewish war, and the Life of Josephus, written by himself.   Tr. from the original Greek according to
Havercamp's accurate ed.   Together with explanatory
notes and observations.   Embellished with elegant
engravings, by the late William Whiston ...   From
the last London ed. of 1827.   Philadelphia: J. Grigg,
1829.   2 v.

The journal of speculative philosophy.   v. 1-4, 1867-
70.   St. Louis, Mo.: George Knapp & Co.   4 v. in 2.
> Editor: Wm. T. Harris.
> Signature: v. 1-2, R. W. Emerson, and note, v. 3-4.

[JUDD, SYLVESTER.]   Margaret: a tale of the real and the
ideal, blight and bloom; including sketches of a
place not before described, called Mons Christi ...
Rev. ed. ...   Boston: Phillips, Sampson, 1851.
2 v.
> Autograph: v. 2, Ellen T. Emerson.   Inscription: v. 1,
> Feb. 24, 1856, Ellen T. Emerson from her Mother.

JUSTINUS, MARCUS JUNIANUS.   Historiae Philippicae,
cum versione Anglica ...; or, The history of Justin,
with an English translation ... by John Clarke ...
5th ed.   London: W. Clarke, 1759.   xvi, 312 pp.
> Bookplate of William Emerson.

JUVENAL.　　Satirae ex editione G. Alex, Ruperti, sedula
　　recensione accuratae.　　Londini: Rodwell et Martin,
　　1819.　　140 pp.
　　　　Autograph: C. C. Emerson, and his notes.

K

[KALEVALA. La Kalévala, épopée nationale de la Fin-
lande ... Tr. ... annoté et accompagné d'études
historiques ... et littéraires, par L. Léouyon le Duc.
1. L'épopée. Paris, 1867.] xlviii, 495 pp.
Copy imperfect: t.p., pp. [i-ii] wanting.
No more published.

KALIDASA. The Mégha dúta; or, Cloud messenger, a
poem in the Sanskrit language, by Cálidása. Tr.
into English verse, with notes and illus., by Horace
Hayman Wilson ... Pub. under the sanction of the
College of Fort William. Calcutta; London: Black,
Perry, 1814. xxii, 175 pp.
Autograph.

———. Sākoontalā; or, The lost ring; an Indian drama.
Tr. into English prose and verse, from the Sanskrit of
Kálidása; by Monier Williams ... 3d ed. Hertford:
Stephen Austin, 1856. xxx, 227 pp.
Autograph.

KANT, IMMANUEL. Critick of pure reason, tr. from the
original. London: William Pickering, 1838. xxxvi,
655 pp.
Autograph and notes.

KAPPIND. [n.p., n.d.] 2 v.
In his Pocket Diary (1820–47) Emerson wrote that he
lent a book, which he describes in this phrase, to "G. P.
B.?", undoubtedly George Partridge Bradford. Emerson's
handwriting in this entry is obscure and the "Kappind"

may be a misreading, but I have been unable to identify it further.

KATER, HENRY, AND LARDNER, DIONYSIUS.   A treatise on mechanics.   Boston: Stimpson and Clapp, 1831. viii, 287 pp.

KAUFMANN, PETER.   The temple of truth; or, The science of ever-progressive knowledge ...   Cincinnati: Truman & Spofford, 1858.   vi, 290 pp.
   Inscription: 6 Oct. 1858, and notes.

KAULBACH, WILHELM, *illus.*   Gallerie zu Goethe's sammtlichen Werken nach Zeichnungen von W. Kaulbach und seiner Schulern, in Stahl gestochen von Steifensand, Weber, Enzing-Muller, Hoffmann u.A.   1. Lief. Elegie.   Faust.   Gotz von Berlichingen.   Wilhelm Meister.   Reinecke Fuchs.   Stuttgart: J. G. Cotta, 1840.   1 v. (5 plates).

KAYE, THOMAS, OF LIVERPOOL, *publishers.*   Plan of Liverpool.   Published for the stranger in Liverpool. [Liverpool.] 1823.   plan.

KEATS, JOHN.   Poetical works.   With a life.   Boston: Little, Brown; New York: Evans and Dickerson, 1854.   xxxvi, 415 pp.
   Autograph and notes.

KEBLE, JOHN.   The Christian year: thoughts in verse for the Sundays and holy-days throughout the year ... From the 31st London ed.   Philadelphia: Geo. S. Appleton; New York: D. Appleton, 1851.   xi, 429 pp.

_____ .   Lyra innocentium: thoughts in verse on Christian children, their ways, and their privileges.   11th ed.   Oxford: James Parker, 1867.   xii, 214 pp.

KELLEY, HALL JACKSON.   A geographical sketch of that part of North America called Oregon ...   To which is attached a new map of the country.   Boston: J. Home, 1830.   80 pp.

KELLOGG, EDWARD.   Labor and other capital: the rights of each secured and the wrongs of both eradicated

... New York: Pub. by the Author, 1849. xxxvi, 298 pp.
> Inscription: From author to R. W. E., 30 Mar. 1850.

KELTY, MARY ANN. Reminiscences of thought and feeling. London: W. Pickering, 1852. iv, 290 pp.
> Inscription.

KENNEDY, GRACE. Anna Ross, a story for children. Philadelphia: American Union Sunday School, [18—?]. 164 pp.

KENYON, JOHN. Poems, for the most part occasional. London: E. Moxon, 1838. xv, 199 pp.
> Inscription: July 1848, to Mr. Emerson. Letter signed by John Kenyon, 4 July 1848, inserted.

KER, JOHN BELLENDEN. An essay on the archaeology of our popular phrases and nursery rhymes. New ed. London: Longman, Rees, Orme, Brown, Green; Southampton: [J.] Coupland, 1837. 2 v.
> Inscription: From Philip Randolph.

KERNER, JUSTINUS ANDREAS CHRISTIAN. The seeress of Prevorst; being revelations concerning the inner-life of man, and the inter-diffusion of a world of spirits in the one we inhabit. From the German, by Mrs. Crowe ... London: J. C. Moore, 1845. xii, 338 pp.

KETT, HENRY. Elements of general knowledge. [Philadelphia? 1805?] 2 v.
> Lent to one of his Harvard classmates by Ralph Waldo Emerson in 1821 (Cameron, III, 856).

KING, EDWARD. Echos from the orient, with miscellaneous poems. London: C. Kegan Paul, 1880. vi, 131 pp.

KING, MOSES. Harvard and its surroundings. 2d ed., thoroughly rev. Copiously illus. with heliotypes, wood engravings, and etchings. Cambridge, Mass.: Moses King, 1878. 92 pp.

KING, THOMAS STARR. Christianity and humanity, a series of sermons. Ed., with a memoir, by Edwin P. Whipple. 4th ed. Boston: James R. Osgood, 1876. lxxx, 380 pp.

KINGSLEY, CHARLES. Glaucus; or, The wonders of the shore. Boston: Ticknor and Fields, 1855. 165 pp.
Inscription: From Philip Randolph.

_____. Westward ho! or, The voyages and adventures of Sir Amyas Leigh, knight, of Burrough, in the County of Devon, in the reign of Her most glorious Majesty, Queen Elizabeth. Rendered into modern English by Charles Kingsley. London: Macmillan, 1881. 2 v.

KINGSTON, WILLIAM HENRY GILES. Picolo Paolo, a tale of Savoy. Boston: D. Lothrop, [1879?]. 64 pp.

KINGSTON HOMOCULTURAL SOCIETY. Kingston Homocultural Society. [London: Tornas, Printers, 18—?]. 1 l.
Broadside.
Bound with: Lane, Charles. A classification of science and arts. London, 1826.

_____. _____. The lectures for the Michaelmas quarter, 1840. [London: Tornas, Printers, 1840?]
Bound with: Lane, Charles. A classification of science and arts. London, 1826.

KIRKLAND, JOHN THURSTON. A discourse delivered in the Stone Church, Summer-Street, the Lord's day after the interment of George Cabot, who died April 18th, 1823. Boston: Wells and Lilly, 1823. 26 pp.

KNOX, ROBERT. The races of men: a philosophical enquiry into the influence of race over the destinies of nations ... 2d ed., with supplementary chapters. London: Henry Renshaw, 1862. viii, 600 pp.
Signature: R. W. Emerson.

KRAITSIR, CHARLES V. Glossology; being a treatise on the nature of language, and on the language of nature. New York: George P. Putnam, 1852. vi, 240 pp.

KRAUSE, WILLIAM E. E. The influence of the United States abroad. San Francisco: Joseph Winterburn, 1868. 16 pp.

KVINOEL, D. C. T.　Commentarius in libros Novi Testamenti historicos.　Lipsiae, 1818-23.　4 v.

Given to Grindall Reynolds of Concord by Ralph Waldo Emerson (Cameron, III, 857).　This is undoubtedly the "Kvinoel" which Emerson listed in his Pocket Diary (1820-47) as having been lent in Feb. 1829, to (Frederick?) Dabney (Harvard, '28).　The book was sold at the Wakeman Sale (New York: American Art Association, 1924), Lot #259.

L

LACROIX, SILVESTRE FRANÇOIS.
   Emerson lent a book by this author to one of his college classmates in 1821. It might have been Elementary treatise on the differential and integral calculus, Elements of algebra, or Elementary treatise on trigonometry (Cameron, III, 856).

The lady's almanac for 1854, by Damrell & Moore & G. Coolidge.   Boston: John P. Jewett, Cleveland, Ohio: Jewett, Proctor & Worthington, [1853].   125 pp.
   Edith's gift to Ellen.
   Notes.

LA FONTAINE, JEAN DE.   Fables.   Nouv. éd.   Paris: Plancher, 1818.   2 v.
   Autographs: Charles C. Emerson.

———.   ———.   Tr. from the French, by Elizur Wright, Jr.   ...   3d ed.   Boston: Tappan and Dennet, 1842.   2 v.
   Inscription: From the publisher.

LAMB, CHARLES.   Mrs. Leicester's School; or, The history of several young ladies, related by themselves. Philadelphia: Henry F. Anners, 1844.   xii, 165 pp.
   Inscription.

———, ed.   Specimens of English dramatic poets, who lived about the time of Shakespeare.   With notes. New York: Wiley & Putnam, 1845.   2 pts. in 1 v.
   Autograph.

———. Works. New ed. London: Edward Moxon, 1855. 4 v.
Set incomplete: v. 1 wanting.

LA MOTTE FOUQUÉ, FRIEDRICH, *Freiherr* DE. Peter Schlemihl, from the German of Lamotte Fouqué, with plates by George Cruikshank. Boston: Wells and Lilly, 1824. viii, 139 pp.
Bound with: The classical journal, v. 1-2, 1830-31. Boston.

———. Undine, eine Erzahlung. New York: Wilhelm Radde, 1846. v, 89 pp.
Autograph: Ellen T. Emerson, and her notes.

[LANDOR, WALTER SAVAGE.] Citation and examination of William Shakespeare, Euseby Treen, Joseph Carnaby and Silas Gough, clerk before the worshipful Sir Thomas Lucy, knight, touching deer-stealing on the 19th day of September in the year of Grace 1582, now first published from original papers. To which is added a conference of Master Edmund Spenser, a gentleman of note, with the Earl of Essex touching the state of Ireland, A.D. 1595. London: Saunders and Otley, 1834. xi, 284 pp.
Autograph and notes.

———. Imaginary conversations of literary men and statesmen. 2d ed., cor. and enl. London: Henry Colburn, 1826. 3 v.
Autograph.

———. The last fruit off an old tree. London: E. Moxon, 1853. x, 520 pp.
Autograph and notes, 1874.

[———.] The Pentameron and Pentalogia. London: Saunders and Otley, 1837. xi, 384 pp.
Autograph and notes.

———. Pericles and Aspasia. London: Saunders and Otley, 1836. 2 v.
Autographs and notes.

———. Works. London: Chapman & Hall, 1868. 2 v.

LANE, CHARLES. A classification of science and arts; or, A map of human knowledge. London: Effingham Wilson, 1826. 20 pp.
Autograph.

LAO-TZŬ. The speculations on metaphysics, polity, and morality, of "the Old philosopher," Lau-Tsze, tr. from the Chinese, with an introduction, by John Chalmers. London: Trübner, 1868. xix, 62 pp.
Inscription: R. W. Emerson with the affecionate regards of Wm. Henry Channing, 1870.

LAPORTE, LAURENT. Sailing on the Nile. Tr. from the French by Virginia Vaughan. Boston: Roberts Bros., 1872. iv, 291 pp.

LARCOM, LUCY. Wild roses of Cape Ann, and other poems. Boston: Houghton, Mifflin, 1881. vi, 272 pp.
Inscription.

LARDNER, DIONYSIUS. A treatise on hydrostatics and pneumatics. 1st American, from the 1st London ed. With notes by Benjamin F. Joslin. Boston: Stimpson and Clapp, 1832. viii, 273 pp.

LASTEYRIE DU SAILLANT, MARIE ANTOINETTE VIRGINIE (DE LAFAYETTE), *Marquise* DE. Vie de Madame de Lafayette par Mme. de Lasteyrie, sa fille, précédée d'une notice sur la vie de sa mère Mme. la Duchesse d'Ayer, 1737-1807. Paris: Jean Tichener, 1868. iii, 484 pp.
Autograph: Ellen T. Emerson, and her marginal notes.

LATHERS, RICHARD. South Carolina, the condition and the prospects of the state. Confiscation of private property and repudiation of the public debt. Address of Richard Lathers, delivered before the New England Society of Charleston, on forefathers' day, December 22, 1873. Charleston, S. C.: The News and Courier Job Presses, 1874. 18 pp.

LATHROP, GEORGE PARSONS. Rose and roof-tree, poems. Boston: J. R. Osgood, 1875. x, 126 pp.
Inscription: Nov. 1875.

LATIMER, HUGH, *Bp. of Worcester.*   Select sermons.
With some account of the author and his writings.
Boston: Hilliard, Gray; Cambridge: Brown, Shattuck,
1832.   xlvii, 288 pp.

LAUGEL, AUGUSTE *i.e.* ANTOINE AUGUSTE.   Les États-
Unis pendant la guerre (1861–1865).   Paris: Germer
Baillière, 1866.   xvi, 363 pp.
Inscription.

LAURIE, JOSEPH.   Homoeopathic domestic medicine, arranged as a practical work for students.   Containing
a glossary of medical terms.   3d American ed., enl.
and improved by A. Gerald Hull.   New York: William
Radde, 1846.   xxx, 438 pp.

LAVALLÉE, THÉOPHILE.   Histoire des Français depuis
le temps des Gaulais jusqu'en 1830.   Paris: Paulin
et Hetzel, 1838–40.   4 v.
Autographs: v. 1, 3, Ellen T. Emerson.

LAW, WILLIAM.   A serious call to a devout and holy
life; adapted to the state and condition of all orders
of Christians.   17th ed.   To which is added, some
account of the author, and three letters to a friend
. . .   Boston: Charles Emer, 1818.   xxvi, 346 pp.

——.   The spirit of prayer; or, The soul rising out of
the vanity of time, into the riches of eternity . . .
Providence: John Miller, 1823.   2 pts. in 1 v.
Mrs. Waldo Emerson's book.
Autograph.

——.   ——.   New York: John S. Taylor, 1844.
139 pp.

LAWSON, WILLIAM, HUNTER, CHARLES D., *et al.*   Ten
years of gentleman farming at Blennerhasset, with
co-operative objects.   London: Longmans, Green,
1874.   viii, 408 pp.

LAZARUS, EMMA.   Poems and translations.   Written be-
tween the ages of fourteen and seventeen.   New
York: Hurd and Houghton, 1867.   viii, 297 pp.
"Corrections" slip inserted at p. [iii].
Inscription: 12 Feb. 1868.

_____. The Spagnoletto, a play in 5 acts. Unpublished manuscript. [n.p.], ᶜ1876. 56 pp.

LEAR, HENRIETTA LOUISA (FARRER). For days and years. A book containing a text, short reading and hymn for every day in the church's year. Selected by H. L. Sidney Lear [pseud.]. New York: E. P. Dutton, 1879. iv, 408 pp.

LE CLERC, JEAN. Ars critica, in qua ad studia linguarum Latinae, Graecae, et Hebraicae. Via munitur; Veterumque emendandorum, Spariorum Scriptorum a Genuinis dignoscendorum, & judicandi de eorum libris ratio traditur. Accendunt in Calce quatuor Indices locupletissimi. Ed. sexto prioribus emendatior. Lugduni Batavorum: Sam. et Joh. Luchtmans, 1778. 3 v.
   Autographs and inscriptions: June 1824.

Lecture. Begins: Man is by nature an active being. [n.p.? n.d.?] 27 pp.
   Bound with: Webster, Daniel. Speech ... on the 14th January, 1814. Alexandria, 1814.

[LEE, HANNAH FARNHAM (SAWYER).] The Huguenots in France and America. Cambridge: John Owen, 1843. 2 v.

LEE, SARAH (WALLIS) BOWDICH. Memoirs of Baron Cuvier. New York: J. J. Harper, 1833. 197 pp.
   Note.

LEIGHTON, ROBERT. Poems. Liverpool: Edward Havell, 1866. xi, 356 pp.
   Inscription: Sept. 1868 (in R. W. E.'s hand), and notes.

_____. Reuben, and other poems. London: Daldy, Isbister, 1875. vii, 272 pp.

_____. Select works. London: William Baynes, 1823. 2 v.
   Inscription: R. W. E. from G. A. Sampson (in R. W. E.'s hand). Note on slip laid in, v. 2, p. [433].

LEIGHTON, WILLIAM. At the court of King Edwin, a
drama ... Philadelphia: J. B. Lippincott, 1878.
157 pp.
Inscription.

——. Change; the whisper of the sphinx. Philadelphia: J. B. Lippincott, 1879. 143 pp.
Inscription: 30 Nov. 1878.

——. Shakespeare's dream, and other poems. Philadelphia: J. B. Lippincott, 1881. 148 pp.
Inscription: By author to R. W. E., Dec. 6, 1880.

——. The sons of Godwin, a tragedy. Philadelphia:
J. B. Lippincott, 1877. 188 pp.
Inscription: By author to Emerson, 12 Dec. 1876.

——. ——. Copy 2.

LE MAOUT, EMMANUEL, AND DECAISNE, J. A general system of botany, descriptive and analytical. In two
parts. Part I.—Outlines of organography, anatomy,
and physiology. Part II.—Descriptions and illustrations of the orders. With 5500 figures by L.
Steinheil and A. Riocreux. Tr. from the original by
Mrs. Hooker. The orders arranged after the method
followed in the universities and schools of Great
Britain, its colonies, America, and India; with additions, an appendix on the natural method, and a
synopsis of the orders, by J. D. Hooker ... London: Longmans, Green, 1873; Boston: Lee and
Shepard, 1873. xii, 1066 pp.

LEMPRIERE, JOHN. A classical dictionary, containing
a copious account of all the proper names mentioned
in ancient authors, with the value of coins, weights,
and measures used among the Greeks and Romans,
and a chronological table. 6th ed., cor. London:
T. Cadell and W. Davies, 1806. xxxii, [864] pp.
Autograph: C. C. Emerson.

LEONOWENS, ANNA HARRIETTE (CRAWFORD). The English governess at the Siamese court: being recollections of six years in the royal palace at Bangkok.

With illus. from photographs presented to the author
by the King of Siam. Boston: Fields, Osgood,
1870. x, 321 pp.

LE SAGE, ALAIN RENÉ. The adventures of Gil Blas of
Santillane. Tr. from the French by Tobias Smollett.
To which is prefixed a life of the author. Phila-
delphia: Jasper Harding, 1846. 4 v. in 1.

――――. Histoire de Gil Blas de Santillane. Paris: A.
Pougin, 1837. 5 v. in 18.
 Set incomplete: t. 1–4, 6–18 wanting.

LESLEY, J. PETER. The iron manufacturer's guide to
the furnaces, forges and rolling mills of the United
States, with discussions of iron as a chemical ele-
ment, an American ore, and a manufactured article,
in commerce and in history. New York: J. Wiley;
London: Trübner, 1859. xxiv, 772 pp. plates,
maps.
 Inscription.

――――. Man's origin and destiny, sketched from the
platform of the physical sciences. 2d ed., enl.
Boston: Geo. H. Ellis, 1881. vi, 442 pp.
 Inscription.

――――. Manual of coal and its topography. Illus. by
original drawings, chiefly of facts in the geology of
the Appalachian region of the United States of North
America. Philadelphia: J. B. Lippincott, 1856.
xii, 224 pp.
 Inscription: From author.

[LESLEY, SUSAN INCHES (LYMAN).] Memoir of the life of
Ann Jean Lyman ... Privately printed. Cam-
bridge, Mass.: [John Wilson], 1876. 543 pp.
 Inscription: By Mrs. Lesley, dated Christmas 1875.

LESSING, GOTTHOLD EPHRAIM. Laocoon, an essay on
the limits of painting and poetry. Tr. from the
German by E. C. Beasley ... With an introduction
by T. Burbidge ... London: Longman, Brown,
Green and Longmans, 1853. xviii, 255 pp.
 Autograph.

A letter to the working women of the United Kingdom of
Great Britain and Ireland, on the readiest and surest
means for their emancipation, by P. A. S., an English
workwoman.   London: B. D. Cousins, [18—?].
8 pp.
    Bound with: Lane, Charles.   A classification of sci-
ence and arts.   London, 1826.

LEVERETT, FREDERICK PERCIVAL.   The new Latin tutor;
or, Exercises in etymology, syntax and prosody,
compiled in part from the best English works, with
additions.   Boston: Hilliard, Gray, Little and
Wilkins, 1829.   348 pp.

Library of useful knowledge.   Natural philosophy . . .
London: Baldwin and Cradock, 1829–[38].   4 v.
Signature: v. 1, 2, R. W. E.; and notes, v. 1.

Library of useful knowledge.   Mathematics I . . .   London: Baldwin and Cradock, 1836.   93, 123, 96 pp.

LIEBER, FRANCIS.   On civil liberty and self-government.
Philadelphia: Lippincott, Grambo, 1853.   2 v.
Set incomplete: v. 2 wanting.

LEIBIG, JUSTUS, *Freiherr* VON.   Familiar letters on
chemistry, and its relation to commerce, physiology,
and agriculture.   Ed. by John Gardner.   New York:
D. Appleton, 1843.   180 pp.
Autograph.

———.   Organic chemistry in its applications to agriculture and physiology.   Ed. from the manuscript of
the author, by Lyon Playfair . . .   1st American ed.,
with an introduction, notes, and appendix, by John
W. Webster . . .   Cambridge: J. Owen; Boston: J.
Munroe, 1841.   xx, 435 pp.

The lily; a coloured annual, for MDCCCXXXI.   New-
York: R. Schoyer, 1831.   vi, 232 pp.
Inscription: Ellen T. Emerson from Aunt Lucy, Jan. 1,
1847.

LINCOLN GUARD OF HONOR.   Organization and objects of
the Lincoln Guard of Honor, and first memorial service, held on the fifteenth anniversary of the death

of Abraham Lincoln, Springfield, Illinois, April 15th,
1880. [Springfield, Ill.: State Journal, 1880.] 14 pp.

LINTON, WILLIAM JAMES. Claribel, and other poems.
London: Simpkin, Marshall, 1865. xi, 266 pp.
Inscription.

Little Annie's first book: chiefly in words of three
letters, by her mother. Philadelphia: George S.
Appleton; New York: D. Appleton, 1849. v, 126 pp.

LITTLE COMPTON, R. I. UNITED CONGREGATIONAL
CHURCH. The one hundred and seventy-fifth
anniversary of the organization of the United
Congregational Church, Little Compton, R. I.,
celebrated June 2d, 1880. Providence:
Press Co., 1880. 76 pp.

Little Nannette, a narrative of facts. From the 3d
English ed. Salem: Whipple and Lawrence, 1825.
36 pp.

Little Red-Riding Hood. New York: John McLoughlin,
[18—?]. 12 pp.

LITTLETON, ADAM. Latin dictionary. In four parts: I.
English–Latin. II. A Latin–classical. III. A
Latin–proper. IV. A Latin barbarous ... With
large amendments and improvements. London: J.
Walthoe, J. J. and P. Knapton, 1735. 1 v. ([1443?]
pp.) 2 maps.

LIVIUS, TITUS. The history of Rome. London: Henry
G. Bohn, 1854-56.
Autograph.

———. ———. Selections from the first five books,
together with the twenty-first and twenty-second
books entire. Chiefly from the text of Alschefski.
With English notes for schools and colleges, by J. L.
Lincoln ... With an accompanying plan of Rome and
a map of the passage of Hannibal. 10th ed. rev.
New York: D. Appleton, 1857. vi, 329 pp.
Signature: J. Haven Emerson.

LIZARS, WILLIAM HORNE, *engr.* Twelve views of the lakes of Westmorland & Cumberland, engraved by Lizars, Edinburgh. Kendal: Hudson & Nicholson, [18—?]. 12 plates.

LLOYD, H. H., & Co., *publishers.* New military map of the border & Southern states. New York, 1861. col. map.
Drawn by Edward S. Hall.

LLOYD, JAMES T. New map of the United States, the Canadas and New Brunswick from the latest surveys, showing every railroad & station finished to June 1862, and the Atlantic and Gulf coasts from the United States superintendant's official reports of the Coast Survey by order of Congress. New York, 1866. col. map.

LLOYD, SAMUEL H. Glimpses of the spirit-land. Addresses, sonnets, and other poems. Printed for private distribution. New-York: J. A. Gray & Green, 1867. 151 pp.

LOCKE, DAVID ROSS. Hannah Jane, by ... (Petroleum V. Nasby) ... Boston: Lee and Shepard; New York: Charles T. Dillingham, 1882. 10 ll.

LOCKE, JOHN. The beauties of Locke, consisting of selection from his philosophical, moral, and theological works, by Alfred Howard. London: T. Davidson, for T. Tegg, [18—?]. 212 pp.
Autograph.

———. Some thoughts concerning education. 8th ed. London: John Osborn and Tho. Longman, 1725. 331 pp.

———. A treatise on the conduct of understanding. Boston: Timothy Bedlington, 1828. 132 pp.
Autograph: Lidian Emerson.
Presented to the Concord Free Public Library by Mrs. Ralph Waldo Emerson.

———. Works.
Lent by Emerson to one of his Harvard classmates in 1821 (Cameron, III, 856).

LOCKER-LAMPSON, FREDERICK. London lyrics. With an illus. by George Cruikshank. London: Chapman and Hall, 1857. viii, 90 pp.

LOCKHART, JOHN GIBSON. Memoirs of the life of Sir Walter Scott, Bart. Boston: Otis, Broaders, 1837–38. 7 v.
  Vol. 5–7 have imprint: Philadelphia: Carey, Lea & Blanchard, 1837–38. Autographs and notes.

LONDON. STATIONERS' COMPANY. A transcript of the registers of the Company of Stationers of London, between 1554–1640 A.D. Second announcement. [London, 1874?] 4 pp.

———. A transcript (page for page) of the registers of the Company of Stationers of London, between 1554–1640 A.D. Ed. by Edward Arber ... [London, 1873?] 6 pp.

———. UNIVERSITY. University of London: Faculties of arts and of law. [Announcements]: session 1833–34. [Signed at end: Thomas Coates, secretary.] London: Richard Taylor, 1833. 8 pp.

LONDON AESTHETIC INSTITUTION. Prospectus. [London: V. Tornas, Printer, 183–?] 4 pp.
  Bound with: Lane, Charles. A classification of science and arts. Boston, 1826.

LONDON MECHANICS INSTITUTION. Prospectus of the day school for the education of youth, to be commenced January 2d, 1832. Conducted by S. Preston ... and qualified assistants. [London: J. Wilson, Printer, 1832] [2] pp.
  Bound with: Lane, Charles. A classification of science and arts ... London, 1826.

LONGFELLOW, HENRY WADSWORTH. The courtship of Miles Standish, and other poems. Boston: Ticknor and Fields, 1858. iv, 215 pp.
  Inscription.

———. The divine tragedy. Boston: James R. Osgood, 1871. iv, 150 pp.

———— .   The golden legend.   Boston: Ticknor, Reed, and Fields, 1851.   301 pp.
Inscription.

———— .   Kavanagh, a tale.   Boston: Ticknor, Reed, and Fields, 1849.   188 pp.
Autograph: R. W. Emerson with the regards of the author. May 19, 1849.
Presented to the Concord Free Public Library by Ralph Waldo Emerson in Feb. 1874 (Cameron, III, 868).

———— .   The New-England tragedies.   I. John Endicott. II. Giles Corey of the Salem Farms.   Boston: Ticknor and Fields, 1868.   179 pp.
Inscription.

———— .   Saggi de' novellieri italiani d'ogni secolo: tratti da' piu celebri scrittori, con brevi notizie intorno alla vita di ciascheduno.   Boston: Gray e Bowen; [Cambridge: E. W. Metcalf], 1832.   vi, 168 pp.
Autograph.
Ms. index.

———— .   The seaside and the fireside.   Boston: Ticknor, Reed, and Fields, 1850.   iv, 141 pp.
Inscription: 25 Dec. 1849.

———— .   The song of Hiawatha.   Boston: Ticknor and Fields, 1855.   iv, 316 pp.

———— .   The Spanish student.   A play, in three acts. Cambridge: J. Owne, 1843.   vi, 183 pp.
Autograph.

———— .   The Spanish student, and other poems.   [New York, Hurst, 18—?]   106 pp.
Bound with the author's Voices of the night.   New York, [18—?].

———— .   Tales of a wayside inn.   Boston: Ticknor and Fields, 1863.   v, 225 pp.
Presentation copy; autograph.

———— .   Voices of the night, ballads and other poems. New York: Hurst, [18—?].   128 pp.
Bound with the author's The Spanish student, and other poems.   [New York, 18—?]

[_____.]   The Waif: a collection of poems ...   3d ed.
Cambridge: J. Owen, 1845.   xi, 144 pp.
Presentation inscription in Longfellow's hand.

LONGUS.   Gli amori pastorali di Dafni e Cloe.   Tr.
dalla lingua Greca dal commendatore Annibal Caro.
Parigi: Ant. Ag Renouard, 1800.   164 pp.

LONSDALE, MARGARET.   Sister Dora, a biography.   From
the 6th English ed.   Boston: Roberts Bros., 1880.
ix, 290 pp.
Autograph: Ellen T. Emerson.

LORD, WILLIAM WILBERFORCE.   Poems.   New York:
D. Appleton; Philadelphia: G. S. Appleton, 1845.
vi, 158 pp.

LORING, GEORGE BAILEY.   The farm-yard club of Jotham:
an account of the families and farms of that famous
town.   Boston: Lockwood, Brooks, 1876.   xv,
603 pp.
Inscription: To R. W. E., Nov. 20, 1876, from the author.

Love culture.   [London?   18—?]   1 l.
Broadside.
Bound with: Lane, Charles.   A classification of
science and arts.   London, 1826.

Love-spirit.   [London, 18—?]   1 l.
Broadside.
Bound with: Lane, Charles.   A classification of science
and arts.   London, 1826.

LOVELACE, RICHARD.   Lucasta.   The poems of Richard
Lovelace, esq., now first edited, and the text care-
fully revised.   With some account of the author, and
a few notes, by W. Carew Hazlitt.   London: John
Russell Smith, 1864.   xlii, 293 pp.
Autographs and notes.

[LOVELACE, WILLIAM KING, *1st Earl of.*]   Art II. Quetelet:
Du systeme sociol.   [n.p., n.d., for review.]   pp. 16-
35.
Apparently proof of a review for the Christian teacher,
no. 43.
Inscription.

[_____.]   Art. III.   Villemain: Literature du moyen age.
Paris.   [n.p., n.d., for review.]   [334]-355.
　　A review extracted from a periodical.
　　Autograph and inscription.

[_____.]   Art. VIII.   Report of the Committee of the
House of Commons on the program of the new house
of Parliament.   [London, Waterlow & sons.]   [n.p.,
n.d., for article.]   pp. [4]-23.
　　An article extracted from a periodical (?).
　　Inscription.

_____ .   On climate in connection with husbandry, with
reference to a work entitled Cours d'agriculture, par
le Comte de Gasparin ...   London: W. Clawes, 1848.
32 pp.
　　"From the Journal of the Royal Agricultural Society of
England, vol. 9, pt. 2 [18—]."
　　Inscription.

[_____.]   Art. V. Histoire du Consulat et de l'Empire.
Par M. A. Thiers.   Paris: Paulin.   Tomes V. VI. VII.
[n.p., n.d., for review.]   pp. [387]-421.
　　A review extracted from a periodical.
　　Inscription.

_____ .   On harbours of refuge, with an abstract of the
discussion upon the paper.   Excerpt minutes of
proceedings of the Institution of Civil Engineers.
By permission of the Council.   London: W. Clawes,
1849.   52 pp.
　　Inscription.

[_____.]   Review of the Agricultural statistics of
France: with a notice of the works of Wm. Rubichon,
Mounier, and Passy, respecting its produce, and the
condition of its rural population.   London: Daniel
Batten, 1848.   44 pp.
　　Inscription.

Low, Nathanael.   An astronomical diary; or, Almanack
for the year of Christian aera 1792.   Bos[ton]: T. &
J. Fleet, [1792?].   24 pp.
　　Autograph: Ward Cotton's property, and notes.

LOWE, ABRAHAM T. Fragments of physiology; or, Essays on life, health, hygiene, disease, and cure of disease. Boston: Henry A. Young, 1877. vii, 220 pp.
Inscription: Rev^d. R. W. Emerson, with the respects of A. T. Lowe.

[LOWE, MARTHA ANN (PERRY).] The olive and the pine ... Boston: Crosby, Nichols, 1859. viii, 156 pp.
Inscription: Miss Ellen Emerson from author (in Emerson's hand).

_____ . The story of Chief Joseph. Boston: D. Lothrop, [1881]. 40 pp.
Inscription: From author to Mrs. Emerson.

[LOWELL, ANNA CABOT (JACKSON)], *comp.* Poetry for home and school. Boston: S. G. Simpkins, 1843. 360 pp.
Inscription: Ellen Emerson from her cousin William, Jan. 1, 1846, and notes.

_____ . Seed-grain for thought and discussion, a compilation. Boston: Ticknor and Fields, 1856. 2 v.
Inscription: v. 1, R. W. Emerson from A. C. L., and note, v. 2.

LOWELL, JAMES RUSSELL. Among my books. 2d series. Boston: James R. Osgood, 1876. 327 pp.
Inscription laid in.

[_____ .] The Biglow papers. Ed., with an introduction, notes, glossary, and copious index, by Homer Wilbur. 4th ed. Boston: Ticknor and Fields, 1856. xxxii, 163 pp.
Autograph.

[_____ .] _____ . 2d series ... Boston: Houghton, Mifflin, 1881. lxxx, 258 pp.

_____ . The cathedral. Boston: Fields, Osgood, 1870. 52 pp.
Inscription.

_____ . Conversations on some of the old poets. Cambridge, [Mass.]: J. Owen, 1845. viii, 263 pp.
Inscription: 1 Jan. 1845.

———. A fable for critics ... Boston: Ticknor and
Fields, 1856. v, 80 pp.
   Autograph.

———. Fireside travels. Boston: Ticknor and Fields,
1864. 324 pp.
   Inscription: Sept. 1864.

[———.] Meliboeus-Hipponax. The Biglow papers.
2d series ... Boston: Ticknor and Fields, 1867.
lxxx, 258 pp.
   Inscription: Ellen T. Emerson from W. H. F., New Years
   1866.

———. My study windows. Boston: James R. Osgood,
1871. 433 pp.
   Inscription: 20 Jan. 1871.

———. Poems. Cambridge: John Owen, 1844. xii,
274 pp.
   Inscription: Poem by J. R. L. and R. W. E.'s signature,
   dated Jan. 7, 1844.

———. ———. Boston: Ticknor, Reed, and Fields,
1849. 2 v.
   Inscription.

———. Three memorial poems. Boston: J. R. Osgood,
1877. 92 pp.
   Inscription: To R. W. E. by author, 15 Dec. 1876.

———. Under the willows, and other poems. Boston:
Fields, Osgood, 1869. viii, 286 pp.
   Inscription: 21 Nov. 1868.

The Lowell offering; a repository of original articles
written exclusively by females actively employed in
the mills ... v. 1, [nos. 1-4, Oct. 1840—Mar.
1841]. Lowell, Mass.: Powers & Bagley; Boston:
Saxton & Pierce, and Jordan. 380 pp.

LOWRIE, F. A. Geographical and statistical chart of
Europe, describing the boundaries, extent, population, sovereigns, governments, debts, revenue, army,
&c. &c., of its several countries, at the present day,

compiled from the most authentic sources.   New
York: William Stoddard, [1830?].   1 l.
  Broadside.

LUCIANUS SAMOSATENSIS.   Dialogues, selected from
  Lucian.   Together with his method of writing history.   Tr. by Wm. Ford.   Dublin: P. Byrne, 1785.
    Given to the Boston Latin Grammar School Library by
    Ralph Waldo Emerson in Oct. 1816.   Inscription: Ralph W.
    Emerson, October 1816.   Presented to the L. G. S. L. by
    R. W. Emerson. (Cameron, III, 855).

[LUMSDEN, JAMES *of Aberdeen.*]   American memoranda, by
  a mercantile man, during a short tour in the summer
  of 1843.   For private circulation.   Glasgow: Bell
  & Bain, 1844.   60 pp.
    Inscription: 15 Feb. 1848.

LUNT, WILLIAM PARSONS.   Gleanings.   Boston: [Pub-
  lished by Author], 1874.   110 pp.

LUSE, JAMES P.   Agassiz: the lessons of his life.
  Lecture delivered before the Louisville Library Association, on February 16, 1874.   [Louisville?
  1874?]   38 pp.

LYELL, SIR CHARLES, *1st Bart.*   Principles of geology:
  being an inquiry how far the former changes of the
  earth's surface are referable to causes now in opera-
  tion.   5th ed.   London: John Murray, 1837.   4 v.
    Autographs, v. 2-4.

LYTTLETON, GEORGE LYTTLETON.   Poems.   Edinburgh:
  A. Kincaid and W. Creech and J. Balfour, 1773.
  110 pp.
    Bound with: Gray, Thomas.   Poems.   Edinburgh, 1773.

M

MACAULAY, THOMAS BABINGTON MACAULAY, *1st Baron*.
The history of England from the accession of
James II.   London: Longman, Brown, Green, and
Longmans; Philadelphia: E. H. Butler, 1849.   2 v.
  Autograph.

McCOMAS, E. W.   The divine problem; a unique theory of
universal being and its evolutions, and of the problem
of divine life, intelligence and beneficence they in-
volve and unfold ...   New York: J. W. Lovell, 1880.
491 pp.

MacCORMAC, HENRY.   The conversation of a soul with
God: a theodicy.   London: Trübner, 1877.   xv,
144 pp.

[_____.]   The Scottish minister; or, The eviction.   A
story of religion and love.   London: Trübner, 1870.
90 pp.
  Inscription.

McCULLOCH, JOHN RAMSAY.   A dictionary, geographical,
statistical, and historical, of the various countries.
places, and principal natural objects of the world.
In which the articles relating to the United States
have been greatly multiplied and expanded, and
adapted to the present condition of the country, and
to the wants of its citizens, by Daniel Haskel ...
New York: Harper, [1843].   2 v.   7 maps.

———. A dictionary, practical, theoretical and historical, of commerce and commercial navigation. Ed. by
by Henry Vethake ... With an appendix ... Philadelphia: A. Hart, late Carey and Hart, 1852. 2 v.

———. A treatise on the principles, practices, and his-
tory of commerce. [London, 1833?] 128 pp.
Bound with: Needham, M. On the manufacture of iron.
London, 1831.

MACDONALD, ALMEDA EVANS. Poems. New York:
Carleton; London: S. Low, 1871. vi, 64 pp.

MACDONALD, GEORGE. England's antiphon. [London]:
Macmillan, [1868]. viii, 332 pp.
Autograph: Ellen T. Emerson, and her notes.

MACHIAVELLI, NICCOLÒ. The art of war. In seven
books. To which is added, Hints relative to war-
fare, by a gentleman of the State of New-York. Albany: Henry C. Southwick, 1815. 349 pp.
Autograph, 1842.

———. The Florentine histories. Tr. from the Italian
ed., prepared in 1843, by G. B. Niccolini, of Florence, by C. Edwards Lester ... New York: Paine
and Burgess, 1845. 2 v.
Autograph.

MACKELLAR, THOMAS. Rhymes atween-times. Philadelphia: J. B. Lippincott, 1873. 336 pp.

MACKIE, CHARLES. Historical description of the Abbey
and Town of Paisley. Glasgow: Joseph Swan, 1835.
viii, 170 pp.
Inscription: From R. Stewart.

MACKINTOSH, SIR JAMES. England. London: Longman,
Rees, Orme, Brown, and Green, and John Taylor, .
1830-32. 3 v.
Autograph and notes.

———. A general view of the progress of ethical philosophy, chiefly during the seventeenth and eight-

eenth centuries.   Philadelphia: Carey and Lea,
1832.   304 pp.
> Signature: R. W. Emerson, and notes.

———.   The history of England.   Philadelphia: Carey &
Lea, 1830–33.   3 v.
> Set incomplete: v. 2, 3 wanting.
> Notes and autograph.

MCLANDBURGH, FLORENCE.   The automaton ear, and other
sketches.   Chicago: Jansen, McClurg, 1876.
282 pp.

Macphail's Edinburgh ecclesiastical journal, and literary
review.   no. 25, Feb. 1848.   Edinburgh: Myles
Macphail; London: Simpkin, Marshall.   80 pp.
> Inscription.

MACPHERSON, JAMES.   The poems of Ossian; tr. by
James Macpherson.   To which are prefixed a preliminary discourse and dissertation on the aera and
poems of Ossian.   Boston: Phillips, Sampson, 1857.
492 pp.

MACRUM, JAMES MARIUS.   The new piano, a lyric poem,
etc.   Pittsburg: Robert S. Davis, 1871.   32 pp.

———.   Solitary house of fancy and feeling, and other
poems.   Dublin: James McGlashan; London: Whittaker, 1846.   x, 215 pp.
> Inscription: 9 Mar. 1859.

MAHĀBHĀRATA.   Nala and Damayanti, and other poems.
Tr. from the Sanscrit into English verse, with mytho-
logical and critical notes, by Henry Hart Milman ...
Oxford: D. A. Talboys, 1835.   viii, 148 pp.
> Inscription: Henry D. Thoreau from Thomas Cholmonde-
> ley (in Thoreau's hand).   Emerson's autograph: May 1862.

———.   BHAGAVADGĪTĀ.   *English.*   A commentary on
the text of the Bhagavad-Gítá; or, The discourse
between Krishna and Arjuna on divine matters.   A
Sanscrit philosophical poem.   With [the text in J. C.
Thomson's English translation and] a few introduc-

tory papers, by Hurrychund Chintamon ...   London:
Trübner, 1874.   83 pp.
    Inscription: From S. A. Dorsey of Louisiana.

MAIN, DAVID M., *ed.*   A treasury of English sonnets, ed.
    from the original sources, with notes and illustra-
    tions.   Manchester: Alexander Ireland, 1880.   viii,
    470 pp.
    Inscription: By Alexander Ireland to R. W. E., 9 Apr.
    1880.

MAINE. GEOLOGICAL SURVEY.   Report on the geology of
    the State of Maine, by Charles T. Jackson, geologist
    of the State of Maine.   2d, 1838.   Augusta: Luther
    Severance.   xiv, 168 pp.
    Inscription: Rev. R. W. Emerson with respects of the
    author.

MALDEN, MASS.   The bi-centennial book of Malden.
    Containing the oration and poem delivered on the two
    hundredth anniversary of the incorporation of the
    Town, May 23, 1849; with other proceedings on that
    day; and matters pertaining to the history of the
    place ...   Pub. for the citizens of Malden.   Bos-
    ton: G. C. Rand, 1850.   251 pp.
    Inscription: R. W. E. from Committee of Publication.

MALLET, PAUL HENRI.   Northern antiquities; or, An his-
    torical account of the manners, customs, religion and
    laws, maritime expeditions and discoveries, language
    and literature of the ancient Scandinavians ...   Tr.
    from the French by Bishop Percy.   New ed., rev.
    throughout and considerably enl.; with a translation
    of the prose Edda from the original Old Norse text;
    and notes critical and explanatory, by I. A. Black-
    well.   To which is added, an abstract of the
    Eyrbyggja saga, by Sir Walter Scott.   London: H. G.
    Bohn, 1847.   578 pp.
    Autograph.

MALTE-BRUN, CONRAD. Universal geography; or, A description of all parts of the world, on a new plan, according to the great natural divisions of the globe ... Improved by the addition of the most recent information ... Boston: Wells and Lilly; New York: E. Bliss and E. White, 1824-31. 8 v. in 17.

MANN, HORACE. Twelve sermons delivered at Antioch College. Boston: Ticknor and Fields, 1861. 314 pp.
Inscription: By Mrs. Mann to Emerson.

MANN, MARY TYLER (PEABODY). Life of Horace Mann, by his wife. Boston: Walker, Fuller, 1865. 602 pp.
Inscription.

MANU. Institutes of Hindu law; or, The ordinances of Menu, according to the gloss of Cullúca. Comprising the Indian system of duties, religious and civil. Verbally tr. from the original, with a preface, by Sir William Jones. A new ed., collated with the Sanscrit text, and elucidated with notes, by Graves Chamney Haughton ... London: Rivingtons and Cochran, 1825. xxii, 450 pp.
Inscription: Henry D. Thoreau from Thomas Cholmondeley.
Autograph: R. W. Emerson. A bequest of Henry D. Thoreau.

MANZONI, ALESSANDRO. I promessi sposi; storia milanese del secolo xvii, scoperta e rifatta da Alessandro Manzoni. 2. ed. torinese. Torino: Giuseppe Pomba, 1827. 3 v.

———. ———. 15. ed. dell' autore. Storia della colonna informe. 14. ed. dell' autore. Milano: Redaelli dei Fratelli Rechiedei, 1869. 615 pp.
Autograph: Ellen Emerson.

Map of Malta and its dependencies. Lithographie von Eml. Hindermann. J. Locherer, Sculp. [Basel, 1832.] map.

Map of St. Helena Sound, and the coast between Charleston and Savannah. Comp. from the U.S. Coast Survey. Boston: A. Williams, 1861.
> Inserted in: Tanner. New universal atlas. Philadel-
> phia, 1845.

Map of the states of Missouri, Illinois, Iowa and Wiscon-
sin; the territory of Minnesota, and the mineral lands
of Lake Superior. Philadelphia: Thomas, Cowperth-
waite, 1850. map.
> Comp. by I. S. Drake. Engraved by Ira S. Drake and
> J. L. Hazzard.

[Map of the United States, 18—?]
> Mutilated copy: consists of N. W. U.S. only; i.e., 86°
> latitude west, 37° longitude north.

Map of the White mountains, N. H., based on the best
surveys. Boston: Geo. K. Snow & Bradlee, [1873?].

MARCET, JANE (HALDIMAND). Conversations on chemistry; in which the elements of that science are famil-
iarly explained and illustrated by experiments.
From the 5th and latest English ed., rev., cor. and
considerably enl. To which are added, notes and
observations by an American gentleman. 2d ed.
Greenfield, Mass.: Denio & Phelps, 1820. xxiv,
420 pp.
> Autograph.

_____ . Conversations on vegetable physiology; comprehending the elements of botany, with their application
to agriculture. New York: G. & C. & H. Carvill,
1830. xii, 354 pp. illus.
> Autograph: E. T. Emerson, and notes by R. W. Emerson.

MARCH, FRANCIS ANDREW. Address at the sixth annual
session of the American Philological Association, at
Hartford, July 14, 1874, by the president. New
York: Rogers & Sherwood, 1874. 19 pp.
> "Reprinted from the American Presbyterian and Prince-
> ton Review for October, 1874."
> Inscription: 4 Nov. 1874.

[MARCHMONT, JOHN, *pseud.*] The Word of God on true
marriage ... Philadelphia: Claxton, Remsen & Haffelfinger, 1877. xii, 284 pp.

MARIETTE, AUGUSTE. Notice des principaux monuments
exposés dans les galeries provisoires du Musée
d'antiquités égyptiennes, de S. A. le khédive á
Boulaq. 4. éd. Paris: A. Franck, 1872. 318 pp.
Autograph.

MARLOWE, CHRISTOPHER. Works. With some account of
the author, and notes, by Alexander Dyce. A new
ed., rev., and cor. London, New York: George Routledge, 1870. liii, 407 pp.

MARSHALL, WILLIAM R. Annual message of Governor
Marshall to the Legislature of Minnesota, delivered
January 10, 1868. Printed by authority. Saint
Paul: Press Printing Co., 1868. 30 pp.
Printed inscription inserted.

MARSTON, JOHN WESTLAND. Poetic culture, an appeal to
those interested in human destiny. London: J. W.
Southgate, 1839. 23 pp.
Bound with: Lane, Charles. A classification of science and arts. London, 1826.

MARTIALIS, MARCUS VALERIUS. Epigrammata ad op-
timorvm librorvm fidem accvrate edita. Editio
stereotypa. Lipsiae: Car. Tavchnitii, [182-?].
408 pp.
Autograph and notes.

———. Épigrammes. Traduction nouvelle et complète,
par feu E. T. Simon; avec le texte latin en regard,
des notes et les meilleures imitations en vers
français, depuis Cl. Marot jusqu'à nos jours; publiée
par le général baron Simon, son fils, et P. R. Auguis
... Paris: F. Guitel, 1819. 3 v.
Autographs and notes.

MARTINEAU, HARRIET. Autobiography. Ed. by Maria
Weston Chapman ... Boston: J. R. Osgood, 1877.
2 v.

_____ . The Crofton boys. New ed. London, New
York: G. Routledge, [1865?]. 192 pp.
Autographs. Inscription: To be returned to Ellen T.
Emerson.

_____ . Eastern life, present and past. London: Edward Moxon, 1848. 3 v.
Inscription and notes, v. 1.

_____ . Feats on the fiord. New ed. London, New
York: George Routledge, [1865?]. 221 pp.
Autograph: Ellen T. Emerson, and her notes.

_____ . Household education. Philadelphia: Lea &
Blanchard, 1849. viii, 212 pp.

_____ . Miscellanies. Boston: Hilliard, Gray, 1836.
2 v.
Set incomplete: v. 1 wanting.
Signature: R. W. Emerson.

MARTINEAU, JAMES. Miscellanies. Boston: Wm.
Crosby and H. P. Nichols, 1852. vi, 472 pp.
Autograph: S. H. Emerson.

MARTLING, JAMES ABRAHAM. London Bridge; or, Capital
and labor. A poem for the times. 2d ed. Boston:
James H. Earle, 1881. 66 pp.

MARVELL, ANDREW. Poetical works. With a memoir of
the author. Boston: Little, Brown; Cincinnati:
Moore, Wilstach, Keys, 1857. liii, 335 pp.
Notes.

MASON, JOHN. A treatise on self-knowledge: showing
the nature and benefit of that important science, and
the way to attain it. Intermixed with various reflections and observations on human nature. Corrected
from the earlier and more perfect editions, with the
life of the author prefixed, by John Mason Good ...
From the London stereotype ed. Philadelphia:
D. Hogan, 1818. [xlviii], 236 pp.
Autograph: Lydian J. Emerson.

MASON, LOWELL. The new carmina sacra; or, Boston
collection of church music. Comprising the most

popular psalm and hymn tunes in general use, together with a great variety of new tunes, chants,
sentences, motetts, and anthems; principally by distinguished European composers; the whole being one
of the most complete collections of music for choirs,
congregations, singing schools and societies, extant.
New York: Mason Bros., [ᶜ1855.]   380 pp.

MASON, LUTHER WHITING.   Second music reader: a course
of exercises in the elements of vocal music and
sight-singing.   With choice note songs for the use of
schools and families.   Boston: Ginn and Heath,
1879.   vi, 96 pp.

MASSACHUSETTS. BOARD OF EDUCATION.   Educational institutions of Massachusetts, 1876.   Boston: Wright &
Potter, 1876.   20 pp.

———— .   Report, together with the report of the secretary
of the Board.   37th, 1872–73.   Boston: Wright &
Potter, 1874.   229, cxv pp.

MASSACHUSETTS. BOARD OF STATE CHARITIES.   Report.
To which are added the reports of the secretary and
the general agent of the Board.   5th, 1869.   Boston:
Wright & Potter.   cv, 444 pp.

MASSACHUSETTS. BUREAU OF STATISTICS OF LABOR.   The
census of Massachusetts: 1875.   Prepared under the
direction of Carroll D. Wright, chief of the Bureau ...
1st ed.   Boston: Albert J. Wright, 1876–77.   3 v.
Vol. 2: 2d ed., Boston, 1877.

MASSACHUSETTS. GENERAL COURT.   JOINT SPECIAL COM-
MITTEE ON SUMNER MEMORIAL.   A memorial of
Charles Sumner ...   Boston: [Wright & Potter],
1874.   316 pp.

———— .   ———— .   Copy 2.

MASSACHUSETTS. STATE BOARD OF AGRICULTURE.   Report
of the secretary, together with the reports of committees appointed to visit the county societies, with
an appendix containing an abstract of the finances of

the county societies. 5th, 1858. Boston: William White. 371 pp.

―――― . Report of the secretary, with an appendix containing reports of delegates appointed to visit the county exhibitions, and also, returns of the finances of the agricultural societies for 1873. 21st, 1874. Boston: Wright & Potter. 408, lxviii pp.

MASSACHUSETTS. ZOOLOGICAL AND BOTANICAL SURVEY. Reports on the herbaceous plants and on quadrupeds of Massachusetts. Pub. Agreeably to an order to the legislature, by the commissioners on the Zoological and botanical survey of the state. Cambridge: Folsom, Wells, and Thurston, 1840. viii, 277 pp.

MASSACHUSETTS HISTORICAL SOCIETY, BOSTON. Collections. 5th ser., v. 1-3, 1871-77. Published at the charge of the Appleton Fund. Boston. 3 v.

―――― . Proceedings of a special meeting, December 16, 1873; being the one hundredth anniversary of the destruction of the tea in Boston Harbor. Boston: John Wilson, 1874. 70 pp.

―――― . II. Proceedings of the Massachusetts historical society, for May, June, July, and August, 1871. [Boston, 1871.]

―――― . II. Proceedings of the Massachusetts historical society, from September, 1875, to January, 1876 (inclusive). [Boston, 1876.]

The Massachusetts quarterly review. [v. 1], no. 4, Sept., 1848. Boston: Coolidge & Wiley.
Autograph.

The Massachusetts sun; or, American oracle of liberty. v. 5, no. 219, May 3, 1775. Worcester,
Facsimile.
Ms. note at foot of p. [1]: This news-paper is the first thing ever printed in Worcester―[Signed] Isaiah Thomas.

MASSEY, GERALD. Poems. A new ed., rev. and enl. Boston: Ticknor and Fields, 1865. xxi, 423 pp.

MASSINGER, PHILIP. Dramatic works of Massinger and Ford. With an introduction by Hartley Coleridge. New ed. ... London, New York: George Routledge, 1869. lxi, 450, vi, 212 pp.

————. Plays. With notes, critical and explanatory, by William Gifford ... A new ed., complete in one vol. Baltimore: J. W. Bond, 1856. x, xlvi, 529 pp.
    Signature: R. W. Emerson.

[MATHER, COTTON. Optanda, Goodmen described, and Good things propounded. Published by authority. Boston: Benjamin Harris, 1692.] 99 [i.e. 90] pp.
    Copy imperfect: t.p. wanting:
    Inscription on flyleaf: Theophilis Cotton. Liber ejus. Aug. 10, 1698.

[MATSON, H.] Jesus the cure of skepticism. Oberlin, Ohio: E. J. Goodrich, [ᶜ1874]. x, 224 pp.

MATTER, JACQUES. Saint-Martin, le philosophe inconnu; sa vie et ses écrits, son maître Martinez et leurs groupes, d'après des documents inédits. Paris: Didier, 1862. xi, 460 pp.

MAURICE, FREDERICK DENISON. The unity of the New Testament. A synopsis of the first three Gospels and of the epistles of St. James, St. Jude, St. Peter, St. Paul, to which is added a commentary of the epistle to Hebrews. First American ed. Boston: Lee & Shepard; New York: Charles T. Dillingham, 1879. ix, 538 pp.

————. ————. Copy 2.

MAY, EDITH J. The sunshine of Greystone: a story for girls. New York: D. Appleton, 1856. 321 pp.
    Autograph: Ellen T. Emerson.

MEACHAM, ALFRED BENJAMIN. Wi-ne-ma (the woman-chief) and her people. Hartford, Conn.: American Publishing Co., 1876. vi, 168 pp.

MEAD, EDWIN DOAK. The philosophy of Carlyle. Boston: Houghton, Mifflin, 1881. 140 pp.
    Presentation letter laid in.

MELVILLE, HERMAN. Typee: a peep at Polynesian life,
during a four months' residence in a valley of the
Marquesas; the revised ed., with a sequel. New
York: Wiley and Putnam, 1846. xiv, 307 pp.
Signature: R. W. Emerson.

MERRICK, PLINY. A letter on speculative free masonry.
Being his answer to Nathan Heard and Gardner Bur-
bank upon their application for his views upon that
subject. Worcester: Dorr and Howland, 1829.
20 pp.

MÉRY, JOSEPH. Nouvelles nouvelles. Paris: L.
Hachette, 1858. 251 pp.

"... Metaphysics belongs to morals ..."
Inscription on ms. leaf: With I. P. G.'s deepest good
wishes. July 18, 1836.
Bound with: Lane, Charles. A classification of science and arts. London, 1826.

MEYER, BERTHA. Aids to family government; or, From
the cradle to the school, according to Froebel. Tr.
from the 2d German ed., by M. L. Holbrook, to which
has been added an essay on the rights of children and
the true principles of family government, by Herbert
Spencer ... New York: M. L. Holbrook, 1879.
208 pp.

MICHAELIS, JOHANN DAVID. Beurtheilung der Mittel,
welche Man anwendet, die ausgestorbene hebräische
Sprache zu verstehen. Göttingen: Abram Van den
Hoeks Witme, 1757. 365 pp.

MICHELET, JULES. L'amour. Paris: L. Hachette, 1858.
xiv, 414 pp.
_____. L'insecte ... 2. éd., rev et cor. Paris:
L. Hachette, 1858. xxxix, 404 pp.
Autograph: Edith Emerson.

MIDDLETON, EMPSON EDWARD. Ah, happy England! A
forecast of a general lament; A poem in five acts.
London: John Camden Hotten, 1871. x, 120 pp.

MILL, JOHN STUART. Principles of political economy, with some of their applications to social philosophy. London: John W. Parker, 1848. 2 v.
Inscription: 15 July 1848, and notes.

———. The subjection of women. London: Longmans, Green, Reader, and Dyer, 1869. 188 pp.
Inscription.

———. Suffrage for women. Speech in the British Parliament, on the household suffrage bill, May 20th, 1867. New York: American Equal Rights Association, 1867. 16 pp.

MILLAR, ROBERT. The history of the propagation of Christianity, and the overthrow of paganism. 3d ed. cor., with additions. London: A Millar, 1731. 2 v.
Set incomplete: v. 2 wanting.
Autograph: John Cotton's. 1740.

MILLER, JOAQUIN. Songs of the Sierras. Boston: Roberts Bros., 1871. 299 pp.

MILLER, LEO. Woman and the divine republic. Buffalo: Haas & Nauert, [c1874]. vi, 213 pp.

MILLER, PHILIP. The abridgement of the Gardeners dictionary: containing the best and newest methods of cultivating and improving the kitchen, fruit, flower garden, and nursery; as also for performing the practical parts of husbandry; together with the management of vineyards, and the methods of making wine in England. In which likewise are included, directions for propagating and improving, from real practice and experience, pasture lands and all sorts of timber trees. 5th ed., cor. & enl. London: John Rivington, 1763. [926] pp.

MILMAN, HENRY HART. The history of the Jews, from the earliest period to the present time. New York: J. & J. Harper, 1830. 3 v. illus., maps.
Notes and initials.

MILTON, JOHN.   Paradise lost, in twelve parts. Night thoughts on life, death and immortality, to which is added, The force of religion, by Edward Young. New ed.   Boston: Phillips, Sampson, 1849.   294, 288 pp.

_____ .   Paradise regained, Samson Agonistes, Comus, Arcades, Lycidas, etc. etc.   Chiswick: T. Whittingham, 1823.   iv, 220 pp.
   Notes.

_____ .   Poetical works. A new ed. with notes, and a life of the author ...   Boston: Hilliard, Gray, 1834. 2 v.
   Autographs: Lydian Emerson, and her notes.   Note on slip inserted, v. 2, p. [3].

_____ .   _____ .   A new ed., with notes, and a life of the author, by John Mitford.   Boston: Phillips, Sampson, 1854.   2 v.

_____ .   Prose works. With a preface, preliminary remarks, and notes, by J. A. St. John.   London: H. G. Bohn, [1848]-53.   5 v.
   Autographs and notes.

_____ .   _____ .   Copy 2.   v. 1, 5.

_____ .   A selection from the English prose works. Boston: Bowles & Dearborn, 1826.   2 v.
   A poem is written in pencil on inside of front cover; a quotation from Landor is written on flyleaf.   Penciled autograph and page notes on inside of back covers.

MITCHEL, ORMSBY MACKNIGHT.   The planetary and stellar worlds.   A popular exposition of the great discoveries and theories of modern astronomy, in a series of ten lectures.   New York: Phinney, Blakeman and Mason, 1861.   xvi, 336 pp.

MITCHELL, SAMUEL AUGUSTUS.   A new map of Texas, Oregon and California, with the regions adjoining, comp. from the most recent authorities.   Philadelphia, 1846.   col. map.
   Inserted in: Tanner, Henry S.   New universal atlas. Philadelphia, 1848.

MOLIÈRE, JEAN BAPTISTE POQUELIN. Oeuvres. Nouv.
ed. Paris: M.-A. Joly, 1734. 6 v.
  The text revised by M.-A. Joly, with a biographical
notice by M. de Serre.
  Autographs: Jerome Bonaparte—Wm[?] Emerson—R. W.
E.—E. T. E.
  Emerson willed this set to his daughter Ellen (Cameron,
III, 862).

MONDAY CLUB. Sermons on the International Sunday-
school lessons for 1879. Boston: Ira Bradley,
[ᶜ1878]. vi, 446 pp.

MONGREDIEN, AUGUSTUS. History of the free-trade movement in England. 15th thousand. London, New
York: Cassell, Petter, Galpin, [pref. 1881]. viii,
188 pp.

MONTAGU, ELIZABETH (ROBINSON). Letters. With some
of the letters of her correspondents. Published by
Matthew Montagu, her nephew and executor ...
Boston: Wells and Lilly, 1825. 3 v. in 1.

[MONTAGUE, BERTHA.] Bertha's visit to her uncle in
England ... Illus. and improved from the London
ed. Boston: Lilly and Wait, and Carter, Hendee &
Babcock, 1831. 2 v.
  Set imperfect: v. 1, all after p. 222 wanting.

MONTAIGNE, MICHEL EYQUEM DE. Essays. In three
books. With marginal notes and quotations of the
cited authors, and an account of the author's life.
To which is added a short character of the author and
translator, by way of letter; written by the Marquess
Hallifax; made English by Charles Cotton ... The
first [and] third and last vol. 2d ed. London:
M. Gilliflower and W. Hensman and J. Hindmarsh,
1693. 2 v.
  Autograph and notes.

———. ———. Made English, by Charles Cotton.
The second vol. 3d ed., with the addition of a com-
pleat index to each volume, and a full vindication of

the author.   London: M. Gilliflower, W. Hensman,
R. Wellington, and H. Hindmarsh, 1700.   728 pp.
    Autograph and notes.

————.   Essais.
    Emerson bequeathed a 3 v. set of the Essais de Mon-
taigne to James Elliot Cabot (Cameron, III, 862).

MONTÉMONT, ALBERT ÉTIENNE DE.   Guide universal de
l'étranger dans Paris; or, Nouveau tableau de cette
capitale ...   3. éd.   Paris: Garnier frères, 1848.
350, 42 pp.
    Autograph.

MONTESQUIEU, CHARLES LOUIS DE SECONDAT.   Grandeur
et décadence des Romains, Politique des Romains,
Dialogue de Sylla et d'Eucrate, Lysimaque, et
Pensées.   Lettres persanes et Temple de Gnide.
Paris: Firmin Didot frères, 1846.   566 pp.

MONTGOMERY, JAMES.   Poetical works.   With a memoir.
Edinburgh: Gall & Inglis, [1870]   xxii, 456 pp.
8 plates.

MOORE, JOSEPH, JR.   Outlying Europe and the nearer
Orient, a narrative of recent travel.   Philadelphia:
J. B. Lippincott, 1880.   554 pp.
    Inscription of author, 26 Mar. 1881.

MOORE, THOMAS.   The Epicurean, a tale.   Philadelphia: Olive-Branch Book Store, 1827.   vi, 192 pp.
    Autograph: Lydia Jackson.

————.   The history of Ireland.   Vol. I.   Philadelphia:
Carey, Lea & Blanchard, 1835.
    Set incomplete.
    Autograph and notes.

————.   Llalla Rookh.   New ed.   Boston: S. G. Goodrich, 1828.   vi, 302 pp.
    Autograph: Ellen Emerson, Concord.

————.   Melodies, national airs, miscellaneous poems
and the odes of Anacreon [pseud.].   Boston: Phillips, Sampson, 1853.   420, 282 pp.

MORGAN, LEWIS HENRY. League of the Ho-dé-no-sau-nee, or Iroquois. Rochester: Sage; New York: M. H. Newman, 1851. xviii, 477 pp.

MORISON, JAMES COTTER. Life and times of Saint Bernard, Abbot of Clairvaux. A.D. 1091–1153. London: Chapman and Hall, 1863. x, 498 pp.

MORISON, JOHN HOPKINS. Disquisitions and notes on the Gospels. Matthew. Boston: Walker, Wise, 1860. x, 538 pp.

MORRIS, WILLIAM. Love is enough; or, The freeing of Pharamond, a morality. Boston: Roberts Bros., 1873. 140 pp.

Mother Goose, old and new. Chicago: Donnelley, Gassette & Loyd, [18—?]. 79 pp.

MOTHERWELL, WILLIAM. Poetical works. With a memoir of his life. 4th ed., greatly enl. Boston: Ticknor and Fields, 1859. xii, 308 pp.

MUDIE, ROBERT. A popular guide to the observation of nature; or, Hints of inducement to the study of natural productions and appearances, in their connexions and relations. New York: J. & J. Harper, 1833. 343 pp.

MÜLLER, FRIEDRICH MAX. Introduction to the science of religion; four lectures delivered at the Royal Institution in February and March, 1870. London: Spottiswoode, 1870. pp.
"Printed in 16 es only, no. 11 ..."
Inscription.

——. Introduction to the science of religion; four lectures delivered at the Royal Institution, with two essays on false analogies and philosophy of mythology. London: Longmans, Green, 1873. ix, 403 pp.
Inscription: 25 May 1873, and notes.

MÜLLER, JOHANNES VON. An universal history, in twenty-four books. Tr. from the German. Boston: Stimpson and Clapp, 1831–32. 4 v.
Autographs. Notes, v. 1.

MUNDT, THEODOR. Geschichte der Literatur der Gegenwart, Vorlesungen. Berlin: M. Simion, 1842. vi, 544 pp.

MURRAY, JOHN, *publisher.* A handbook for travellers in central Italy ... 3d ed., carefully rev. and augm. London, 1853. 2 v. map.
Autograph and notes.

_____ . Handbook for travellers in northern Italy. Part I: Comprising the continental states of Sardinia, Lombardy and Venice, Parma, Piacenza, and Modena. Part II: Lucca, Piza, Florence, and North Tuscany. 5th ed., carefully rev. and cor. to the present time. London, 1854. xxxi, 388 pp. map, plans.
Autograph.

_____ . A handbook for travellers in Southern Italy; being a guide for the continental portion of the kingdom of the two Sicilies ... 2d ed., entirely rev. and cor. to the present time. London, 1855. viii, 392 pp.
Autograph.

_____ . Handbook to London as it is. New ed., rev. London, [1869]. 327 pp.

My dear friend. Could we be resolved to cease altogether the action of speaking from old memory ...
Ms. form letter.
Bound with: Lane, Charles. A classification of science and arts. London, 1826.

_____ . _____ . Copy 2.

N

Narina: the story of a little princess, and her silver-feathered shoes; with other moral tales. Boston: T. H. Carter, [1844?]. 140 pp.
   Inscription: Ellen Emerson from Mr. Bradford (in R. W. E.'s hand).

NASSE, ERWIN. On the agricultural community of the middle ages, and inclosures of the sixteenth century in England. Tr. from the German by H. A. Ouvry ... London: Macmillan, 1871. 100 pp.

NATIONAL ANTI-SLAVERY BAZAAR, BOSTON. The Liberty bell, by friends of freedom ... Boston, 1851. viii, 308 pp.

National reform supposes social reform; social reform supports individual reform; individual reform supports regeneration; individual regeneration supports *Redeeming Lane*. [London, 18—?] 1l.
   Broadside.
   Bound with: Lane, Charles. A classification of science and arts. London, 1826.

[NEEDHAM, M.] On the manufacture of iron. [London, 1831.] 32 pp.

NEPOS, CORNELIUS. Vitae excellentium imperatorum & in eas. Iani Gebhardi Spicilegium. Amstelodami: Ianssoniana, 1644. 497 pp.

Neues Taschen–Liederbuch. Eine Auswahl der beliebtesten und bekanntesten Trink-, Scherz-, Ernst-,

Studenten-, Freiheits-, Vaterlands-, Volks-, Jäger-,
Soldaten-, Opern-, Liebs-, Wander-, und Gesell-
schafts-Lieder.   New York: Wilhelm Radde, 1855.
viii, 184 pp.

New church magazine for children.   [v. 1], no. 1-6;
v. 7, no. 9-10; v. 3, no. 4-6; v. 13, no. 1.   July-
Dec. 1843; Sept.-Oct. 1849; Oct.-Dec. 1846; Jan.
1855.   Boston.   1 v. (various pagings).

The new doxology, creed, and liturgy; or, The new and
universal prayer book, with a succinct prologue and
illustration, for the use of the second Christian age
and dispensation, by the cupbearer, the wordbearer,
the minstrel of the word, the mediate, and the representative ...   Shrewsbury: J. Crumpton, [18—?].
12 pp.
> Autograph.
> Bound with: Lane, Charles.   A classification of science
> and arts. London, 1826.

The New England historical & genealogical register, and
antiquarian journal.   Published quarterly under the
direction of the New England Historic-Genealogical
Society.   [v. 10, no. 2 (whole number 38), April,
1856.] Boston: Samuel G. Drake.   [105]-200 pp.

A new English-German and German-English dictionary;
containing all the words in general use, designating
the various parts of speech in both languages with
the genders and plurals of the German nouns.   Comp.
from the dictionaries of Lloyd, Nöhden, Flügel, Sporschil ...   Philadelphia: G. W. Mentz, 1838.   2 v.
in 1.

NEW HAMPSHIRE. GEOLOGICAL SURVEY.   Final report on
the geology and mineralogy of the State of New
Hampshire; with contributions towards the improve-
ment of agriculture and metallurgy, by Charles T.
Jackson.   Published by order of the Legislature.
Concord, N. H.: Carroll & Baker, 1844.   viii, 376 pp.
> Inscription: Jan. 1845.

A new invention for heating and cooking by gas, desig-
nated in its various forms as I. The Cambridge gas
furnace; II. The Cambridge gas stove; III. The Cambridge gas oven; IV. The Cambridge gas range;
V. The Cambridge gas boiler. [n.p., n.d.] 8 pp.

The New-Jerusalem magazine. v. 1, no. 1-12, Sept.
1827—August 1828. Boston: A. Howard. iv,
384 pp.
> Signature: R. W. Emerson, and notes.

_____ . _____ . Copy 2.
> The fire in the Emerson house on July 24, 1872, de-
> stroyed a back file of this magazine (Cameron, III, 858).

New York (State) State Survey. Special report on the
presentation of the scenery of Niagara Falls, and
fourth annual report on the triangulation of the State
for the year 1879. James T. Gardner, director. Albany: Charles Van Benthuysen, 1880. 96 pp.
> Printed presentation slip: With the compliments of
> Frederick Law Olmsted.

New York. Church of the Messiah. Services in commemoration of the fifty-fourth anniversary of the
founding of the Church of the Messiah, and the recent
redemption of the church, from debt, at the church,
corner of Park avenue & Thirty-fourth st., Tuesday
and Wednesday, March 18th and 19th 1879. 1825–
1879. [New York: S. Hamilton's Son, 1879.]
60 pp.

Newcomb, Harvey. Sabbath school teacher's aid: a
collection of anecdotes for illustrating religious
truth, arranged under a variety of subjects, for the
use of sabbath school teachers, especially the
teachers of infant classes. Boston: Massachusetts
Sabbath School Society, 1840. xiv, 333 pp.
> Autograph: Edith Emerson, Concord.

Newton, Sir Isaac. The chronology of antient kingdoms
amended. To which is prefix'd, a short chronicle
from the first memory of things in Europe, to the con-

quest of Persia by Alexander the Great.   With three plates of the Temple of Solomon.   Dublin: S. Powell, 1728.   x, 378 pp.

NEWTON, JOHN.   Olney hymns, in three parts: I. On select passages of Scriptures.   II. On occasional subjects.   III. On the progress and changes of the spiritual life.   Poems.   London: Religious Tract Society, [18—?].   xviii, 375 pp.
   Autograph: Ellen T. Emerson.

_____ . _____ .   London, New York: T. Nelson, 1856. xv, 348 pp.
   Inscription: Ellen T. Emerson from her Mother, Feb. 24, 1857, and (R.W.E.'s?) notes.

NEWTON, RICHARD HEBER.   Studies in the life of Jesus. No. XX.   The character of Jesus, the Christ of God. Preached in the Anthon Memorial Church.   New York: S. W. Green's Son, 1880.   43 pp.

NICHOL, JOHN.   Fragments of criticism.   Printed for private circulation.   Edinburgh: J. Nichol, 1860. 244 pp.

NICHOL, JOHN PRINGLE.   The planet Neptune: an exposition and history.   Edinburgh: John Johnstone, 1848. vi, 133 pp.

NICHOLAS, LL[EWELLY?]N.   (Hinneh Ha-adam) "Behold the man!"   Being a short dissertation on a right view of the divine humanity, and its glorification ... London: Henry Pownceby, 1835.   28 pp.
   Notes.
   Bound with: Lane, Charles.   A classification of science and arts.   London, 1826.

NOBLE, SAMUEL.   The plenary inspiration of the scriptures asserted, and the principles of their composition investigated, with a view to the refutation of all objections to their divinity.   In six lectures (very greatly enl.,) delivered at Albion Hall, London Wall. With an appendix, illustrative and critical.   From

the London ed.   Cincinnati: Book Committee of the
Western Convention, 1839.   xiv, 316 pp.
  Autograph and inscription: To R. W. E. by Mrs. Rosa.

NODIER, CHARLES.   Contes en prose et en vers.   t. 2.
Bruxelles: Société belge de librairie Houman, 1844.
254 pp.

NOEL, RODEN BERKELEY WRIOTHESLEY.   Beatrice, and
other poems.   London: Macmillan, 1868.   vii, 324 pp.
  Inscription.

———.   The House of Ravensburg.   London: Dalby,
Isbister, 1877.   vi, 147 pp.
  Printed inscription laid in at front.

———.   The red flag, and other poems.   London:
Strahan, 1872.   iv, 250 pp.

NÖROTH, J., tr.   Blüthern der neuern englischen und
amerikanischen Poesie, ins Deutsche.   Boston:
Schoenhof & Moeller, [1874].   viii, 126 pp.

NORTHERN SUNDAY-SCHOOL ASSOCIATION.   The true object
and means of Sunday-school instruction; being an affectionate address to Sunday-school teachers, by one
of themselves ...   Belfast, 1847.   32 pp.

NORTON, ANDREWS.   Address delivered before the Uni-
versity in Cambridge, at the interment of Professor
Frisbie July XII, MDCCCXXII.   Cambridge: Hilliard
and Metcalf, 1822.   24 pp.
  Bound with: Webster, Daniel.   A discourse delivered at
Plymouth, December 22, 1820.   Boston, 1821.

———.   ———.   Copy 2.
  Autograph: E. B. Emerson.
  Bound with: Everett, Edward.   Speech ... March 9,
1826.   Washington, 1826.

———.   A discourse on religious education; delivered
at Hingham, May 20, 1818, before the trustees of the
Derby Academy; being the annual Derby lecture.
Published by request.   Boston: Wells and Lilly,
1818.   27 pp.
  Bound with: Webster, Daniel.   Speech ... on the 14th
January, 1814.   Alexandria, 1814.

_____ . Thoughts on true and false religion.   First
published in the Christian disciple.   Boston: Wells
and Lilly, 1820.   40 pp.
  Bound with: Webster, Daniel.   A discourse delivered at
  Plymouth, December 22, 1820.   Boston, 1821.

NORTON, CHARLES ELIOT.   The dimensions and proportions of the Temple of Zeus at Olympia.   Presented
October 10, 1877.   Boston, 1877.
  Detached copy of Proceedings of the American Academy
  of Arts and Sciences, v. 13, Oct. 1877, 145-170 pp.

_____ . Historical studies of church building in the
Middle Ages: Venice, Siena, Florence.   New York:
Harper, 1880.   vi, 331 pp.

NOTT, SAMUEL.   The telescope; or, Sacred views of
things past, present and to come.   Boston: Perkins
& Marvin, 1832.   180 pp.
  Autograph: Lydia Jackson.

Nouvelle biographie générale depuis les temps les plus
reculés jusqu'à nos jours, avec les renseignements
bibliographiques et l'indication des sources à con-
sulter.   Sous la direction de dr. Hoefer ...   [Paris:
Firmin Didot frères, 185-?]   3, [1] pp.
  Prospectus.

_____ . Paris: Firmin Didot frères, 1852-66.   46 v.
  Autographs.

_____ . Titres et couvertures des tomes 1 à 9.   Paris:
Firmin Didot frères, 1854.   34 11.
  Includes preliminary leaves for t. 1-8, paper covers for
  t. 3-9.

Nursery; a monthly magazine for youngest readers.
v. 11, no. 66, June 1872.   Boston: John L. Shorey,
161-188 pp.

NUTTALL, THOMAS.   An introduction to systematic and
physiological botany.   2d ed., with additions.
Cambridge, Mass.: Hilliard and Brown, 1830.   xi,
363 pp.
  Autograph.

O

OBERHOLTZER, SARA LOUISA (VICKERS). Come for arbutus, and other wild bloom. Philadelphia: J. B. Lippincott, 1882. 147 pp.
    Frontispiece autographed (?). Letter inserted: To R. W. E. from author, Dec. 10, 1881.

Observations on the necessity of betrothment, or the internal, mental, marriage, previous to wedlock, or the external, animal, marriage. Illus. by arguments and diagrams, drawn from the science of phrenology. London: W. Strange, 1838. 16 pp.
    Bound with: Lane, Charles. A classification of science and arts. London, 1826.

Observations on the present system of education; with some hints for its improvement. 4th ed. London: Cowie, 1837. 25 pp.
    Bound with: Lane, Charles. A classification of science and arts. London, 1826.

Ocean telegraphy; the twenty-fifth anniversary of the organization of the first company ever formed to lay an ocean cable. Printed for private circulation only. New York, 1879. 64 pp.

OEGGER, J. G. E. The true Messiah; or, The Old and New Testaments, examined according to the principles of the language of nature. Boston: E. P. Peabody, 1842. 27 pp.

OEHLENSCHLAGER, ADAM GOTTLOB, AND GRILLPARZER,
FRANZ. Correggio: a tragedy, by Oehlenschlager.
Sappho: a tragedy, by Grillparzer. With a sketch of
the autobiography of Oehlenschlager. Tr. from the
German, by E. L. Boston: Phillips and Sampson,
1846. xxxix, 303 pp.
  Presented to the Concord Free Public Library in Feb.
  1874, by Ralph Waldo Emerson (Cameron, III, 868).

ØRSTED, HANS CHRISTIAN. The soul in nature, with
supplementary contributions. Tr. from the German,
by Leonora and Joanna B. Horner. London: H. G.
Bohn, 1852. xlv, 465 pp.
  Autograph and note.

[OGILBY, WILLIAM.] The menageries. Quadrupeds,
described and drawn from living subjects. London:
Charles Knight, 1829. 3 v.
  Set incomplete: v. 2, 3 wanting.

OHIO AND MISSISSIPPI RAILROAD. Map of the Ohio and
Mississippi Railroad connecting the cities of Cincinnati & St. Louis, exhibiting the principal tribu-
tary lines, also the railways uniting the eastern
terminus with Boston, New York, Philadelphia &
Baltimore. Cincinnati: Klaupnech & Menzel,
[185-?].

OHIO ASSOCIATION OF THE NEW CHURCH. Three addresses on Emanuel Swedenborg as a scientist,
philosopher and theologian. Delivered at the
twenty-seventh annual meeting of the Ohio Association of the New Church, at Cincinnati, Ohio, on Sunday evening, October 10th, 1880. New York: E. H.
Swinney, 1880. 40 pp.
  Addresses by Thomas French, Jr., Frank Sewall, and
  John Goddard.

OLD, WILLIAM WATKINS. A string of pearls. London:
Derby, Bemrose, 1874. vii, 129 pp.
  Inscription: April 1874.

[OLDHAM, JOHN.]   Poems, and translations.   London:
Jos. Hindmarsh, 1683.   215 pp.
   Bound with the author's works indicated below.

[_____.]   Satyrs upon the Jesuits: written in the year
1679.   And some pieces by the same hand.   The 2d
ed. more corrected.   London: Joseph Hindmarsh,
1682.   148 pp.

[_____.]   Some new pieces never before publisht.
London: Jo. Hindmarsh, 1681.   134 pp.

[OLIPHANT, MARGARET OLIPHANT (WILSON).]   A little
Pilgrim ...   Boston: Roberts Bros., 1882.   123 pp.
   Autograph: Ellen T. Emerson.

OMAR KHAYYAM.   Rubáiyát of Omar Khayyám, the
astronomer-poet of Persia.   Rendered into English
verse.   3d ed.   London: Bernard Quaritch, 1872.
xxiv, 36 pp.
   Inscription: From C. E. Norton, Dec. 1873.

O'REILLY, JOHN BOYLE.   Songs, legends, and ballads.
Boston: Pilot Publishing Co., 1878.   viii, 318 pp.
   Inscription: 15 Jan. 1879, to R. W. E.   Letter from au-
thor inserted.

OSGOOD, DAVID.   Some facts evincive of the atheistical,
anarchical, and in other respects, immoral principles
of the French Revolution, stated in a sermon delivered on the 9th of May, 1798, the day recommended
by the President of the United States for solemn
humiliation, fasting, and prayer.   Boston: Samuel
Hall, 1798.   27 pp.

OSSOLI, SARAH MARGARET (FULLER), Marchesa D'.   Memoirs.   Boston: Phillips, Sampson, 1852.   2 v.
   Autograph and notes.

_____.   Woman in the nineteenth century.   London:
H. G. Clarke, 1845.   212 pp.
   Presentation copy to Emerson from the author, with
autograph inscription; also with a later presentation inscription by Emerson.   Sold at the Moncure Conway Sale
on May 24, 1916, by Stan V. Henkels of Philadelphia.

OTIS, HARRISON GRAY.   An address to the members of
the City Council on the removal of the municipal
government, to the Old State House.   Boston: John
H. Eastburn, 1830.   15 pp.
   Bound with: Webster, Daniel.   Speech of ... on the
14th January, 1814.   Alexandria, 1814.

OTTO, EMIL.   German conversation-grammar: a new and
practical method of learning the German language.
9th ed., compl. rev.   Boston: S. R. Urbino; New
York: Leypoldt & Holt; F. W. Christern, 1866.
viii, 440 pp.

The overland monthly devoted to the development of the
country.   v. 13, no. 6, Dec. 1874.   San Francisco:
John H. Carmany; New York: American News Co.
[489]-584, [7]-8 pp.

Over-songs.   [Cambridge: Welch, Bigelow], 1864.   28 l.
Contains a poem by Emerson.

OVIDIUS NASO, PUBLIUS.   Electra, ex Ovidio et Tibullo,
in usum regiae scholae Etonensis.   Ed. altera,
recensita, et in gratiam rudiorum notis aucta.
Etonae: E. Williams, 1815.   xii. 141 pp.

_____.   Metamorphoses.   Tr. into English verse by
various authors; and originally published by Sir Samuel Garth.   London: Brettell for J. Walker, 1807.
449 pp.

[_____.   Metamorphosis.   n.p., n.d.]   316 pp.
   Copy imperfect: t.p. and all before dedication wanting.
   Autographs: John Cotton's book, 1726, Nathaniel Cush-
ing, and note.

[OXFORD UNIVERSITY.]   Dean Ireland's scholarship.
[Examination questions.]   1844, 1845.   [n.p.]
2 v.

[_____.]   Hertford scholarship, 1843.   [Examination
questions.]   1843, 1845, 1848.   [n.p.]   3 v.
   Title varies slightly.

[_____.]   _____.   Copy 2.   1848.

[_____.]   Lusby scholarship, Magdalen Hall.   [Ex-
amination questions.]   1844, 1847, 1848.   [n.p.]
3 v.

_____.   _____.   Copy 2.   1847.

[_____.]   Suggestions for an improvement of the examination statute.   Oxford: Francis Macpherson,
1848.   33 pp.

[_____.]   University college fellowships.   [Examina-
tion questions.]   1847, 1848.   [n.p.]   2 v.

_____.   _____.   Copy 2.   1847.

_____.   BODLEIAN LIBRARY.   A catalogue of books pur-
chased for the Bodleian Library, with a statement of
monies received and expended, during the year end-
ing November 8, 1847.   [Oxford: Clarendon Press,
1847?]   44 pp.

P

PACIFIC RAILROAD COMPANY. Map of the state of
  Missouri, showing different railroad routes surveyed
  by the Pacific Railroad Co. as reported to the Legis-
  lature of the State of Missouri in December 1852.
  St. Louis, Mo.: Julius Hutowa, [1852?]. map.
    Inserted in: Tanner, Henry S. New universal atlas.
  Philadelphia, 1845.

PACIUS, JULIUS. Porphyrii isagogen, et Aristotelis
  organvm, comentarius analyticus, ad illvstrem et
  generosvm dominum, dominum Ladislavm VVilenvm.
  Aureliae Allobrogum: Vignonianis, 1605. 536 pp.
    Bound with: Aristotle. Όργανον. Geneva, 1605.
  Notes.

[PAINE, THOMAS.] Common sense. [1st ed.] Philadelphia: R. Bell, 1776. 77 pp.
    Autograph. Signature: N. Bond.

PALEY, WILLIAM. The principles of moral and political
  philosophy ... 5th ed. cor. London: J. Davis,
  1788. 2 v.
    Autograph and notes.

PALFREY, FRANCIS WINTHROP. Memoir of William Francis
  Bartlett. Boston: Houghton, Osgood, 1879.
  309 pp.

[PALFREY, SARAH HAMMOND.] The chapel, and other
  poems. Christo et ecclesiae, by E. Foxton
  [pseud.]. New York: G. P. Putnam's Sons, 1880.
  130 pp.

[_____.] Herman; or, Young knighthood, by E. Foxton [pseud.]. Boston: Lee and Shepard, 1866. 2 v.
Inscription: v. 1 (in R. W. E.'s hand). Signature: v. 2, R. W. Emerson.

_____. Prémices, by E. Foxton [pseud.]. Boston: Ticknor and Fields, 1855. iv, 196 pp.
Autograph: L. J. Emerson.

_____. Sir Pavon and St. Pavon, by E. Foxton [pseud.]. Boston: Lee and Shepard, 1867. 84 pp.
Inscription Ellen T. Emerson from Edward, Jan. 1, 1868.

PARKER, AMOS ANDREW. Poems at fourscore ... 2d ed., rev. ... Keene, N. H.: Sentinel Printing Co., 1877. 208 pp.
Inscription.

PARKER, DANIEL. Phrenology, and other poems. Lowell: S. W. Huse, 1859. 40 pp.

PARKER, JOHN HENRY. A concise glossary of terms used in Grecian, Roman, Italian and Gothic architecture, abridged from the 4th ed. of the larger work. Illus. by four hundred and forty woodcuts. Oxford: John Henry Parker, 1846. 297 pp.
Inscription: From George Bancroft, 25 Jul. 1848.

PARKER, LIZZIE G. Miscellaneous selections from the writings of the late Lizzie G. Parker, of Wellsburg, West Virginia. Wellsburg, W. Va.: Alfred Glass, 1873. viii, 194 pp.

PARKER, THEODORE. Speeches, addresses, and occasional sermons. Boston: W. Crosby and H. P. Nichols; New York: C. S. Francis, 1852 [c1851]. 2 v.
Inscriptions: v. 1, Dec. 14, 1851 (by author); v. 2, R. W. Emerson from the author (in R. W. E.'s hand). Notes.

_____. Ten sermons of religion. Boston: Crosby, Nichols; New York: C. S. Francis, 1853. vi, 395 pp.
Inscription: author to R. W. E., July 1, 1853.

_____. Theodore Parker's experience as a minister, with some account of his early life, and education for the ministry; contained in a letter from him to the members of the twenty-eighth Congregational Society of Boston.   Boston: R. Leighton, Jr., 1859. 182 pp.

PARSONS, THOMAS WILLIAM.   The old house at Sudbury. Cambridge, [Mass.]: J. Wilson, 1870.   vi, 114 pp.

PASCAL, BLAISE.   Pensées de Pascal, précédées de sa vie, par Mme. Périer, sa soeur, suivies d'un choix des pensées de Nicole et de son Traité de la paix avec les hommes.   Paris: Firmin-Didot frères, 1847. xxxvi, 504 pp.
   Autograph: Ellen Emerson, May, 1855.

PASSOW, ARNOLD, *ed.*   Τραγούδια 'ρωμαικά.   Popvlaria carmina graeciae recentioris edidit Arnoldus Passow.   Lipsiae: B. G. Tevbneri, 1860.   xi, 650 pp.

[PATMORE, COVENTRY KERSEY DIGHTON.]   The angel in the house ...   London: J. W. Parker, 1854-[56]. 2 v.
   Inscription: R. W. Emerson from the author (in Emerson's hand) and notes.

[_____.] _____.   The espousals ...   Boston: Ticknor, and Fields, 1856.   x, 204 pp.
   Autograph.

_____. _____.   Book I. The betrothal.   Book II. The espousals.   2d ed.   London: John W. Parker, 1858. viii, 303 pp.

_____.   Poems.   London: E. Moxon, 1844.   iv, 157 pp.
   Inscription: R. W. Emerson from Coventry Patmore (in Emerson's hand).

_____.   The victories of love.   Boston: T. O. H. P. Burnham, 1862.   96 pp.

_____, *comp.*   The children's garland from the best poets, selected and arranged.   Cambridge, Mass.: Sever and Francis, 1863.   xi, 354 pp.
   Autograph: Edith Emerson.

PATON, ALLAN PARK.   Poems.   2d series.   London:
Longman, 1848.   vii, 124 pp.
Inscription from publishers: 25 Feb. 1848.

PAULET, E.   Dharma; or, Three phases of love.   London: Smith, Elder, 1865.   3 v.

PAULI, REINHOLD.   The life of Alfred the Great, tr. from
the German of R. Pauli.   To which is appended
Alfred's Anglo-Saxon version of Orosius, with a
literal English translation, and an Anglo-Saxon alphabet and glossary, by B. Thorpe ...   London:
H. G. Bohn, 1853.   ix, 582 pp.
Autograph.

PAYNE, JOHN.   The masque of shadows, and other
poems.   London: Basil Montagu Pickering, 1870.
222 pp.
Inscription.

PEABODY, ELIZABETH.   Sabbath lessons; or, An abstract
of sacred history; to which is annexed, a geographical sketch of the principal places mentioned in
sacred history.   Salem: Thomas C. Cushing, 1810.
123 pp.
Autograph: Mrs. Emerson, 1826.

PEABODY, ELIZABETH PALMER.   Chronological history of
the United States, arranged with plates on Bem's
principle.   New York: Sheldon, Blakeman, 1856.
312 pp.
Inscription.

_____.   Crimes of the house of Austria against man-
kind.   Collected from accredited history.   New-
York: R. Garrigue, 1852.   x, 230 pp.
Ms. writing on preliminary leaf.

_____.   Memorial of William Wesselhoft.   To which is
added his last address to the Homoeopathic Association.   Boston: Nathaniel C. Peabody, 1859.   54 pp.

PEACOCK, THOMAS BROWER.   The vendetta, and other
poems.   Rev., with additional poems.   Topeka,
Kan.: Democrat Printing House, 1876.   viii, 161 pp.
Printed inscription inserted.

PEASE, AARON G.   Philosophy of trinitarian doctrine: a
contribution to theological progress and reform.
Rutland, Vt.: G. P. Putnam's Sons, 1875.   xii,
183 pp.

[PEASE, E. DARWIN], *supposed author.*   The old trunk
and new carpet-bag.   Ed. by Robert Bluebeard
Kydd ...   [n.p., ᶜ1872.]   306 pp.
  Inscription: R. W. E. from author.

[PENROSE, ELIZABETH (CARTWRIGHT).]   History of England, from the invasion of Julius Caesar to the reign
of Victoria, by Mrs. Markham [pseud.].   A new ed.,
rev. and enl., with questions, adapted to schools in
the United States, by Eliza Robbins ...   New York:
D. Appleton, 1853.   viii, 387 pp.
  Autograph: Ellen Emerson, Lenox, Mass., and notes.

[_____.]   A history of France, from the conquest of
Gaul by Julius Caesar to the reign of Louis Philippe:
with conversations at the end of each chapter, by
Mrs. Markham [pseud.].   Prepared for the use of
schools by the addition of a map, notes and questions, and a supplementary chapter, bringing down
the history to the present time, by Jacob Abbott.
New York: Harper, 1853.   x, 629 pp.
  Autograph: Ellen T. Emerson.

PERCY, THOMAS, *Bp. of Dromore, ed.*   Reliques of
ancient English poetry: consisting of old heroic
ballads, songs, and other pieces of our earlier poets,
(chiefly of the lyric kind.)   Together with some few
of later date.   ...   London: J. Dodsley, 1765.
3 v.
  Set incomplete: v. 2 wanting.
  Autographs.
  Book plates: v. 1, The Rt. Honble. Isaac Barné; v. 3,
Francis Freeling.

PERKINS, JACOB.   Steam navigation.   Improvements.
Part I. The Bailer.   London: J. Ridgeway, 1833.
15 pp.

PERRIN, JEAN BAPTISTE.   The elements of French and
English conversation; with new, familiar, and easy
dialogues, each preceded by a suitable vocabulary,
in French and English.   Designed particularly for
the use of schools.   Rev. and cor., by C. Pseud-
homme.   New York: Evert Duyckinck, 1827.
216 pp.

PERRY, MATTHEW CALBRAITH.   Narrative of the expedi-
tion of an American squadron to the China seas and
Japan, performed in the years 1852, 1853 and 1854,
under the command of M. C. Perry, United States
Navy, by order of the Government of the United
States ...   Pub. by order of the Congress of the
United States.   Washington: Beverley Tucker,
1856.   2 v.

Pestalozzian Academy, conducted by Francis Wilby, and
assistants, for youth of both sexes, removed from
Curtain Road, to Worship Square.   [London: Archer,
Printer, 18—?]   2 pp.
   Bound with: Lane, Charles.   A classification of sci-
ence and arts.   London, 1826.

PESTALOZZIAN ASSOCIATION.   Rules and orders, with a
short prelection.   [London: W. Strange, 18—?]
8 pp.
   Bound with: Lane, Charles.   A classification of science and arts.   London, 1826.

———.   ———.   Copy 2.

Peter Puzzlewig's mirthful game of happy hits at useful
knowledge of every-day things.   Albany: Richard H.
Pease, [18—?].   6 pp.

PETERSON, HENRY.   The modern Job.   Philadelphia:
H. Peterson, 1869.   124 pp.

PFEIFFER, EMILY.   Sonnets & songs.   New ed.   London: C. Kegan Paul, 1880.   ix, 103 pp.
   Letter from author's husband, 2 Jan 1881, inserted.

PHELPS, ALMIRA (HART) LINCOLN.   Familiar lectures on
botany.   Including practical and elementary botany,

with generic and specific descriptions of the most
common native and foreign plants, and a vocabulary
of botanical terms. For the use of higher schools
and academies. 3d ed. Hartford: F. J. Huntington,
1832. xii, 440 pp.

——— . Familiar lectures on botany, explaining the
structure, classification, and uses of plants, illustrated upon the Linnaean and natural methods, with a
flora for practical botanists. For the use of colleges, schools, and private students. New ed., rev.
and enl. ... New York: Mason Bros., 1856.
297 pp.
   Wrapper addressed to Emerson, laid in.

[PHELPS, ELIZABETH (STUART).] The last leaf from
Sunny side, by H. Trusta [pseud.]. With a memorial
of the author, by Austin Phelps. 10th thousand.
Boston: Phillips, Sampson, 1853. iv, 342 pp.
   Inscription: Ellen's birthday present from Eddie 1854.

[———.] The tell-tale; or, Home secrets. Told by old
travellers. By H. Trusta [pseud.]. 10th thousand.
Boston: Phillips, Sampson, 1853. 262 pp.

PHELPS, HUMPHREY, *firm, publishers.* Map of the State
of New York, with the latest improvements. Sold by
W. Hooker, J. A. Buntus. [N.Y.?, 1831?] col. map.

[PHILLIPS, GEORGE SEARLE.] Memoirs of William Wordsworth, comp. from authentic sources; with numerous
quotations from his poems, illustrative of his life
and character, by January Searle [pseud.] ... London: Partridge & Oakey, 1852. 312 pp.

PHILLIPS, HENRY. Poems translated from the Spanish
and German. Philadelphia, 1878. iv, 76 pp.
   "One hundred copies printed, exclusively for private
circulation."
   Printed inscription.

PHILLIPS, WENDELL. Sir Henry Vane. [n.p., 1881?]
8 pp.
   From the Phi Beta Kappa address at Harvard College,
1881.

———. Speeches, lectures, and letters. Boston:
James Redpath, 1863. iv, 562 pp.

[PHILO-DICAIOS, *pseud.*]. The triumphs of justice over
unjust judges: exhibiting, I. The names and crimes
of four and forty judges hang'd in one year in England ... II. The case of the Land Chief Justice
Tresilian, hang'd at Tylewan, and all the rest of the
judges of England (save one) banisht in R. Richard
and the 2d's time. III. The crime of Empson and
Dudley ... IV. The proceedings of the Ship-money-
judges in the reign of King Charles the First. V.
Diverse other presidents both ancient and modern.
To which is added, VI. The judges oath, and some
observations thereupon ... [London]: Re-printed,
1732. 27 pp.
   Copy imperfect: pp. 21-27 wanting.

Phrenology. [London: Cunningham and Salmon,
Printers, 18—?] 4 pp.
   Bound with: Lane, Charles. A classification of sci-
   ence and arts. London, 1826.

Phrenology. [no. 2-3. Stroud: B. Bucknall, 18—?]
12 pp.
   Bound with: Lane, Charles. A classification of science and arts. London, 1826.

PICKERING, CHARLES. The races of man, and their geographical distribution ... New ed. To which is
prefixed, An analytical synopsis of the natural history of man, by John Charles Hall ... London:
H. G. Bohn, 1851. lxxii, 445 pp.

Picture riddler ... Boston: Munroe & Francis, [ᶜ1845].
120 pp.

PIERPONT, JOHN. Introduction to the national reader; a
selection of easy lessons, designed to fill the same
place in the common schools of the United States,
that is held by Murray's introduction, and the com-
pilations of Guy, Mylius, and Pinnock, in those of
Great Britain. 27th ed. Boston: Charles Bowen,
1837. 168 pp.

PINDARUS.   Odes, literally tr. into English prose, by
   Dawson W. Turner ...   To which is adjoined a
   metrical version, by Abraham Moore.   London:
   Henry G. Bohn, 1852.   xxvii, 434 pp.
   Autograph and notes.

PINEIDER, F. E G., *firm, publishers*.   Guide manuel de
   Rome, et de ses environs; avec un plan topographique
   de la ville.   Florence, [187–?].   160 pp.

PINKNEY, EDWARD C.   Poems.   Baltimore: Joseph
   Robinson, 1838.   72 pp.

The Pitts-Street Chapel lectures, delivered in Boston by
   clergymen of six different denominations, during the
   winter of 1858 ...   Boston: J. P. Jewett; Cleveland,
   O.: H. P. B. Jewett, 1858.   vi, 366 pp.
   Inscription to M. M. Emerson.

PLATO.   The Cratylus, Phaedo, Parmenides, and
   Timaeus of Plato.   Tr. from the Greek by Thomas
   Taylor.   With notes on the Cratylus, and an ex-
   planatory introduction to each dialogue ...   Lon-
   don: B. and J. White, 1793.   xvi, 554 pp.
   Autograph and notes.

——.   Dialogues.   Tr. into English, with analyses
   and introductions, by B. Jowett ...   3d ed. rev. and
   cor. throughout, with additions and an index of subjects and proper names.   Oxford: Clarendon Press,
   1875.   5 v.
   Printed inscription slip tipped in: v. 1, From the author.

——.   Oeuvres. Tr. par Victor Cousin ...   Paris:
   Bossange Frères, 1822–40.   13 v.
   Autograph.

——.   Plato's best thoughts, comp. from Prof.
   Jowett's translation of the dialogues of Plato, by
   C. H. A. Bulkley ...   New York: Scribner, Arm-
   strong, 1876.   vii, 475 pp.
   Autograph.

——.   La république; ou, Du juste, et de l'injuste.
   Tr. par M. de la Pillonnière.   Londres: Du traduc-
   teur, 1726.   xx, 319 pp.

_____. Socrates. A translation of the Apology, Crito and parts of the Phaedo of Plato. New York: Charles Scribner's Sons, 1879. xvii, 159 pp.

_____. Works; viz. his fifty-five dialogues, and twelve epistles, tr. from the Greek; nine of the dialogues by the late Floyer Sydenham, and the remainder by Thomas Taylor; with occasional annotations on the nine dialogues tr. by Sydenham, and copious notes, by the latter translator; in which is given the substance of nearly all the existing Greek ms. commentaries on the philosophy of Plato, and a considerable portion of such as are already published ... London: T. Taylor, 1804. 5 v.
Autographs and notes.

_____. _____. A new and literal version chiefly from the text of Stallbaum ... London: E. G. Bohn, 1848-54. 6 v.
Notes and autographs.

Platonic parables, May 1, [1837] ... London: Published for Society, 1837. 24 pp.
Bound with: Lane, Charles. A classification of science and arts. London, 1826.

PLAYFAIR, JOHN. Dissertation second, exhibiting a general view of the progress of mathematical and physical science, since the revival of letters in Europe. [Boston, 1820?] 2 v. in 1.
Inscription: R. W. E. from E. B. E. Autograph and notes.

PLETSCH, OSCAR. Jahr ein, Jahr aus im Elternhaus. In 40 Bildern. Mit neuen und altern Reimen. In Holzschnitt aus gefuhrt von H. Burkner. Dresden: J. Heinrich Richter, [1861]. [80] pp.

[PLIMSOLL, I.] The vicar of Charles. A poem in commemoration of Plymouth's great preacher, in a preceding age; who, though dead, yet speaketh. Plymouth: W. Cann, 1868. 38 pp.
Inscription: Dr. Plimsoll, Feb. 17, 1876.

PLINIUS SECUNDUS, C.   The natural history of Pliny.
Tr., with copious notes and illustrations, by the late
John Bostock ...   and H. T. Riley ...   London:
H. G. Bohn, 1865–67.   6 v.
Autograph.

PLOTINUS.   Select works of Plotinus, the great restorer
of the philosophy of Plato: and extracts from the
treatise of Synesius on providence.   Tr. from the
Greek.   With an introduction containing the substance of Porphyry's life of Plotinus, by Thomas
Taylor ...   London: The Author, 1817.   lxxxiii,
600 pp.
Autograph and notes.   Contents in manuscript on verso
of flyleaf.

PLUTARCHUS.   The beauties of Plutarch; consisting of
selections from his works, by Alfred Howard.   Boston: F. S. Hill, 1831.   192 pp.
Notes.

_____.   Chaeronensis varia scripta quae moralia vulgo
vocantur.   Ad optimorum librorum fidem accurate
edita.   Ed. stereotypa.   Lipsiae: Caroli Tauchnitii,
1829 [i. e., 186–?].   6 v.
Set incomplete: v. 2, 5 wanting.
Notes.

_____.   _____.   Nova impressio.   Lipsiae: Ottonis
Holtze, 1866.   6 v.
Set incomplete: v. 1, 3, 4, 6 wanting.
Notes.

_____.   Lives, tr. from the original Greek; with notes
critical and historical, and a life of Plutarch, by
John Langhorne, and William Langhorne.   New ed.,
with corrections and additions, by Francis Wrang-
ham ...   New York: Samuel Campbell, 1822.   8 v.
Set incomplete: v. 7 wanting.
Autographs and notes, 1828.

_____.   Morals.   Tr. from the Greek, by several hands
...   5th ed. rev. and cor. from the many errors of the
former eds.   London: W. Taylor, 1718.   5 v.
Autographs and notes.

———— . ———— . Tr. from the Greek by several hands.
Cor. and rev. by William W. Goodwin ...   With an
introduction by Ralph Waldo Emerson.   Boston:
Little, Brown, 1870.   5 v.
> Set incomplete: v. 2, 3, 5 wanting.
> Autograph and notes.

Poems of the "Old South," by Henry Wadsworth Longfellow, Oliver Wendell Holmes, John Greenleaf Whittier, Julia Ward Howe, Edward Everett Hale, and
James Freeman Clarke ...   Boston: William F. Gill,
1877.   35 pp.
> Inscription: Ralph Waldo Emerson (gift of publisher)
> 25 Dec. 1877.

POLLOK, ROBERT.   The course of time, a poem in ten
books.   3d American from the 3d Edinburg ed.
Boston: Crocker and Brewster; New York: Jonathan
Leavitt, 1828.   247 pp.
> Autograph: Lydia Jackson.

POPE, ALEXANDER.   An essay on man, in four epistles
to H. St. John, Lord Bolingbroke, to which are now
added several other pieces with the universal prayer.
Andover: Flagg & Gould, 1815.   vi, 96 pp.
> Autograph: E. B. Emerson.

———— . Poetical works.   With a life by Alexander
Dyce.   Boston: Little, Brown, 1853.   3 v.
> Autograph and notes.

———— . ———— . To which is prefixed a life of the
author ...   Boston: Phillips, Sampson; New York:
James C. Derby, 1855.   2 v. in 1.

———— . ———— . Ed. by H. F. Cary, with a biographical
notice by the author.   London, New York: George
Routledge, 1872.   xvi, 478 pp.

PORTER, EDWARD GRIFFIN, AND STEPHENSON, H. M.
Souvenir of 1775.   Prepared at the request of the
Lexington Centennial Committee.   Boston: James
R. Osgood, [ᶜ1875].   16 pp.

PORTEUS, BEILBY, *Bp. of London.* A summary of the principal evidences for the truth and divine origin of the Christian revelation. Designed chiefly for the use of young persons. New York: American Tract Society, [184-?]. 122 pp.

POTTER, JOHN, *Abp. of Canterbury.* Archaeologia graeca; or, The antiquities of Greece ... To which is added an appendix, containing a concise history of the Grecian states, and a short account of the lives and writings of the most celebrated Greek authors, by G. Dunbar ... 1st Am. from the last Edinburgh ed., with additions and corrections by Charles Anthon ... New York: Collins, 1825. xvi, 707 pp.
Autographs.

POWELL, E. P. Anniversary sermon preached on the sixth anniversary of his connection with Plymouth Church, Adrian, Mich., May 3, 1867. Adrian, Mich.: Times and Expositor Office, 1867. 12 pp.

Practical rules, for conducting a conversational meeting. [n.p., n.d.] 1 l.
Appears to be the rules of the Society for Mutual Instruction, Holborn.
Bound with: Lane, Charles. A classification of science and arts. London, 1826.

PRANG, LOUIS, & COMPANY, *firm, publishers.* European war map, no. 3, showing all the R. R.'s and other means of communications. Boston, °1870.
Consists of N. E. France, Holland, and N. W. Germany.

PRESBYTERIAN CHURCH IN THE U. S. A. BOARD OF EDUCATION. My own hymn book, illustrated with fourteen engravings ... Philadelphia, [18—?]. 71 pp.
Autograph.

PRESTON, ELLIOTT W. Lord Byron vindicated; or, Rome and her pilgrim. By "Manfred" [pseud.] ... London: Simpkin, Marshall, 1876. xxxi, 147 pp.

PRESTON, HARRIET WATERS. Aspendale. Boston:
Roberts Bros., 1871. 219 pp.

PRESTON, S. At Fairseat, near Wrotham, Kent, youth are
boarded, and educated on the principles of Pesta-
lozzi. [n.p., 18—?] 1 l.
Prospectus.
Bound with: Lane, Charles. A classification of science and arts. London, 1826.

PRINCE, THOMAS. An account of the revival of religion
in Boston, in the year 1740-1-2-3. Boston:
Samuel T. Armstrong, 1823. 55 pp.

PROCLUS DIADOCHUS. The commentaries of Proclus on
the Timaeus of Plato, in five books; containing a
treasury of Pythagoric and Platonic physiology. Tr.
from the Greek, by Thomas Taylor ... London: The
Author, 1820. 2 v.
Notes, v. 2.

———. ———.
Given to the Concord Free Public Library by Ralph
Waldo Emerson in Aug. 1873 (Cameron, III, 868).

———. The six books of Proclus, the Platonic succes-
sor, on the theology of Plato, tr. from the Greek; to
which a seventh book is added ... Also, a translation from the Greek of Proclus' Elements of theology.
To which are added a translation of the treatise of
Proclus On providence and fate; a translation of extracts from his treatise entitled, Ten doubts concerning providence; and a translation of extracts from his
treatise, On the subsistence of evil; as preserved in
the Biblioteca Gr. of Fabricius ... London: A. J.
Valpy, 1816. 2 v.
Notes.

———. ———.
Given to Concord Free Public Library by Ralph Waldo
Emerson in Aug. 1873 (Cameron, III, 868).

[PROCTER, BRYAN WALLER.] English songs and other small
poems, by Barry Cornwall [pseud. New ed.] London: Edward Moxon, 1846. xvi, 284 pp.
Inscription.

_____ . _____ , by Barry Cornwall [pseud.   New ed.,
with additions.]   London: Chapman and Hall, 1856.
xl, 284 pp.
   Inscription.

_____ .   Essays and tales in prose, by Barry Cornwall
[pseud.]   Boston: Ticknor, Reed, and Fields, 1853.
2 v.
   Inscribed.

Prospectus of a new London Elementary Oriental Institute, to enable gentlemen proceeding to India, and
more especially those intended for civil and military
offices, to speak, on their arrival the most important
and useful of the native languages, and to read and
unite them in their appropriate characters.   [London:
Kingsbury, Parbury, and Allen, 1826.]   3 pp.
   Bound with: Lane, Charles.   A classification of science
and arts.   London, 1826.

The psyche. A new weekly periodical.   On Saturday,
June 8, 1839, will be published, no. 1, price three-
pence, The psyche ...   London: William Everett,
[1839?].   1 l.
   Broadside.
   Prospectus of: The psyche; a magazine of belles lettres
the drama, poetry, music and the fine arts.
   Bound with: Lane, Charles.   A classification of science and arts.   London, 1826.

Psychological speculations.   Essay I, the theological
departments of psychology, concerning time, space,
sense, &c.   With a general syllabus of psychology.
By the spirit of the blue mountains.   London: Burgess and Hill, 1827.   52 pp.
   Notes.
   Bound with: Lane, Charles.   A classification of science and arts.   London, 1826.

_____ . _____ .   Copy 2.
   Notes.

Public Ledger almanacs for the years 1870, 1871, 1872,
1873, 1874, 1875.   Philadelphia: George W. Childs,
[1875].   346 pp.

PULTE, JOSEPH HIPPOLYT. Organon der Weltgeschicht
... Cincinnati: W. Radde; Philadelphia: C. E.
Rademacher, 1846. iii, 123 pp.
Inscription.

[Punch; or, The London charivari. London, 1856-83.]
portfolio.
Scattered numbers in a folder; also clippings and illustrations of English buildings.

PURANAS. *Bhâgavatapurana.* Le Bhâgavata Purâna; ou,
Histoire poétique de Krichna, tr. et publié par M.
Eugene Burnouf ... Paris: Imprimerie Royal, 1840-
47. 3 v.
Inscriptions in v. 1-3. Vol. 1, Henry D. Thoreau from
Cholmondeley (in E.'s hand), R. W. Emerson from Henry D.
Thoreau.

PUSEY, EDWARD BOUVERIE. Daniel the prophet: nine
lectures delivered in the Divinity School of the University of Oxford. With copious notes. 3d ed.,
26th thousand. Oxford: James Parker, 1869. civ,
651 pp.
Inscriptions.

PUTNAM, SAMUEL P. Prometheus, a poem. New York:
G. P. Putnam's Sons, 1877. 140 pp.
Letter from author, 3 Dec. 1877, inserted at front.

Q

QUINCY, JOSIAH. An address to the citizens of Boston, on the XVIIth of September, MDCCCXXX, the close of the second century from the first settlement of the city. Boston: J. H. Eastburn, 1830. 68 pp.
Inscription.
Bound with: Webster, Daniel. Speech of ... on the 14th January, 1814. Alexandria, 1814.

_____ . The history of the Boston Athenaeum, with biographical notices of its deceased founders. Cambridge: Metcalf, 1851. xii, 263 pp.

_____ . An oration, delivered July 4, 1832, before the City Council and inhabitants of Boston. Boston: John H. Eastburn, 1832. 21 pp.

_____ . Speeches delivered in the Congress of the United States, by Josiah Quincy, member of the House of Representatives for the Suffolk district of Massachusetts, 1805–1813. Ed. by his son, Edmund Quincy ... Boston: Little, Brown, 1874. xii, 412 pp.

QUINCY, JOSIAH PHILLIPS. The protection of majorities; or, Considerations relating to electoral reform. With other papers. Boston: Roberts Bros., 1876. 163 pp.

R

RABELAIS, FRANÇOIS. Works. Tr. from the French with explanatory notes, by Duchat, Motteux, Ozell and others ... London: Tarkington, Allen, 1807. 4 v.
Notes, v. 1.

RACINE, JEAN. Choix des tragédies. 2. éd., corrigée et enrichie de notes ... par L. T. Ventoriellae ... Londres: S. Low, 1832. 2 v. in 1.

RAE-BROWN, COLIN. The dawn of love: an idyll of modern life. London: James Nisbet, 1873. 52 pp.

Railway improvement. [London]: Reynell and Weight, 1845. 34 pp.
"From the Westminster review [no. 82] of September, 1845."

RALSTON, WILLIAM RALSTON SHEDDEN. The songs of the Russian people, as illustrative of Slavonic mythology and Russian social life. London: Ellis & Green, 1872. xvi, 439 pp.
Inscription: May 1872 to R. W. E. with author's compliments.

[RANDALL, JOHN WITT.] Consolations of solitude ... Boston: John P. Jewett, 1856. 261 pp.
Ms. note on t.p.: With corrections and alterations by the author.
Inscription: Presentation from author to R. W. E., Aug. 1856, and notes.

[RANDOLPH, RICHARD.] Aspects of humanity, brokenly mirrored in the ever-swelling current of human speech

...   Philadelphia: J. B. Lippincott, 1869.   vi,
55 pp.

————. ————.   Copy 2.

————.   Sober thoughts on staple themes.   Philadelphia: Claxton, Remsen & Haffelfinger, 1871.   x,
159 pp.

RANTOUL, ROBERT.   An oration delivered at Concord on
the celebration of the seventy-fifth anniversary of the
events of April 19, 1775.   Delivered before the
Massachusetts Legislature, and published by their
order.   Boston: Dutton & Wentworth, 1850.   135 pp.

RAVEN, NIL, [*pseud.?*].   Two years in Wall Street; or,
Why was I born?   Consisting of riches, jokes, dis-
appointments, and other affairs of a show-y nature.
For all who are in the world, the flesh and Wall
Street.   New York, 1877.   72 pp.
   Inscription: Presentation copy to R. W. E. from author,
30 June 1877.

RAYMOND, ROSSITER WORTHINGTON.   Statistics of mines
and mining in the states and territories west of the
Rocky Mountains for 187-.   Washington, 1873.
   Given to the Concord Free Public Library by Ralph
Waldo Emerson in Aug. 1873 (Cameron, III, 868).

READE, CHARLES.   Clouds and sunshine, and Art: a
dramatic tale.   Boston: Ticknor and Fields, 1855.
288 pp.
   Signature: Emerson (in Ellen's hand).

————.   Peg Woffington, a novel.   Boston: Ticknor and
Fields, 1855.   303 pp.
   Inscription: Ellen from Papa, Christmas 1854 (in R. W.
E.'s hand).

READE, JOHN EDMUND.   Poetical works.   New ed.
London: Longman, Brown, Green, Longmans &
Roberts, 1857.   4 vols.

Reasons for repealing the laws of Massachusetts, which
render the members of manufacturing companies per-

sonally liable for their debts.   Boston: Dutton and
Wentworth, 1830.   12 pp.

REAVIS, LOGAN URIAH.   Thoughts for the young men of
America; or, A few practical words of advice to those
born in poverty and destined to be reared in orphan-
age.   New York: Samuel R. Wells, 1871.   62, 40 pp.

REDPATH, JAMES.   The public life of Capt. John Brown,
with an auto-biography of his childhood and youth.
Boston: Thayer and Eldridge, 1860.   407 pp.
    Inscription: From author to Emerson, undated.

REED, SAMPSON.   An address delivered before the Boston Society of the New Jerusalem and the teachers
and pupils of the Sabbath and week-day schools, on
Thanksgiving Day, November 25, 1841.   Boston:
Otis Clapp, 1842.   12 pp.
    Inscription.
    Bound with: Everett, Edward.   Speech ... March 9,
    1826.   Washington, 1826.

———— .   A biographical sketch of Thomas Worcester, for
nearly fifty years the pastor of the Boston Society of
the New Jerusalem, with some account of the origin
and rise of that society.   Together with a memorial
address read before the Society by James Reed ...
Boston, Mass.: New Church Union, 1880.   140 pp.

———— .   Observations on the growth of the mind.
Originally printed at Boston, in 1826.   London:
T. Goyder, Simpkin and Marshall, 1827.   49 pp.
    Notes.
    Bound with: Lane, Charles.   A classification of sci-
    ence and arts.   London, 1826.

———— .   ———— .   5th ed.   Boston: T. H. Carter, 1865.
99 pp.
    Autograph.

Reflections on the European Revolution of 1848.   By a
Superior Spirit ...   London: Longman, Brown, Green
and Longmans, 1848.   vii, 192 pp.

REID, SIR GEORGE HOUSTOUN.   An essay on New South
Wales, the mother colony of the Australias.   Syd-

ney: Thomas Richards, Govt. Printer; London,
New York: Trübner, 1876.   vi, 173 pp.

RÉNAN, ERNEST.   The life of Jesus.   People's ed.
London: Trübner, Paris: M. Levy frères, [18—?].
xii, 311 pp.
   Inscription: To Emerson by translator.

[RENNIE, JAMES.]   Insect architecture.   [London: C.
Knight, 1830?]   420 pp.
   Copy imperfect: all before p. [1] and pp. 217–420 want-
ing.
   Bound with the author's Insect transformations.   Lon-
don, 1830.

———.   Insect transformations.   London: Charles
Knight, 1830.   xii, 420 pp.

REVERE, LUKE.   Tim Orton, and other poems.   New
York: Baker & Godwin, Printers, 1874.   20 pp.

Review of the report of the case of the Commonwealth
versus David Lee Child, for publishing in the Massachusetts journal a libel on John Keyes.   Boston:
J. H. Eastburn, 1829.   16 pp.

La revue géographique internationale, journal illustré
d'enseignement et d'émigration ...   no. 1, 10 mars
1876.   Paris: Bureau du journal au comptoir géographique.   16 pp.

REW, WALTER.   Dion, a tragedy; and poems.   London:
Trübner, 1877.   vi, 224 pp.
   Card of author inserted.

———.   Maud Vivian; a drama; and poems.   London:
E. Moxon, 1873.   190 pp.
   Inscription: From Walter, with profound respects.

Rhymes for the nursery.   Monroe and Francis' ed.
New York: C. S. Francis, [c1837].   112 pp.

RICE, ALLEN THORNDIKE, ed.   Essays from the North
American Review.   New York: D. Appleton, 1879.
vi, 482 pp.
   Inscription on embossed stamp: With the editor's compliments.

RICE, HARVEY. Mount Vernon, and other poems. 4th ed., enl. Columbus: Follett, Foster, 1862. vi, 221 pp.

RICHARDSON, SAMUEL. The history of Sir Charles Grandison. In a series of letters. 5th ed. London: J. Rivington, 1766. 7 v.
Set incomplete: v. 2–7 wanting.

RICHTER, JOHANN PAUL FRIEDRICH. The Campaner Thal: or, Discourses on the immortality of the soul. Tr. from the German, by Juliette Bauer. London: Charles Gilpin, 1848. xii, 87 pp.
Inscription: From the translator.

———. Titan, a romance. From the German, tr. by Charles T. Brooks ... Boston: Ticknor and Fields, 1862. 2 v.
Autographs.

[———.] Walt and Vult; or, The twins. Tr. from the Flegeljahre of Jean Paul [pseud.], by [Eliza Buckminster Lee] ... Boston: J. Munroe; New York: Wiley & Putnam, 1846. 2 v.
Inscription: From translator.

RICKETSON, DANIEL. The autumn sheaf: a collection of miscellaneous poems. New Bedford, [Mass.]: The Author, 1869. ix, 300 pp.
Inscription: 27 April 1869.

———. The history of New Bedford, Bristol County, Massachusetts: including a history of the old Township of Dartmouth and the present townships of Westport, Dartmouth, and Fairhaven, from their settlement to the present time. New Bedford, [Mass.]: The Author, 1858. xii, 412 pp.
Inscription: From author, Sept 9, 1859.

RICORD, FREDERICK WILLIAM. English songs from foreign tongues. New York: Charles Scribner's Sons, 1879. xiii, 216 pp.

RIDLEY, JAMES. The tales of the genii; or, The delightful lessons of Horam the son of Asmar. Tr. from the

Persian, by Sir Charles Morell [pseud.]. London: J. Wallis, [18—?]. x, 247 pp.

RIPLEY, EZRA. A history of the fight at Concord, on the 19th of April, 1775. With a particular account of the military operations and interesting events of that ever memorable day; showing that then and there the first regular and forcible resistance was made to the British soldiery, and the first British blood was shed by armed Americans, and the Revolutionary War thus commenced. 2d ed. Concord: Herman Atwill, 1832. iv, 40 pp.
  Note.
  Bound with: Everett, Edward. Speech ... March 9, 1826. Washington, 1826.

——. ——. Copy 2.

RIPLEY, GEORGE, *comp.* Philosophical miscellanies. Tr. from the French of Cousin, Jouffroy, and B. Constant. With introductory and critical notices. Boston: Hilliard, Gray, 1838. 2 v.
  Autograph.

——. ——. Copy 2.

RITSON, JOSEPH. Ancient songs and ballads, from the reign of King Henry the Second to the Revolution. London: Payne and Foss, by T. Davison, 1829. 2 v.
  Autographs.

ROBBINS, CHANDLER. A reply to some essays lately published by John Cotton (of Plymouth) relating to baptism ... Also, A vindication of the author from several injurious aspersions contained in Mr. Cotton's Remarks on some letters that passed relative to this point. Boston: Thomas and John Fleet, 1773. viii, 76 pp.

ROBERTSON, FREDERICK WILLIAM. Sermons preached at Trinity Chapel, Brighton. 1st series. 3rd Ameri-

can, from the 5th London ed.   Boston: Ticknor and
Fields, 1859.   368 pp.
  Inscription: Mother from Edith.

————.   Sermons, preached at Trinity Chapel, Brighton.
2d series.   From the 4th London ed.   Boston: Ticknor and Fields, 1850.   xvi, 342 pp.

————.   Sermons preached at Trinity Chapel, Brighton.
3d series.   From the 2d London ed.   Boston: Ticknor and Fields, 1858.   324 pp.
  Inscription: To Mother from Ellen.

ROBINSON, HENRY CRABB.   Diary, reminiscences, and
correspondence.   Sel. and ed. by Thomas Sadler ...
Boston: Fields, Osgood, 1869.   2 v.
  Note, v. 1.

ROBINSON, HUGH.   Scholae Wintoniensis; phrases Lat-
inae.   [The Latin phrases of Winchester School.
Cor. and aug.   2d ed.   By Nicholas Robinson.
London, 1658]   377 pp.

ROBINSON, NICHOLAS.   The Christian philosopher; or, A
divine essay on the principles of man's universal redemption ...   London, 1758.   2 v.
  Set imperfect: v. 1 wanting.
  Christmas card laid in at p. 239.

ROEDEREV, PIERRE LOUIS.   Mémoire pour servir à l'his-
toire de la société palie en France.   Paris: Firmin
Didot frères, 1835.   ii, 484 pp.
  Autograph.

RÖLKER, BERNARD.   A German reader for beginners.
Cambridge: John Bartlett, 1854.   xi, 288 pp.
  Autographs. Inscription: Bequeathed by Ellen T. Emer-
  son; Miss Anna E. Rolker, Nov. 20, 1906.

ROGÉ, CHARLOTTE FISKE (BATES).   Risk, and other
poems.   Boston: A. Williams, 1879.   vii, 133 pp.
  Inscription: Dec. 1879.

ROGERS, JAMES EDWIN THOROLD.   Cobden and modern
political opinion.   Essays on certain political
topics.   London: Macmillan, 1873.   xvi, 382 pp.

ROGERS, NATHANIEL PEABODY. A collection from the newspaper writings of Nathaniel Peabody Rogers. Concord, N. H.: J. R. French, 1847. xxiv, 380 pp. Notes.

ROGET, PETER MARK. Animal and vegetable physiology, considered with reference to natural theology. Philadelphia: Carey, Lea & Blanchard, 1836. 2 v. Autograph and notes, v. 1.

ROLLIN, CHARLES. The ancient history of the Egyptians, Carthaginians, Assyrians, Babylonians, Medes & Persians, Macedonians, and Grecians. Boston: Munroe & Francis; Philadelphia: J. Bioren, & T. L. Plowman; Portsmouth: W. & D. Tredwell; Portland: T. Clark, 1805. 8 v. Bookplate of Wm. Emerson.

——. [Ten maps for Rollin's Ancient history. Octavo ed.] Boston: Etheridge & Bliss, 1807. 10 maps.

ROOT, E. D. Sakya Buddha: a versified, annotated narrative of his life and teachings; with an excursus, concerning citations from the Dhammapada, or Buddhist Canon. New York: Charles P. Somerby, 1880. viii, 171 pp.

ROOT, GEORGE FREDERICK. The young men's singing book; a collection of music for male voices. With the assistance of Lowell Mason. New York: Mason Bros., [ᶜ1855]. 256 pp.

Rosa; o, Il giorno delle disyrazie, traduzione dall'inglese M ... T ... Roma: Società tipografica, 1828. 27 pp.

ROSENKRANZ, KARL. Hegel's Naturphilosophie und die Bearbeitung derselben durch den italienischen Philosophen A. Véra. Berlin: Nicolaische, 1868. vi, 180 pp. Inscription: R. W. Emerson with regards of W. Z. H.

ROSENMÜLLER. In his Pocket Diary (1820–47) Emerson wrote that he lent a book, described only with this one word, to (Fred-

erick?) Dabney (Harvard, '28) in Feb. 1829. It was
probably one of the various Biblical commentaries written
by Ernest Friedrich Karl Rosenmüller (1768–1835) or
Johann Georg Rosenmüller (1736–1815), but it is impossi-
ble to identify which one.

ROSS, ALEXANDER MILTON. The birds of Canada, with
descriptions of their habits, food, nests, eggs, times
of arrival and departure. Toronto: Henry Rowsell,
1871. viii, 132 pp. illus.
Inscription: 23 Sept. 1873.

_____ . Recollections and experiences of an abolition-
ist; from 1855 to 1865. Toronto: Rowsell and
Hutchinson, 1875. xv, 224 pp.
Inscription: 29 July 1875.

ROSSETTI, CHRISTINA GEORGINA. Poems. [Author's ed.
3d thousand.] Boston: Roberts Bros., 1866. x,
256 pp.

_____ . _____ . Copy 2.
Inscription: From L. L. Whitney; Christmas present.

ROSSETTI, DANTE GABRIEL. Poems. [Author's ed.]
Boston: Roberts Bros., 1870. xi, 282 pp.

_____ . _____ . Boston: Roberts Bros., 1879. viii,
280 pp.
Inscription: For Mrs. Emerson from E. P.

ROSSINI, GIOACHINO ANTONIO. Cinderella; an opera, in
three acts. Music by Rossini. Correctly printed
from the acting copy ... [Baltimore, 1839?]
Notes and signature: Ellen Emerson.

ROUSSEAU, JEAN JACQUES. Les confessions. Éd.
stéréotype ... Paris: Pierre Didot et Firmin Didot,
1808. 4 v.
Notes.

_____ . The confessions. Period first. New York:
Calvin Blanchard, 1856. 309 pp.

_____ . Eloisa; or, A series of original letters collected
and published by J. J. Rousseau ... Tr. from the
French ... New ed. To which is now first added,

The sequel of Julia; or, The new Eloisa. Found
among the author's papers after his decease. Together with a portrait of Rousseau. London:
H. Baldwin, 1784. 4 v.
    Notes.

_____ . Émile; ou, De l'éducation. Paris: Le Prieur,
1794. 6 v.
    Autographs and inscription: W. E.—E. B. Emerson.
    Notes by R. W. E.

_____ . Emilius; or, An essay on education. Tr. from
the French, by Mr. Nugent ... London: J. Nourse
and P. Vaillant, 1763. 2 v.

_____ . Julie; ou, La nouvelle Héloïse; ou, Lettres de
deux amants, habitants d'une petite ville au pied des
Alpes; recueillies et publiées par J.-J. Rousseau ...
Éd. stéréotype. Paris: Pierre Didot et Firmin
Didot, 1817–29. 4 v.
    Set incomplete: t. 1 wanting.
    Tome 4 published by Hector Bossange.

_____ . Oeuvres. Second supplément à la collection.
t. 1–3. Genève, 1789. 3 v.
    Autograph.

_____ . Works. Tr. from the French. Edinburgh:
J. Dickson & C. Elliot, 1774. 10 v.
    Set incomplete: v. 1–6 wanting.
    Notes.

ROYCE, SAMUEL. Deterioration and race education.
With practical application to the condition of the
people and industry. New York: E. O. Jenkins,
1878. 504 pp.
    Inscription. Letter from author inserted.

ROYSE, NOBLE KIBLEY. Some ancient melodies and
other experiments. Cincinnati: Robert Clarke, 1882.
v, 220 pp.
    Inscription: Cincinnati, Feb. 22, '82 from author.

RUCKERT, FRIEDRICH. Five little stories, as lullabies
for my little sister. For Christmas. From the

German of Friedrich Ruckert, by N. L. F.   Boston:
Joseph H. Francis; New York: C. S. Francis, 1841.
30 pp.

RUSKIN, JOHN.   Fors clavigera.   Letters to the workmen
and labourers of Great Britain.   New York: J. Wiley,
1871.   119 pp.

———.   ———.   Part II.   New York: John Wiley, 1872.
160 pp.

———.   Lectures on architecture and painting, delivered
at Edinburgh, in November, 1853.   With illus. drawn
by the author.   New York: John Wiley, 1854.   vi,
189 pp.
   Signature: R. W. Emerson.   Inscription: From Munroe
and Co. for Mr. Emerson.

———.   Modern painters.   By a graduate of Oxford.
Part III.   1st American from the 3d London ed.
Rev. by the author.   New York: John Wiley, 1848.
222 pp.
   Autograph.   Signature: R. W. Emerson.   Notes.

———.   Modern painters, of many things.   Part IV.
1st American ed.   New York: Wiley & Halsted,
1856.   xiii, 348 pp.
   Autograph.

———.   Munera pulveris.   Six essays on the elements
of political economy.   New York: J. Wiley, 1872.
xxvii, 164 pp.
   Autograph.

———.   The poetry of architecture: cottage, villa, etc.
To which is added suggestions on works of art.   By
"Kata Phusin," conjectured nom-de-plume of John
Ruskin ...   New York: J. Wiley, 1873.   246 pp.

———.   Sesame and lilies.   Two lectures delivered at
Manchester in 1864.   1. Of kings' treasuries.
2. Of queens' gardens ...   New York: J. Wiley,
1872.   xvi, 119 pp.

———.   Time and tide, by Weare and Tyne.   Twenty-

five letters to a working man of Sunderland on the laws of work. 2d ed. London: Smith, Elder, 1868. viii, 199 pp.
    Autograph.

_____ . The two paths: being lectures on art, and its application to decoration and manufacture, delivered in 1858–59. New York: John Wiley, 1859. viii, 217 pp.
    Signature: R. W. Emerson.

RUSSELL, LADY RACHEL (WRIOTHESLEY) VAUGHAN. Letters. Boston: Wells and Lilly, 1820. 2 v. in 1.
    Autograph.

_____ . Letters from the manuscript in the Library at Woburn Abbey. With an introduction, vindicating the character of Lord Russell against Sir John Dalrymple, &c. and the trial of Lord William Russell for high treason. London: J. F. Dave, 1826. xxiv, 264 pp.
    Inscription: Mrs. R. Emerson from Mr. George A. Sampson, and notes.

S

Sacred socialism. South Wellington Road, Stockport, September 5th 1840. [n.p., 1840?] 1 l.
> Broadside.
> Bound with: Lane, Charles. A classification of science and arts. London, 1826.

[SADĀNANDA YOGĪNDRA.] A lecture on the Vedánta, embracing the text of the Vedánta-Sāra [by J. R. Ballantyne]. Printed for the use of the Benares College, by order of the Gov't., N. W. P. Allahabad: Presbyterian Mission Press, 1850. 84 pp.
> Autograph. Inscription: Henry D. Thoreau from Thomas Cholmondeley.

SADDHARMAPUNDARIKA. Le lotus de la bonne loi, tr. du sanscrit, accompagné d'un commentaire et de vingt et un mémoires relatifs au Buddhisme, par m. E. Bournouf ... Paris: Imprimerie Nationale, 1852. iv, 897 pp.
> Inscription: Henry D. Thoreau from Thomas Cholmondeley.

SA'DI. Flowers culled from the Gûlistân; or, Rose garden, and from the Bostan; or, Pleasure garden of Sadi ... London: Williams & Norgate, 1876. xvi, 175 pp.
> Inscription.

——. The Gûlistân; or, Rose garden. Tr. from the original, by Francis Gladwin. Calcutta printed.

London: Reprinted for Black, Parry, & Kingsbury, by
W. Bulmer, 1808.   xxii, 303 pp.
   Autograph.

———.   ———.   With an essay on Saadi's life and
genius, by James Ross, and a preface, by R. W.
Emerson.   Boston: Ticknor and Fields, 1865.
379 pp.
   Notes.

———.   ———.   Copy 2.
   Given to Concord Free Public Library by Ralph Waldo
Emerson in Aug. 1873 (Cameron, III, 868).

SADLER, THOMAS.   Edwin Wilkins Field, a memorial
sketch.   London: Macmillan, 1872.   xi, 175 pp.
port.

The Sage of Mentor.   In five cantos.   By the Unknown
... Chicago: Ottaway, 1881.   48 pp.
   Inscription: From the author.

SAINSBURY, SAMUEL.   Human interests, reflections, etc.
London: Tinsley Bros., 1877.   xii, 164 pp.
   Inscription: From author to R. W. E.

ST. JOHN, BAYLE.   Montaigne the essayist, a biography.
London: Chapman and Hall, 1858.   2 v.   illus.
   Autographs and notes.

ST. JOHN, CHARLES HENRY.   Country love and city life,
and other poems.   Boston: A. Williams, 1880.   vi,
200 pp.

ST. JOHN, JAMES AUGUST.   The history of the manners
and customs of ancient Greece.   London: R. Bent-
ley, 1842.   3 v.
   Autographs and notes.

ST. LOUIS.   BOARD OF EDUCATION.   Report of the Board
of directors of the St. Louis public schools.   19th,
25th, 1872/73, 1878/79.   St. Louis: Democrat Litho.
and Printing Co.   2 v.
   Publisher varies: 1878/79, G. I. Jones.

ST. PAUL'S SCHOOL, LONDON.   Prolusiones literariae,
praemiis quotannis propositis dignatae, et in D. Pauli

schola habitae a. S. H. MDCCCXLIII. Subjiciuntur et nonnullae comitiis Hibernis nuper recitatae ... Londoni: B. Fellowes, 1843. 37 pp.

SAINT-PIERRE, JACQUES HENRI BERNARDIN DE. Studies of nature. Tr. by Henry Hunter ... London: C. Dilly, 1796. 5 v.

SAINTE-BEUVE, CHARLES AUGUSTIN. Causeries du lundi. Paris: Garnier frères, 1852–62. 15 v.
  Set incomplete: t. 1, 2, 4–6, 8–15 wanting.
  Autographs.

——. Port-Royal. Paris: L. Hachette, 1867. 6 v.
  Inscription: v. 1, Ellen T. Emerson from E. W. Ward, New Yrs., 1865.

——. Portraits de femmes. Nouv. éd., rev. et cor. ... Paris: Didier, 1856. 482 pp.

SALVINI, ANTONIO MARIA. Gli efesiaci di Senofonte Efesio volgarizzati. Parigi: Ag. Renouard, 1800. 108 pp.

SALYARDS, JOSEPH. Idothea; or, The divine image. A poem. New Market, Va.: Henkel, Calvert, 1874. 308 pp.

SAMSON, GEORGE WHITEFIELD. The atonement viewed as assumed divine responsibility; traced as the fact attested in divine revelation; shown to be the truth uniting Christian theories; and recognized as the grace realized in human experience. Philadelphia: J. B. Lippincott, 1878. iv, 320 pp.

SANBORN, FRANKLIN BENJAMIN. Memoirs of John Brown, written for Samuel Orcutt's History of Torrington, Ct., by F. B. Sanborn, with memorial verses by William Ellery Channing. Concord, Mass.: J. Munsell, 1878. 107 pp.
  Inscription: 7 Mar. 1878.

——, AND LEIGHTON, R., JR. Poems read at the opening of the fraternity lectures, 1858–59. America, by F. B. Sanborn. Character, by R. Leighton, Jr.

Boston: Printed for the Fraternity, 1859. 59 pp.
Inscription.

SAND, GEORGE, *pseud. of Mme.* DUDEVANT. Le compag-
non du Tour de France. Paris: Perrotin, 1843.
459 pp.
Autograph.

——. La comtesse de Rudolstadt. Nouv. éd., rev.
et cor. ... Paris: Charpentier, 1845. 2 v.

——. Consuelo. Tr. from the French, by Fayette
Robinson. New York: Stringer & Townsend, 1851.
254 pp.

——. Jeanne. Bruxelles: Wouters, 1844. 2 v.

——. La mare au diable. 2. éd. Paris: Desessart,
1846–47. 2 v.
Signature: v. 2, R. W. Emerson.

——. Oeuvres. Bruxelles: Meline, Cans, 1842–47.
6 v.
Set incomplete: v. 1–3, 5, 6 wanting.
Signature: R. W. Emerson.
Contents: Horace, Consuelo, Mouny-Robin, Jean Ziska.

——. Le péché de M. Antoine. Bruxelles: C.
Muquardt, 1846. 3 v.
Initials.

——. La petite Fadette. Nouv. éd. Paris: Michel
Lévy frères, 1865. 287 pp.

SANFORD, HENRY SHELTON. The different systems of
penal codes in Europe; also, a report on the adminis-
trative changes in France, since the Revolution of
1848. Washington: B. Tucker, 1854. 404 pp.

SANTAREM, MANUEL FRANCISCO DE BARROS, 2. *Visconde*
DE. Researches respecting Americus Vespucius,
and his voyages. Tr. by E. V. Childe. Boston:
C. C. Little & J. Brown, 1850. 221 pp.

SARBIEWSKI, MACIEJ KAZIMIERZ. Carmina. Nova ed.,
prioribus longe auctior & emendatior ... Parisiis:
J. Barbou, 1759. viii, 383 pp.
Notes.

SARGENT, EPES. The woman who dared. Boston:
Roberts Bros., 1870. vi, 270 pp.

SARMIENTO, DOMINGO FAUSTINO, *Pres. Argentine Republic.* Civilisation et barbarie; moeurs, coutumes,
caractères des peuples argentins. Facundo Quiroga
et Aldao. Tr. de l'espagnol et enrichi de notes par
A. Giraud ... Paris: A. Bertrand, 1853. xlvi,
383 pp.
  Inscription.

SAUVEUR, LAMBERT. Petites causeries. Boston: Lee
et Shepard; New York: F. W. Christern, 1875.
178 pp.
  Inscription: To R. W. E. from author, 5 June 1875.

SAY, JEAN BAPTISTE. A treatise on political economy;
or, The production, distribution, and consumption of
wealth. Tr. from the 4th ed. of the French by C. R.
Prinsep ... To which is added, a translation of the
introduction, and additional notes, by Clement C.
Biddle. Boston: Wells and Lilly, 1821. 2 v.
  Set incomplete: v. 1 wanting.
  Marginal notes.

SAYN-WITTGENSTEIN, KAROLINE ELZBIETA (IWANOWSKA).
Bouddhisme et Christianisme. Rome: J. Aurelgi,
1868. 254 pp.
  Inscription: From author to Emerson, sending the volume
  through Longfellow.

[SCHAAD, JOHN CHRISTIAN.] Ocean waves in lyric
strains, a requiem; and other poems. By the Hermit
of St. Eirene ... Pittsburgh, Pa.: W. S. Haven,
1856. viii, 88 pp.

SCHELLING, FRIEDRICH WILHELM JOSEPH VON. Sammtliche
werke ... Stuttgart: J. G. Cotta, 1856–57. 2 v.

SCHICKARDI, WILHELM. Horologivm Hebraevm, sive con-
silium, quomodo sancta lingua spacio xxiv, horarum,
a totidem collegis, seu eorundem semisse sufficienter
apprehendi queat, septies comprobatum, & impressum
iam quantâ fieri potuit diligentiâ ... A. N. H.,

s. t. D. ... Londini: Thomae Paine: venit apud
Philemonem Stephanum, & Christophorum Meredith,
1639.   139 pp.

SCHILLER, JOHANN CHRISTOPH FRIEDRICH VON.   Corre-
spondence between Schiller and Goethe, from 1794 to
1805.   Tr. by George H. Calvert.   Vol. I.   New
York: Wiley and Putnam, 1845.   xi, 392 pp.
  No more published.
  Autograph.

_____ .   Historical works.   From the German, by George
Moir ...   Edinburgh: Constable, 1828.   2 v.
  Autograph, v. 2, and notes.

_____ .   Song of the bell.   A new translation, by W. H.
Furness.   With poems and ballads from Goethe,
Schiller, and others, by F. H. Hedge.   Philadelphia:
Hazard and Mitchell, 1850.   48 pp.
  Inscription: 5 Apr, 1850, from the translator.

_____ .   Wallenstein's camp.   Tr. from the German by
George Moir.   With a memoir of Albert Wallenstein,
by G. Wallis Haven.   Boston: James Monroe, 1837.
v, 142 pp.

SCHLEGEL, AUGUST WILHELM VON.   A course of lectures
on dramatic art and literature.   Tr. from the original
German by John Black.   Philadelphia: Hogan &
Thompson, 1833.   xii, 442 pp.
  Autograph and notes.

SCHLEGEL, FRIEDRICH VON.   The philosophy of history;
in a course of lectures, delivered at Vienna.   Tr.
from the German, with a memoir of the author, by
James Burton Robertson ...   London: Saunders and
Otley, 1835.   2 v.

SCHLEIERMACHER, F.   Critical essay on the gospel of
St. Luke.   With an introduction by the translator,
containing an account of the controversy respecting
the origin of the three first Gospels since Bishop
Marsh's dissertation.   London: J. Taylor, 1825.
cliv, 320 pp.

Emerson's copy with his signature and note.   Sold by
the Parke-Bernet Galleries in New York City at the Win-
ter-McVoy Sale on Feb. 18, 1942.   Resold by the City
Book Auction in New York City on June 24, 1950.

SCHMIDT, JOHANN ADOLF ERDMANN.   Neugriechisch-
deutsches und deutsch-neugriechisches Wörterbuch.
Zum gebrauch der Deutschen und Griechen.   Leipzig: E. B. Schwickert, 1825–27.   2 v.

SCHMIDT, JULIAN.   Portraits aus dem neunzehnten
Jahrhundert.   Berlin: Wilhelm Hertz, 1878.   473 pp.

The school; or, Lessons in morals ...   no. 1.   Boston:
Cottons & Barnard, [ᶜ1827].   36 pp.

SCHREVEL, CORNELIS.   Lexicon manual Graeco-Latinum
et Latino-Graecum: studio atque opera Josephi Hill,
Joannis Entick, nec non Gulielmi Bowyer, adauctum.
Insuper quoque ad calcem adjectae sunt sententiae
Graeco-Latinae, quibus omnia Gr. ling. primitiva
comprehenduntur.   Item tractatus duo: alter De reso-
lutione verborum, De Articulis alter; uterque peruti-
lis, et aeque desideratus.   Ed. XIX, et prima Americana, prioribus auctior et emendatior.   Philadel-
phiae: Johnson & Warner, et Kimber & Conrad, 1808.
vi, [326] pp.

SCHWEGLER, ALBERT.   Handbook of the history of philos-
ophy.   Tr. and annotated by James Hutchinson
Stirling ...   2d ed.   Edinburgh: Edmondston &
Douglas, 1868.   xiv, 486 pp.
    Autograph.

SCOTT, SIR WALTER, Bart.   Complete works.   With a
biography, and his last additions and illus.   New
York: Conner & Cooke, 1833–34.   7 v.
    Set incomplete: v. 2–7 wanting.
    Signature: R. W. Emerson, and notes.

———.   Guy Mannering.
    Emerson lent a copy of this to one of his Harvard class-
mates in 1821 (Cameron, III, 856).

_____ .   The lady of the lake.
   Emerson lent a copy óf this to one of his Harvard classmates in 1821 (Cameron, III, 856).

[_____ .]   The life of Napoleon Buonaparte, Emperor of
the French.   With a preliminary view of the French
Revolution.   Philadelphia: Carey, Lea & Carey,
1827.   3 v.
   Autograph.

_____ .   Poetical works.   Containing Lay of the last
minstrel, Marmion, Lady of the Lake, Don Roderick,
Rokeby, ballads, lyrics, and songs.   With a life of
the author.   New York: D. Appleton; Philadelphia:
G. S. Appleton, 1845.   xxiv, 624 pp.

_____ .   Scotland.   London: Longman, Rees, Orme,
Brown, and Green and John Taylor, 1831.   2 v.

_____ .   Tales of a grandfather; being stories taken from
Scottish history.   Humbly inscribed to Hugh Little-
john.   2d series.   Philadelphia: Carey, Lea &
Carey, 1829.   2 v.
   Set incomplete: v. 1 wanting.
   Inscription: R. W. Emerson to W. Emerson Jr.

_____ .   Waverley novels.   Parker's ed.,   rev. and
cor. with a general preface, an introduction to each
novel, and notes, historical and illustrative, by the
author.   Boston: Samuel H. Parker, 1829–34.   54 v.
   Set incomplete: v. 43, 49, 50 wanting.
   Autographs.

SCOTT, WILLIAM BELL.   Hades; or, The transit; and,
The Progress of mind, two poems.   London: Henry
Renshaw, 1838.   47 pp.

_____ .   Memoir of David Scott, R. S. A.; containing
his journal in Italy, notes on art and other papers.
Edinburgh: Adam & Charles Black, 1850.   443 pp.
port., plates.
   Inscription: 1851.

———. The year of the world; a philosophical poem &
"Redemption from the fall." Edinburgh: William
Tait; London: Simpkin and Marshall, 1864. xii,
113 pp.

SCOUGAL, HENRY. Life of God in the soul of man; or,
The nature and excellency of the Christian religion.
Boston: Lincoln & Edmands, 1823. 80 pp.
  Inscription: From Rev. Dr. Channing (in R. W. E.'s
hand).

———. ———. Copy 2.

SCRIBE, AUGUSTIN EUGÈNE. Nouvelles ... Maurice—
Carlo Broschi—La maîtresse anonyme. Paris:
Michel Lévy frères, 1856. 320 pp.

———. Oeuvres choisies ... Paris: Firmin Didot
frères, 1845. 5 v.
  Autographs.

SEAMAN'S AID SOCIETY, BOSTON. Sixth annual report of
the managers of the Seaman's Aid Society of the city
of Boston. Written by Mrs. S. J. Hale, and read at
the annual meeting, Jan. 9, 1839 ... Boston: James
B. Dow, 1839. 35 pp.

Search the Scriptures; or, The way of truth is the way of
life ... San Francisco: A. L. Bancroft, 1881.
148 pp.

SEARS, EDMUND HAMILTON. The fourth gospel, the heart
of Christ. 2d ed. Boston: Noyes, Holmes, 1872.
viii, 551 pp.

———. Regeneration ... 5th ed. Boston: American
Unitarian Association, 1856. 248 pp.
  Autograph. Signature: Lydian Emerson.

———. Sermons and songs of the Christian life. Boston: Noyes, Holmes; Philadelphia: Claxton, Remsen,
and Hoffelfinger, 1875. x, 334 pp.
  Autograph: Ellen T. Emerson, New Years, 1875.

[SEDGWICK, CATHARINE MARIA.] [Live and let live; or,

Domestic service illustrated. New York: Harper, 1837.] viii, 216 pp.
> Bookplate: No. 309, Sunday-School Library of the Unitarian Society in Concord.

[____.] A love token for children. Designed for Sunday-school libraries. New York: Harper, 1838. 142 pp.

[____.] ____. New York: Harper, 1871. 142 pp.

____. Morals of manners; or, Hints for our young people. New York: Wiley and Putnam, 1846. 63 pp.
> Autograph: Ellen T. Emerson.

SEDGWICK, ELIZABETH BUCKMINSTER (DWIGHT). A talk with my pupils. New York: J. Hopper; Boston: Crosby & Nichols, 1863. ii, 235 pp.

[SEELEY, SIR JOHN ROBERT.] Ecce Homo; a survey of the life and work of Jesus Christ. Boston: Roberts Bros., 1866. 355 pp.
> Signature: R. W. Emerson.

SEIDLER, LOUISE. Erinnerungen und Leben. Aus handschriftlichen Nachlass zusammengestellt und bearbeitet von Hermann Uhde. Berlin: Wilhelm Hertz, 1874. x, 479 pp.

A selection of hymns and psalms, for social and private worship. 3d ed., cor. Cambridge: Hilliard and Metcalf, 1825. xix, 364 pp.
> Signature: R. W. Emerson.

SENECA, LUCIUS ANNAEUS. Morals by way of abstract. To which is added, a discourse, under the title of An after thought, by Sir Roger L'Estrange. Keene, [N. H.]: John Prentiss, 1806. xiv, 372 pp.
> Autograph and notes.

Sentences, to be read at breakfast time. [n.p., n.d.] 1 l.
> Broadside.

Bound with: Lane, Charles.   A classification of science and arts.   London, 1826.

A sermon preached at the closing of a Sunday school,
October 31, 1830.   By a pastor.   Boston: Leonard
C. Bowles, 1831.   17 pp.

SEWEL, WILLIAM.   The history of the rise, increase, and
progress, of the Christian people called Quakers;
intermixed with several remarkable occurrences.
Written originally in Low Dutch, and also tr. into
English, by William Sewel.   3d ed., cor.   Philadelphia: Benjamin & Thomas Kite, 1832.   2 v.
    Autograph and notes, v. 1.   Inscription: v. 1, C. C.
Emerson from Mrs. J. T. Wigglesworth.

[SEWELL, ELIZABETH MISSING.]   History of the early
church from the first preaching of the gospel to the
Council of Nicea.   For the use of young persons.
New York: D. Appleton, 1860.   viii, 383 pp.

SHAKESPEARE, WILLIAM.   The beauties of Shakespeare;
selected from his works.   To which are added the
principal scenes in the same author.   The 7th ed.,
cor., rev., and enl.   London: G. Kearsley, F. & C.
Rivington, I. Walker, [ca. 1800].   xii, 393 pp.
    Autograph.

_____ .   Dramatic works.   From the correct ed. of
Isaac Reed.   With copious annotations ...   London: J. Walker, G. Offer, 1820.   12 v.

_____ .   _____ .   With a glossary.   Chiswick: Printed
by C. Whittingham for Thomas Tegg, 1823.
    On deposit in Folger Library.

_____ .   _____ .   With the corrections & illustrations of
Dr. Johnson, G. Stevens, & others.   Rev. by Isaac
Reed.   [Stereotype ed.?] ...   New York: Collins &
Hannay, 1825.   10 v.
    Set incomplete: v. 1-3, 5-10 wanting.

_____ .   King Lear.   Ed. by Horace Howard Furness.
Philadelphia: J. B. Lippincott, 1880.   vi, 503 pp.
    "A New variorum edition of Shakespeare, v. 5."

_____ . Plays, complete in one volume.   [Chiswick:
C. Whittingham, 18—?]   666 pp.
  Autograph: Lydian Emerson.

_____ . Poems.   London: Edward Moxon, 1840.   60 pp.

_____ . _____ . London: William Pickering, 1842.
lxxxix, 288 pp.
  Autograph.   Notes on inside back cover.

_____ . Poems and songs.   London: W. Strange,
[1830?].   vii, 96 pp.

_____ . Sonnets, and A lover's complaint.   Reprinted
in the orthography, and punctuation of the original
edition of 1609 ...   London: J. R. Smith, 1870.
[76] pp.
  Inscription: From Dr. A. M. Ross.

_____ . Works.   Comprising his dramatic and poetical
works, complete, accurately printed from the text of
the corrected copy left by the late George Stevens.
With a glossary and notes and a memoir, by Alexander Chalmers ...   Complete in one volume.   New
York: Oliver S. Felt, [18—?].   xi, 1027 pp.
  Signature: R. W. Emerson, and notes.

SHAKESPEARE SOCIETY OF PHILADELPHIA.   Twenty-seventh
annual dinner.   Philadelphia, 1879.   [4] pp.
  Inscription: From W. H. Furness.

SHATTUCK, LEMUEL.   A history of the Town of Concord;
Middlesex County, Massachusetts, from its earliest
settlement to 1832; and of the adjoining towns, Bedford, Acton, Lincoln, and Carlisle; containing various notices of County and State history not before
published.   Boston: Russell, Odiorne; Concord: J.
Stacy, 1835.   viii, 392 pp.
  Inscriptions: R. W. E. to M. M. E., M. M. E. to Mrs.
  Ripley.

_____ . _____ . Copy 2.
  Autograph and notes.

[SHELLEY, MARY WOLLSTONECRAFT (GODWIN).]   Eminent
literary and scientific men of France.   London:

Longman, Orme, Brown, Green, & Longmans, 1838–
39.   2 v.
  Set incomplete: v. 2 wanting.
  Autograph.

SHELLEY, PERCY BYSSHE.   Alastor; or, The new ptolemy
    ...   London: Saunders and Otley, 1852.   172 pp.

———.   Poetical works.   1st American ed. (complete):
  with some remarks on the poetical faculty and its influence on human destiny; embracing a biographical
  and critical notice, by G. G. Foster.   New York:
  J. S. Redfield, 1845.   750 pp.
  Autograph: Margaret Fuller, and her notes.

SHEPHERD, WILLIAM.   History of the American Revolu-
  tion.   [London, 1830?]   64 pp.
  Bound with: Needham, M.,   On the manufacture of iron.
  London, 1831.

SHEPPARD, ELIZABETH SARA.   Charles Auchester, a
  memorial, by E. Berger [pseud.] ...   New York:
  Harper, 1853.   194 pp.
  Signature: R. W. Emerson.

———.   Counterparts; or, The cross of love.   ... London: Smith, Elder, 1854.   3 v.
  Autographs.

[———.]   Rumour.   ... London: Hurst and Blackett,
  1858.   3 v.
  Autographs.

SHERWOOD, MARY MARTHA (BUTT).   Julian Percival.
  Salem: Whipple and Lawrence, 1827.   35 pp.

SHEW, JOEL.   Children, their hydropathic management in
  health and disease; a descriptive and practical work,
  designed as a guide for families and physicians.
  Illustrated with numerous cases.   New York: Fowler and Wells, 1852.   xvii, 432 pp.

SHIPPEN, RUSH RHEES.   Daily praise and prayer ...
  Boston: American Unitarian Association, 1876.
  379 pp.

Short stories illustrative of Gospel truth. 4th series
... Dublin: Dublin Tract Repository, [18—?].
288 pp.

SIBLEY, JOHN LANGDON. Biographical sketches of
graduates of Harvard University, in Cambridge,
Massachusetts. Vol. I. 1642–1658. With an appendix, containing an abstract of the steward's ac-
counts, and notices of non-graduates, from 1649–50
to 1659. Cambridge: Charles William Sever, 1873.
xx, 618 pp.

SIDNEY, SIR PHILIP, AND SELDEN, JOHN. The defence of
poesy, by Sir Philip Sidney. Table tales, by John
Selden. With some account of the authors. Cambridge: Hilliard & Brown, 1831. xlvii, 294 pp.
Autograph and notes.

SIMCOX, GEORGE AUGUSTUS. Prometheus unbound, a
tragedy. London: Smith, Elder, 1867. xxii,
108 pp.
Inscription: To R. W. E. from W. H. Channing, Oct,
1867, and note.

SIMMONS, GEORGE FREDERICK. Six sermons. Boston:
J. Munroe, 1856. 134 pp.
Signature: Ellen T. Emerson.
Ms. poem at end, in her hand.

SINCLAIR, CATHERINE. Holiday house. A series of
tales from the 5th London ed. Philadelphia: Geo.
S. Appleton; New York: D. Appleton, 1849. x,
318 pp.
Autograph: Ellen T. Emerson.

[SMEDLEY, EDWARD.] The history of France. Part I.
From the final partition of the empire of Charlemagne,
A.D. 843, to the peace of Cambray, A.D. 1529.
Published under the superintendence of the Society
for the Diffusion of Useful Knowledge. London:
Baldwin and Cradock, 1836. xii, 507 pp.
Signature: R. W. Emerson.

SMITH, ADAM.   The theory of moral sentiments; or, An
Essay towards an analysis of the principles, by
which men naturally judge concerning the conduct
and character, first of their neighbors, and afterwards
of themselves.   To which is added, a dissertation
on the origin of languages.   1st American from the
12th Edinburgh ed.   Philadelphia: Anthony Finley,
1817.   vii, 598 pp.
  Autograph and notes.

SMITH, GERRIT.   The theologies.   Peterboro, N. Y.:
C. A. Hammond, [18—?].   28 pp.

SMITH, JAMES.   The divine drama of history and civili-
zation.   London: Chapman and Hall, 1854.   xii,
644 pp.
  Inscriptions: Henry James and his address, R. W. Emerson from Henry James (in E.'s hand).   Marginal notes.

SMITH, ROSWELL CHAMBERLAIN.   Atlas, for schools,
academies, and families.   An atlas, to accompany
The productive geography.   Philadelphia: W. Marshall, Hartford: Daniel Burgess, c1835.   18 ll.
col. maps.

——— .   An introductory geography, designed for children, illus. with one hundred and twenty six engravings, and twenty maps.   8th ed.   St. Louis: S. W.
Meech, 1848.   viii, 175 pp.

SMITH, SIR WILLIAM.   A history of Greece, from the
earliest times to the Roman conquest.   With supplementary chapters on the history of literature and
art.   Boston: Jenks, Hickling and Swan, 1854.
xxviii, 632 pp.
  Autograph.

——— .   A smaller history of Rome, from the earliest
times to the establishment of the empire.   With a
continuation to A.D. 476, by Eugene Lawrence ...
New York: Harper, 1876.   xxx, 365 pp.

SMITH, WILLIAM.   Old Yorkshire, with an introduction

by Canon Raine ... London: Longmans, Green, 1881. x, 313 pp.

SMITH, WILLIAM HENRY. Bacon and Shakespeare. An inquiry touching players, play-houses, and play-writers in the days of Elizabeth. To which is appended an abstract of a ms. respecting Tobie Matthew. London: John Russell Smith, 1857. viii, 162 pp.
  Autograph and notes.

SMITH, WILTON MERLE. "What you are speaking so I cannot hear what you say," Emerson. An address by Wilton Merle Smith, at East Northfield, Mass. [n.p., 18—?] 21 pp.

SMITHSONIAN INSTITUTION. Report ... 1854—56, 1862, 1865, 1869—71. Washington: Govt. Print. Off. 8 v.
  33d Cong., 1st sess., Senate, Misc. doc., no. 73; 33d Cong., 2d sess., Senate, Misc. doc., no. 24; 34th Cong., 3d sess., Senate, Misc. doc., no. 54; 37th Cong., 3d sess., Senate, Misc. doc. [no. 25]; [?]; 41st Cong., 3d sess., House, Ex. doc., no. 153; 42d Cong., 1st sess., House, Ex. doc., no. 20; [?].
  Vols. for 1854, 1855 called also 8th, 9th.
  Title varies slightly.
  Publisher varies: 1854-55, Beverly Tucker; 1857, A. O. P. Nicholson.

SMYTH, WILLIAM. Lectures on modern history, from the irruption of the northern nations to the close of the American Revolution. [2d ed.] Cambridge: J. and J. J. Deighton; London: W. Pickering, 1840. 2 v.

SNIDER, DENTON JAQUES. Delphic days. St. Louis, Mo.: Friedrich Roesslein, 1880. 126 pp.
  Inscription: To R. W. Emerson from the author, 26 May 1880.

SNORRI STURLUSON. The Heimskringla; or, Chronicle of the Kings of Norway. Tr. from the Icelandic, with a preliminary dissertation, by Samuel Lang ... Lon-

don: Longman, Brown, Green and Longmans, 1844.
3 v.
Autographs.   Note, v. 2.

SNOW, CALEB HOPKINS.   A history of Boston, the metropolis of Massachusetts, from its origin to the present
period; with some account of the environs.   2d ed.
Boston: A. Bowen, 1828.   iv, 427 pp.
Autograph and marginal notes.

SNOW, GEORGE D'OYLY.   A theologico-political treatise.
London: Trübner, 1874.   xiii, 164 pp.

SOAVE, FRANCESCO.   Novelle morali ad uso della
giovenuto.   Nuova ed. ... Lione: Blache, 1818.
2 v.
Set incomplete: pte. 1 wanting.
Autograph.

Socialism.   no. 1.   [n.p., 18—?]   1 l.
Broadside.
Bound with: Lane, Charles.   A classification of sci-
ence and arts.   London, 1826.

Socialism.   no. 2.   [n.p., 18—?]   1 l.
Broadside.
Bound with: Lane, Charles.   A classification of sci-
ence and arts.   London 1826.

SOCIETY FOR MUTUAL INSTRUCTION.   A few friends of
truth and goodness, having formed a small society for
the purpose of mutual instruction, assemble every
Wednesday evening, at six or seven o'clock, at no. 7,
Castle Street, Holborn ...   [London, 18—?]   1 l.
Broadside.
Bound with: Lane, Charles.   A classification of sci-
ence and arts.   London, 1826.

[SOCIETY FOR MUTUAL INSTRUCTION.]   Proposal for uniting the friends of free enquiry in a society or school
for mutual instruction in metaphysics, morals, and
theology.   [London: Hetherington, Printer, 18—?]
1 l.
Broadside.
Bound with: Lane, Charles.   A classification of science and arts.   London, 1826.

SOCIETY FOR THE DIFFUSION OF USEFUL KNOWLEDGE, LON-
DON. Lives of eminent persons, consisting of Gali-
leo, Kepler, Newton, Mahomet, Wolsey, Sir E. Coke,
Lord Somers, Caxton, Blake, Adam Smith, Niebuhr,
Sir C. Wren, and Michael Angelo. Published under
the superintendence of the Society. London: Baldwin
and Cradock, 1833. 13 pts. in 1 v.
Autograph and notes.

Some account of Thomas Dormer; with hints on early
rising. Cambridge: Hilliard and Metcalf, 1821.
16 pp.
Bound with: The classical journal. 1830-31. Boston.

SOMERVILLE, MARY (FAIRFAX). On the connexion of the
physical sciences. London: John Murray, 1834.
458 pp.
Signature: R. W. Emerson.

SOPHOCLES. The Oedipus tyrannus. Harvard university, Sanders theatre, May 17, 19, and 20, 1881.
[Cambridge]: The Greek Dept., [1881]. [161] pp.

_____. Sophocles. Tr. by Thomas Francklin ...
London: A. J. Valpy, 1832. xi, 363 pp.
Autograph.

_____. Tragedies. Literally tr. into English prose,
with notes. 3d ed. improved. New York: William
Jackson, 1837. 307 pp.
Autographs and notes.

_____. _____. A new translation, with a biographical
essay, and an appendix of rhymed choral odes and
lyrical dialogues, by E. H. Plumptre ... London:
Daldy, Isbister, 1879. xcv, 502 pp.
Inscription: Dec. 25, 1879, to R. W. E., by author.
Sheet with notes, inserted.

SOULE, RICHARD. A dictionary of English synonymes
and synonymous or parallel expressions, designed as
a practical guide to aptness and variety of phraseol-
ogy. Boston: Little, Brown, 1871. iv, 456 pp.
Inscription: To R. W. E. by author.

———, AND WHEELER, WILLIAM A. A manual of English pronunciation and spelling: containing a full alphabetical vocabulary of the language, with a preliminary exposition of English orthoëpy and orthography; and designed as a work of reference for general use, and as a text-book in schools. Boston: Soule and Williams, 1861. xxix, 467 pp.
> Inscription: By author to R. W. E.

SOUTHEY, ROBERT. Chronicle of the Cid, from the Spanish. 1st American ed. Lowell: Daniel Bixby, 1846. xvi, 486 pp.
> Inscription: From publisher, and notes.

Specimens of the earlier English poets. London: S. W. Simpon, 1824. 275 pp.
> Autograph and notes.

Speech of a Frenchman, on the proposed bill of [Mr. Warburton] for the dissection of human bodies, delivered at the British Forum, Monday 23rd March, 1829. [London: Cunningham, 1829.] 8 pp.
> Bound with: Lane, Charles. A classification of science and arts. London, 1826.

SPENCE, JOSEPH. Anecdotes, observations, and characters, of books and men. Collected from the conversation of Mr. Pope, and other eminent persons of his time. With notes, and a life of the author, by Samuel Weller Singer. 2d ed. London: J. R. Smith, 1858. xxxii, 396 pp.
> Autograph and notes.

SPENCE, WILLIAM. Address delivered at the anniversary meeting of the Entomological Society of London, on the 24th January, 1848. London: Richard and John Taylor, 1848. 20 pp.

———. Tracts on political economy. viz. 1. Britain independent of commerce; 2. Agriculture the source of wealth; 3. The objections against the corn bill refuted; 4. Speech on the East India trade. With prefatory remarks on the causes and cure of our present distresses, as originating from neglect of

principles laid down in these works. London: Longman, Hurst, Rees, Orme, and Brown, 1822. 265 pp.
Inscription.

SPENCER, HERBERT. Education: intellectual, moral, and physical. New York: D. Appleton, 1861. xviii, 283 pp.

_____ . Positivism in theology, first principles. London: Williams & Norgate, 1862. 34 pp.

SPENSER, EDMUND. Spenser and the Fairy queen, by John S. Hart. Philadelphia: Hayes & Zell, 1854. x, 434 pp.
Inscription: Ellen T. Emerson from Mrs. Hemenway, Jan. 1, 1855.

_____ . Works. With observations on his life and writings. London: George Routledge, 1844. 530 pp.
Autograph and notes.

_____ . _____ . With a selection of notes from various commentators; and a glossarial index: to which is prefixed some account of the life of Spenser, by Henry John Todd ... New ed. London, New York: George Routledge, 1872. lx, 556 pp.

[SPERRY, MRS. N. S.] Instauration; or, The new era. Hartford: C. Lockwood & Brainard, Printers, 1872. 311 pp.
Presented to the Concord Free Public Library by Ralph Waldo Emerson in Feb. 1874. Withdrawn from circulation, 1921 (Cameron, III, 868).

[_____ .] Recognition of the creator of daily life. Hartford, 1873.
Presented to the Concord Free Public Library by Ralph Waldo Emerson in Feb. 1874. Withdrawn from circulation, 1921 (Cameron, III, 868).

SPIERS, ALEXANDER. French and English, and English and French pronouncing dictionary. Newly composed from the French dictionaries of the French Academy, Laveaux, Boiste, Bescherelle, Landais, etc., and from the English dictionaries of Johnson, Webster, Worcester, Richardson, etc. Carefully

rev., cor., and enl. ... by G. P. Quackenbos.   New
York: D. Appleton, 1856.   2 v. in 1.
  Notes of R. W. E.

SPIESS, H.   Das Ziel der Menschheit.   Ein Beitrag zum
  Begründen eines nichtig eren Standpunktes für die
  Beurtheilung politischer Fragen ...   Galveston,
  [Tex.]: Buch und Accidenz Druckerei der Union,
  1867.   iv, 41 pp.
    Inscription and notes.

Spiritual culture; or, Thoughts for the consideration of
  parents and teachers ...   Boston: Joseph Dowe,
  1841.   xii, 108 pp.
    Inscription: R. W. Emerson from his friend, A. Bronson
  Alcott, Concord, 5 July 1841, and notes.

Spiritual-living man.   [n.p., 18—?]   [8] pp.
    Bound with: Lane, Charles.   A classification of science
  and arts.   London, 1826.

SPRAGUE, CHARLES.   An ode, pronounced before the inhabitants of Boston, September the seventeenth,
  1830, at the centennial celebration of the settlement
  of the City.   Boston: John H. Eastburn, 1830.
  22 pp.
    Inscription.
    Bound with: Webster, Daniel.   Speech of ... on the 14th
  January, 1814.   Alexandria, 1814.

———— .   The prize ode recited at the representation of
  the Shakespeare jubilee, Boston, Feb. 13, 1824.
  [Boston, 1824?]   8 pp.
    Bound with: Webster, Daniel.   A discourse delivered at
  Plymouth, December 22, 1820.   Boston, 1821.

[SPRAGUE, MARY APLIN.]   An earnest trifler.   Boston:
  Houghton, Osgood, 1880.   249 pp.

STAËL-HOLSTEIN, ANNE LOUISE GERMAINE (NECKER),
  Baronne de.   De l'Allemagne.   Paris: Firmin Didot
  frères, 1850.   592 pp.
    Autograph: Ellen T. Emerson.

_____.   Germany.   Tr. from the French.   New York:
Eastburn, Kirk, 1814.   3 v. in 2.
> Set incomplete: v. 1 wanting.
> Notes.

_____.   Lettres sur les écrits et le caractère de J.-J.
Rousseau.   Éd. rev. et cor.   Paris: Treuttel et
Würtz, 1820.   101 pp.

STALLO, JOHN BERNHARD.   General principles of the
philosophy of nature: with an outline of some of its
recent developments among the Germans, embracing
the philosophical systems of Schelling and Hegel,
and Oken's system of nature.   Boston: W. Crosby
and H. P. Nichols, 1848.   xii, 520 pp.

STANLEY, ARTHUR PENRHYN.   Addresses and sermons,
delivered during a visit to the United States and
Canada in 1878.   New York: Macmillan, 1879.   vii,
255 pp.
> Autograph: Ellen T. Emerson.

STANLEY, THOMAS.   The history of the Chaldaick philosophy.   London: A. and J. Churchill, 1701.   658 pp.
> Inscription and notes in front.

The statesman supplement.   Saturday, October 2, 1858.
[London.]   12 pp.
> Inscribed by Emerson.
> Contents:—Biographical memoir of Thomas Carlyle
> [by Ballantyne].   Note.

STEARNS, CHARLES WOODWARD.   The Shakespeare treasury of wisdom and knowledge.   New York: G. P.
Putnam, 1871.   viii, 436 pp.
> Inscription: 1871.

STEARNS, JONATHAN FRENCH.   Bedford sesqui-centennial
celebration, Aug. 27, 1879.   Historical discourse.
Also, a sketch of the celebration.   Boston: Alfred
Mudge, 1879.   84 pp.
> Inscription.

STEDEFELD, G. FR.   Hamlet, ein Tendenzdrama Shakespeare's gegen die skeptische und kosmopolitische

Weltanschauung des Michael de Montaigne. Mit
einem Anhange über Leben und Lehre Montaigne's
von R. W. Emerson. Frei übersetzt und mit Anmerk-
ungen begleitet. Berlin: Gebrüder Paetel, 1871.
48+ pp.

STEDMAN, EDMUND CLARENCE. Hawthorne, and other
poems. Boston: J. R. Osgood, 1877. viii, 134 pp.

_____. Octavius Brooks Frothingham and the new faith.
New York: G. P. Putnam's Sons, 1876. 50 pp.

_____. Poetical works. Complete ed. Boston: J. R.
Osgood, 1873. xii, 342 pp.

_____. Victorian poets. Boston: J. R. Osgood, 1876.
xxiii, 441 pp.
    Autograph: F. B. Sanborn, 1875.

STEECE, TECUMSEH. A Republican military system.
New York: John A. Gray & Green, 1863. 30 pp.
    Autograph.

STEELE, ANNE. Works. Comprehending poems on subjects chiefly devotional: and miscellaneous pieces in
prose and verse; heretofore published under the title
of Theodosia ... Boston: Munroe, Francis and
Parker, 1808. 2 v.
    Signature: v. 1, Mrs. R. W. Emerson.

STERLING, JOHN. Essays and tales, collected and
edited, with a memoir of his life, by Julius Charles
Hare ... London: John W. Parker, 1848. 2 v.
    Autographs and notes.

_____. Poems. London: Edward Moxon, 1839. xiii,
245 pp.
    Inscription: Gift of John Sterling to Ralph W. Emerson,
    Concord, T. C., London 1840 Jan 1 (in Carlyle's hand).

_____. Strafford, a tragedy. London: E. Moxon, 1843.
224 pp.
    Inscription and notes. Two pictures laid in.

STEWART, DUGALD. Works ... Cambridge, [Mass.]:
Hilliard and Brown, 1829. 7 v.
    Signature and notes.

STEWART, GEORGE, JR.   The story of the great fire in St. John, N. B., June 20th, 1877.   Toronto: Belford Bros., [ᶜ1877].   vii, 273 pp.
Inscription: With compliments of the author.

STICKNEY, ALBERT.   A true republic.   New York: Harper, 1879.   271 pp.
Inscription by the author to R. W. E.

STIRLING, JAMES HUTCHISON.   As regards protoplasm. New and improved ed., completed by addition of Part II., in reference to Mr. Huxley's second issue, and of preface, in reply to Mr. Huxley in "Yeast." London: Longmans, Green, 1872.   76 pp.
Inscription.

——.   Burns in drama, together with Saved leaves; ed. by James Hutchison Stirling.   Edinburgh: Edmonston, 1878.   iv, 250 pp.
Inscription.

——.   Jerrold, Tennyson and Macaulay, with other critical essays.   Edinburgh: Edmonston & Douglas, 1868.   243 pp.
Autograph.

——.   Lectures on the philosophy of law.   Together with Whewell and Hegel, and Hegel and W. R. Smith, a vindication in a physico-mathematical regard. London: Longmans, Green, 1873.   v, 139 pp.
Inscription.

——.   The secret of Hegel: being the Hegelian system in origin, principle, form, and matter.   London: Longman, Green, Longman, Roberts, & Green, 1865. 2 v.
Autographs and notes.

STIRLING=MAXWELL, SIR WILLIAM.   Annals of the artists of Spain.   London: John Ollivier, 1848.   3 v.
Inscription.

STODDARD, CHARLES WARREN.   Poems.   San Francisco: A. Roman, 1867.   123 pp.
Inscription: 28 August 1867.

STODDARD, RICHARD HENRY.   Songs of summer.   Boston:
Ticknor and Fields, 1857.   vii, 229 pp.
  Inscription.

STÖCKHARDT, JULIUS ADOLPH.   The principles of chemistry, illustrated by simple experiments.   Tr. by C. H.
Pierce.   Boston: Phillips, Sampson, 1858.   xix,
681 pp.

STOKES, HENRY SEWELL.   Memories: a life's epilogue.
New ed., with A lament for the Princess Alice.
London: Longmans, Green, 1879.   x, 273 pp.
  Printed inscription.

STONE, THOMAS TREADWELL.   The rod and the staff.
Boston: American Unitarian Association, 1856.   vi,
398 pp.
  Inscription: Return this book to M. M. Emerson.

STORY, WILLIAM WETMORE.   Poems.   Boston: Little,
Brown, 1856.   307 pp.
  Given to the Concord Free Public Library by Ralph
Waldo Emerson in Feb. 1874.   (Cameron, III, 869).

STOWE, HARRIET ELIZABETH (BEECHER).   Dred; a tale of
the great Dismal Swamp.   Boston: Phillips, Sampson, 1865.   2 v.

——— .   A key to Uncle Tom's cabin; presenting the
original facts and documents upon which the story is
founded.   Together with corroborative statements
verifying the truth of the work.   Boston: J. P.
Jewett, 1853.   iv, 262 pp.

——— .   My wife and I; or, Harry Henderson's history.
New York: J. B. Ford, 1872.   viii, 474 pp.

——— .   Sunny memories of foreign lands.   Illus. from
designs by Hammatt Billings.   Boston: Phillips,
Sampson; New York: J. C. Derby, 1854.   lxvii,
326 pp.
  Set incomplete: v. 2 wanting.
  Inscription: M. M. Emerson the gift of Maria Thoreau.
Ms. slip inserted.

——— .   Uncle Tom's cabin; or, Life among the lowly.

Illustrated ed. . . . Original designs by Billings; engraved by Baker and Smith. Boston: J. P. Jewett, Cleveland, O.: Jewett, Proctor, and Worthington, 1853. 2 v. in 1.

STRETTON, HESBA. The fishers of Derby Haven. London: Religious Tract Society, [18—?]. 208 pp.
Autograph: Ellen T. Emerson.

STUART, HECTOR A. Nat Zoan, a romance of Borneo. "Caliban" . . . San Francisco: Wm. P. Harrison, 1876. 103 pp.
Inscription: Sept 1876. Author's corrections.

SUE, EUGÈNE. The wandering Jew. Complete edition in one volume. London, New York: George Routledge, [1867?]. 3 pts. in 1 v.

Suggestive aids. [n.p., 18—?] 1 l.
Broadside.
Bound with: Lane, Charles. A classification of science and arts. London, 1826.

SULLIVAN, WILLIAM. The moral class book; or, The law of morals; derived from the created universe, and from revealed religion. Intended for schools . . . Boston: Richardson, Lord & Holbrook, 1831. x, 282 pp.

Summer points from Middlebury. [Middlebury?, Vt., 1874?] 7 pp.

SUMNER, CHARLES. Validity and necessity of fundamental conditions on states. Speech in the Senate of the United States, June 10, 1868. Washington, 1868. 8 pp.

———. Works. Boston: Lee and Shepard, 1870–77. 12 v.
Inscription on flyleaf: Subscriber's copy. Charles Sumner.

SUPLÉE, THOMAS DANLY. The life of Theodorick Bland Pryor, first mathematical-fellow of Princeton College. San Francisco: Bacon, 1879. 199 pp.
Inscription. Letter from author inserted at front.

SUTTON, HENRY.   The evangel of love.   London: C. A.
Bartlett, 1847.   230 pp.

SWEDENBORG, EMANUEL.   Angelic wisdom concerning the
divine love and the divine wisdom.   Tr. from the
Latin.   Originally published at Amsterdam
MDCCLXIII.   Boston: Otis Clapp; New York: John
Allen; Cincinnati: J. F. Desilver, 1847.   viii,
256 pp.
> Autograph and notes.

———— .   The animal kingdom, considered anatomically,
physically, and philosophically.   Tr. from the Latin,
by James John Garth Wilkinson ...   London: W.
Newbery; Boston: Otis Clapp, 1843–44.   2 v.
> Autographs and note.

———— .   The Apocalypse revealed; wherein are disclosed
the arcana there foretold, which have hitherto re-
mained concealed.   From the Latin.   A new ed. rev.
and cor.   Boston: Otis Clapp, 1836.   3 v.
> Autograph: v. 3, Lydian Emerson, in R. W. E.'s hand,
> and his notes. Inscription: v. 1, To Mrs. R. W. E. from
> S. Searle.

———— .   The delights of wisdom concerning conjugial
love: after which follow the pleasures of insanity
concerning scortatory love.   Originally published in
Latin, at Amsterdam, MDCCLXVII.   Boston: T. Harrington Carter, and Otis Clapp, 1843.   438 pp.
> Clippings laid in. Notes.

———— .   The doctrine of life for the New Jerusalem, from
the Commandments of the Decalogue tr. from the
Latin from the 6th London ed.   Boston: Allen and
Goddard, 1831.   54 pp.

———— .   ———— .   Another issue.   1836.

———— .   The doctrine of the New Jerusalem concerning
the Lord.   Stereotype ed.   Boston: Otis Clapp,
1833.   iv, 94 pp.

———— .   The economy of the animal kingdom, considered
anatomically, physically, and philosophically.   Tr.

from the Latin by Augustus Clissold ... London:
W. Newbery; Boston: O. Clapp, 1845–46. 2 v.
> Inscription: R. W. Emerson, gift of the London Sweden-
> borg Association (in Emerson's hand). Notes.

——— . The memorabilia; or, Memorable relations of the
things seen and heard in heaven and hell. With an
introduction by George Bush. New York: John
Allen; Boston: Otis Clapp, 1846. 64 pp.

——— . Oeconomia regni animalis, in transactiones
divisa, quarum haec tertia de fibra, de tunica arach-
noidea, et de morbis fibrarum agit, anatomice, phy-
sice, et philosophice perlustrata. Ex autographo
ejus in Bibliotheca Academiae Regiae Holmiensis
asservato nunc primum edidit Jac. Joh. Garth Wilkinson ... Londini: W. Newbery, 1847. xii, 262 pp.
> Inscription: 30 Aug. 1837.

——— . Of the New Jerusalem, and its heavenly doctrine, as revealed from heaven; to which are prefixed
some observations concerning the new heaven and
new earth. Tr. from the Latin. Originally published in the year 1758 ... 4th American ed., from
the 5th London ed. Boston: Otis Clapp, 1835.
72 pp.

——— . On the intercourse between the soul and the
body, which is supposed to take place either by
physical influx, or by spiritual influx, or by pre-
established harmony. From the Latin. Boston:
Adonis Harvard, 1828. iv, 56 pp.
> Autograph.

——— . Ontology. From a photolithographic copy of the
original Latin manuscript still preserved in the Library of the Academy of Sciences at Stockholm. Tr.
by Philip B. Cahell ... Philadelphia: J. B. Lippincott, 1880. 40 pp.

——— . Opuscula quaedam argumenti philosophici. Ex
autographo ejus in Bibliotheca Academiae Regiae

Holmiensis asservato nunc primum edidit Jac. Joh.
Garth Wilkinson ...   Londini: W. Newbery, 1846.
x, 126 pp.
> Inscription.

————— .   The principia; or, The first principles of
natural things, being new attempts toward a philosophical explanation of the elementary world.   Tr.
from the Latin by Augustus Clissold ...   London:
W. Newbery; Boston: O. Clapp, 1845–46.   2 v.
> Autograph.   Inscription: R. W. Emerson, gift of the
> London Swedenborg Association (in Emerson's hand).
> Notes.

————— .   A treatise concerning heaven and its wonders,
and also concerning hell; being a notation of things
heard and seen.   From the Latin, originally published at London, 1758.   A new translation.   London: Thomas Goyder, 1823.   xxxii, 452 pp.
> Notes.

————— .   The true Christian religion, containing the universal theology of the new church, foretold by the
Lord in Daniel VII. 13, 14; and in Revelation XXI.
1, 2.   A new translation from the original Latin ed.,
printed at Amsterdam, in the year 1771.   Boston:
T. Harrington Carter, and Otis Clapp, 1843.   xvi,
576 pp.
> Autograph.

SWEETSER, MOSES FOSTER.   The White Mountains: a
handbook for travellers ...   Boston: James R. Osgood, 1876.   xiv, 436 pp.   illus., 6 maps.
> Inscription: 6 June 1876.   Letter inserted.

SWETT, SAMUEL.   History of Bunker Hill battle.   2d ed.
Much enl. with new information derived from the sur-
viving soldiers present at the celebration on the 17th
June last, and notes.   Boston: Munroe and Francis,
1826.   58 pp.   plan.
> Bound with: Everett, Edward.   Speech ... March 9,
> 1826.   Washington, 1826.

SYMINGTON, ANDREW JAMES. Harebell Chimes; or, Summer memories and musings. London: Houlston & Stoneman; Edinburgh: Wm. Blackwood, 1849. xv, 256 pp.
    Inscription: Dec. 1848.

_____ . The reasonableness of faith, with an appendix containing hymns and verses of consolation and hope. London: Houlston, 1870. 112 pp.
    Inscription.

SYNCRETIC ASSOCIATION. Prospectus of the Syncratic Association, Suffolk Street Gallery. London: William Stevens, Printer, [18—?]. 4 pp.
    Bound with: Lane, Charles. A classification of science and arts. London, 1826.

T

TACITUS, CORNELIUS. Opera ex recensione Io. Augusti
Ernesti denuo curavit J. J. Ohenlinus cum notis
selectis ... Bostoniae: Wells et Lilly, 1817. 3 v.
Set incomplete: v. 2 wanting.

——— . Works. With an essay on his life and genius,
notes, supplements, etc., by Arthur Murphy ... New
ed., with the author's last corrections. London:
Jones, 1831. xviii, 742 pp.
Inscription: C. C. Emerson.

TAINE, HIPPOLYTE ADOLPHE. Essais de critique et
d'histoire. Paris: L. Hachette, 1858. xv, 412 pp.
Autograph.

——— . Histoire de la littérature anglaise. 2. éd. rev.
et aug. Paris: L. Hachette, 1866–69. 5 v.
Inscription, v. 1.

TANNAHILL, ROBERT. Poetical works. With a sketch
of his life. New ed. rev. and cor. Glasgow: Purvis
and Aitken, 1825. xi, 142 pp.

TANNER, HENRY SCHENCK. A new universal atlas containing maps of the various empires, kingdoms,
states and republics of the world. With a special
map of each of the United States, plans of cities &c.
Comprehended in seventy sheets and forming a series of one hundred and seventeen maps, plans and
sections. Philadelphia: Carey & Hart, 1845. 71 ll.
col. maps.

TARBELL, JOHN ADAMS. Homoeopathy simplified; or, Domestic practice made easy. Containing explicit directions for the treatment of disease, the management of accidents, and the preservation of health. 2d ed. Boston: Sanborn, Carter, and Bazin, 1856. 360 pp.

TASSO, TORQUATO. Aminta. Alceo. Egle. Favole teatrali del secolo XVI. [v. 4.] Venezia: Antonio Zotta e Figli, 1784. 304 pp.
Autograph and note, Oct. 1822.

_____. La Gerusalemme liberata, e l'Aminta. Ed. stereotipa. Parigi: Firmino Didot, 1819. 2 v.
Autographs and notes.

TAYLOR, BAYARD. Home pastorals, ballads and lyrics. Boston: J. R. Osgood, 1875. viii, 214 pp.

_____. The masque of the gods. Boston: James R. Osgood, 1872. 47 pp.

_____. The national ode, the memorial freedom poem. Boston: W. F. Gill, 1877. 74 pp.

_____. The picture of St. John. Boston: Ticknor and Fields, 1866. vi, 220 pp.

_____. The prophet, a tragedy. Boston: J. R. Osgood, 1874. 300 pp.
Inscription ms. slip tipped in: From the author.

TAYLOR, EDWARD. Jacob Behmen's Theosophick philosophy unfolded ... With a short account of the life of Jacob Behmen. London: Tho. Salusbury, 1691. 434 pp.
Autograph.

TAYLOR, EMILY, *ed*. Sabbath recreations; or, Select poetry of a religious kind, chiefly taken from the works of modern poets; with original pieces never before published. 1st American ed.; in which many pieces have been withdrawn from the English copy, and others substituted, by John Pierpont. Boston: Bowles & Dearborn, 1829. x, 278 pp.
Autograph and notes, including notes of Ellen L. Tucker.

TAYLOR, SIR HENRY. Philip van Artevelde; a dramatic romance, in two parts. Cambridge: J. Munroe, 1835. 2 v.

———. A Sicilian summer, St. Clement's eve, The eve of the conquest, and other poems. New ed. London: Chapman & Hall, 1868. xii, 263 pp.
Inscription: 23 April 1873.

TAYLOR, JANE. Essays in rhyme on morals and manners. Boston: Wells and Lilly, 1816. 183 pp.

———. Hymns for infant minds. New York: American Tract Society, [18-?]. 104 pp.

———. ———. Copy 2.

———. Memoirs, correspondence and poetical remains. New ed. Boston: Perkins & Marvin, 1832. xii, 346 pp.
Autograph: L. J. Emerson.

TAYLOR, JEREMY. The rule and exercise of holy dying ... London: R. Baynes; Glasgow: Richard Griffin, 1820. xvi, 296 pp.
Signature: R. W. Emerson, 1824.

TAYLOR, THOMAS. A dissertation on the philosophy of Aristotle, in four books. London: The author, 1812. 577 pp.
Given to the Concord Free Public Library by Ralph Waldo Emerson in Aug. 1873 (Cameron, III, 869).

TEBBETS, THEODORE. A memoir of William Gibbons. New York: Printed for His Friends, [1862]. 129 pp.
Inscription: To Mrs. R. W. E. from A. H. Gibbons.

TEETGEN, ALEXANDER. Fruit from Devon: (Lyrical vignettes of the North Coast); and other poems, with an appendix and résumé. London: Williams and Norgate, 1870. viii, 245 pp.
Inscription inserted at front.

———. Palingenesia; or, The modern apostate. London: Williams & Norgate, 1868. vi, 122 pp.
Inscription.

TENNYSON, ALFRED TENNYSON, *1st Baron.*   Enoch Arden,
&c.   Boston: Ticknor and Fields, 1864.   204 pp.
  Autograph.   Inscription: With publisher's regards, July
1864.

_____ .   Idyls of the King.   Boston: Ticknor and Fields,
1859.   227 pp.
  Autograph and notes.

_____ .   In memoriam.   Boston: Ticknor, Reed, and
Fields, 1850.   216 pp.
  Autograph.

_____ .   Maud, and other poems.   Boston: Ticknor and
Fields, 1855.   160 pp.
  Autograph.

_____ .   Poems.   Boston: William D. Ticknor, 1842.
2 v.
  Inscription: v. 1, R. W. Emerson from C. S. Wheeler (in
R. W. E.'s hand).   Signature: v. 2, R. W. E.

_____ .   Poems, chiefly lyrical.   London: Effingham
Wilson, 1830.   154 pp.
  Signatures: R. W. E., signed twice.

_____ .   Poetical works.   Boston: Ticknor and Fields,
1866.   2 v. in 1.
  Autograph and notes.

_____ .   Queen Mary; a drama.   Author's ed., from ad-
vance sheets.   Boston: J. R. Osgood, 1875.   284
pp.
  Inscription: From Mrs. Osgood, June 1875.

[TERENTIUS.]   Afri comoediae.   Ad editationem R.
Bentleii diligentissime expressae.   Ed. stereotypa.
Lipsiae: Car. Tovchnitii, 1819.   xxvii, 270 pp.

TERESA, SAINT.   Life of St. Teresa, written by herself.
Tr. from the Spanish by John Dalton.   1st American
ed.   Philadelphia: Peter F. Cunningham, 1867.   xii,
431 pp.
  Inscription: Ellen T. Emerson from Col. Greene, Nov. 14,
1867 (in Ellen's hand) and notes.

TESCHEMACHER, JAMES ENGLEBERT. A concise application of the principles of structural botany to horticulture, chiefly extracted from the works of Lindley, Knight, Herbert, and others, with additions and adaptations to this climate. Boston: Charles C. Little and James Brown, 1840. v, 90 pp.

THACHER, JAMES. History of the Town of Plymouth, from its first settlement in 1620, to the present time: with a concise history of the aborigines of New England, and their wars with the English, &c. Boston: Marsh, Capen & Lyon, 1835. iv, 401 pp.

THACKERAY, WILLIAM MAKEPEACE. Doctor Birch and his young friends. New York: D. Appleton, 1857. 49 pp.
> Book plate of Georgius Dexter.

———. The history of Pendennis ... With illustrations on wood by the author. New York: Harper, 1850. 2 v.
> Signature: R. W. Emerson.

There is a charm in the very name of Love Spirit, which in a certain measure softens the opposition it cannot disarm ... [n.p., 18—?] [8] pp.
> Bound with: Lane, Charles. A classification of science and arts. London, 1826.

Think. Think deeply ... [n.p., 18—?] 1 l.
> Broadside.
> Bound with: Lane, Charles. A classification of science and arts. London, 1826.

———. ———. Copy 2.

———. ———. Copy 3.

THOMAS, JOSEPH. Universal pronouncing dictionary of biography and mythology. Philadelphia: J. B. Lippincott, 1870. 2 v.

THOMAS À KEMPIS. On the imitation of Christ in three books; with the book of the sacraments. Tr. from the Latin by John Payne. 4th ed. London: James Phillips, 1797. xxxix, 334 pp.

THOMAS, GEORGE.   The discovery of a new world of being.   London: Longman, Green, 1871.   271 pp.
    Inscription: 19 Jan. 1874.

THOMSON, JAMES.   The seasons.   In four books with
Britannia.   To which are added the following pieces;
I. Ode on St. Cecilia's day, by Mr. Pope.   II. Alexander's feast; or, The power of musick, by Mr. Dryden.   III. Ode on solitude, by Mr. Pope.   IV. The
dying Christian to his soul, an ode, by the same.
V. The universal prayer, by the same.   VI. Elegy,
to the memory of an unfortunate lady, by the same.
VII. Veni creator spiritus, translated in paraphase,
by Mr. Dryden.   To which is prefixed, the Life
and literary character of Mr. Thomson.   Illustrated
with a new set of designs.   Dublin: W. Smith, 1773.
vii, 214 pp.
    Signature: R. W. E.

_____ .   The seasons; with The Castle of indolence.
New York: W. B. Gilley, 1819.   287 pp.
    Autograph: Ellen LeR. Tucker (?).

_____ .   _____ .   Chiswick: C. Whittingham, 1822.
158 pp.
    C. C. Emerson's copy.

THOREAU, HENRY DAVID.   Early spring in Massachusetts.
From the Journal of Henry D. Thoreau ...   Boston:
Houghton, Mifflin, 1881.   vii, 318 pp.
    Inscription slip inserted: Feb 24, '81—R. W. E. from
    Blake.

_____ .   Essays and other writings, ed., with a prefatory
note, by Will H. Dircks.   London: Walter Scott,
[18—?].   xv, 271 pp.

_____ .   Letters to various persons.   Boston: Ticknor
and Fields, 1865.   229 pp.
    Signature: R. W. Emerson.

_____ .   _____ .   Copy 2.
    Notes by Emerson.

——. Walden; or, Life in the woods. Boston: Ticknor and Fields, 1854. 357 pp.
Inscription: Lydian Emerson from her friend Henry Thoreau. Picture laid in: Thoreau's Cove, Walden Pond.

——. A week on the Concord and Merrimack rivers. Boston: James Munroe, 1849. 413 pp.

——. ——. Copy 2.
Inscription to Mrs. Emerson, and notes by R. W. Emerson.

——. ——. 10th ed. Boston: Houghton, Mifflin, [ᶜ1867]. 415 pp.

——. A Yankee in Canada, with Anti-slavery and reform papers. Boston: Ticknor and Fields, 1866. 286 pp.
Inscription.

THORNTON, JOHN WINGATE. The historical relation of New England to the English commonwealth. Boston: A. Mudge, 1874. 105 pp.
Inscription: March 1875.

THORNTON, ROBERT JOHN. A grammar of botany; containing an explanation of the system of Linnaeus, and the terms of botany, with botanical exercises, for the use of schools and students ... New York: J. Eastburn, 1818. iv, 317 pp.
Autograph: L. Emerson.

THORPE, BENJAMIN. Northern mythology, comprising the principal popular traditions and superstitions of Scandinavia, North Germany, and the Netherlands. Compiled from original and other sources. London: Edward Lumley, 1851-52. 3 v.
Set incomplete: v. 1 wanting.

THUCYDIDES. History of the Peloponnesian War. Tr. from the Greek of Thucydides. A new ed., cor. and rev. New York: Harper, 1836. 2 v.
Autograph and notes.

TIARKS, JOHANN GERHARD. A practical grammar of the German language and exercises. [Leipzig: B. G. Teubner, 18—?]. viii, 357 pp.

Autographs: Ellen T. Emerson, Oct. 10, 1855, Edith Emerson, Dec. 7, 1857.

TIBBLES, THOMAS HENRY. The Ponca chiefs. An Indian's attempt to appeal from the tomahawk to the courts. A full history of the robbery of the Ponca tribe of Indians, with all the papers filed and evidence taken in the Standing Bear habeas corpus case, and full text of Judge Dundy's celebrated decision. With some suggestions towards a solution of the Indian question, by Zylyff [pseud.] With an introduction by Inshtatheamba (Bright Eyes), and dedication by Wendell Phillips. 2d ed. Boston: Lockwood, Brooks, 1880. viii, 146 pp.

TICKNOR, GEORGE. Life, letters, and journals. Boston: J. R. Osgood, 1876. 2 v.
Autographs and notes.

_____ . Outlines of the principal events in the life of General Lafayette. From the North American review. Boston: Cummings, Hilliard, 1825. 64 pp.
Ms. note on t.p.: By Professor Ticknor.
Autograph.
Bound with: Everett, Edward. An oration delivered at Plymouth, December 22, 1824. Boston, 1825.

_____ . _____ . Copy 2.
Bound with: Webster, Daniel. A discourse, delivered at Plymouth, December 22, 1820. Boston, 1826.

[TILESTON, MARY WILDER (FOOTE)], *comp.* Sunshine in the soul; poems selected by the editor of "Quiet hours." Boston: Roberts Bros., 1877. 127 pp.
Inscription: Ellen T. Emerson from Alicia, 1877.

_____ . Sursum corda. Boston: Roberts Bros., 1877. vi, 316 pp.

TOLMAN, HARRIET SMITH. James Tolman. Boston: Rand, Avery & Frye, 1869. 88 pp.

TORONTO. UNIVERSITY. UNIVERSITY COLLEGE. Annual convocation, 1862. Toronto: Henry Rowsell, 1862. 10 ll.

TOUSSENEL, ALPHONSE.   Passional zoology; or, Spirit of
the beasts of France.   Tr. by M. Edgeworth Lazarus.   New York: Fowler and Wells, 1852.   v,
356 pp.
  Autographs.

Tributes to William Lloyd Garrison, at the funeral services, May 28, 1879.   Boston: Houghton, Osgood,
1879.   v, 56 pp.

TROWBRIDGE, JOHN TOWNSEND.   The emigrant's story,
and other poems.   Boston: J. R. Osgood, 1875.   vi,
170 pp.
  Inscription.

————.   The vagabonds, and other poems.   Boston:
Fields, Osgood, 1869.   iv, 172 pp.

TRUMBULL, HENRY CLAY.   The knightly soldier: a biography of Henry Ward Camp, Tenth Conn.   Boston:
Nichols and Noyes; New York: O. S. Felt, 1865.
.xii, 331 pp.

TRYON, THOMAS.   A treatise of dreams & visions,
wherein the causes, natures and uses of nocturnal
representations, and the communications both of good
and evil angels, as also departed souls to mankind,
are theosophically unfolded; that is, according to the
word of God, and the harmony of created beings ...
To which is added, A discourse of the causes, natures and cure of phrensie, madness or distraction.
2d ed.   London: T. Sowle, 1695.   299 pp.

TUCKERMAN, FREDERICK GODDARD.   Poems.   London:
Smith, Elder, 1863.   iv, 235 pp.

TUCKERMAN, HENRY THEODORE.   A memorial of Horatio
Greenough, consisting of a memoir, selections from
his writing, and tributes to his genius.   New York:
G. P. Putnam, 1853.   vi, 245 pp.
  Autograph and notes.

TULLOCH, JOHN.   Rational theology and christian philosophy in England in the seventeenth century.   2d
ed.   Edinburgh: William Blackwood, 1874.   2 v.
  Inscription: v. 1, From the author.

TURNER, EDWARD. Elements of chemistry, including the
recent discoveries and doctrines of the science. 4th
American, from the 3d London ed. With notes and
emendations, by Franklin Bache. Philadelphia:
Grigg & Elliot, 1833. xiii, 622 pp.
  Signature: R. W. Emerson.

TURNER, SHARON. The sacred history of the world, as
displayed in the creation and subsequent events to
the deluge. Attempted to be philosophically considered, in a series of letters to a son. Stereotype ed.
New York; J. & J. Harper, 1832-38. 3 v.
  Set incomplete: v. 2-3 wanting.
  Autograph: Lydia Jackson.

TUTHILL, LOUISA CAROLINE (HIGGINS). Onward! Right
onward! 8th ed. Boston: Wm. Crosby and H. P.
Nichols, 1849. iv, 169 pp.
  Inscription: Ellen Emerson, from her teacher, A. M.
Whiting.

TYNDALL, JOHN. Address delivered before the British
Association assembled at Belfast, with additions.
London: Longmans, Green, 1874. viii, 65 pp.
  Printed presentation slip from author, inserted.

_____. The glaciers of the Alps. Being a narrative of
excursions and ascents, an account of the origin and
phenomena of glaciers, and an exposition of the
physical principles to which they are related.
Boston: Ticknor and Fields, 1861. xx, 446 pp.
  Note.

[_____.] Science and man. Presidential address, delivered before the Birmingham and Midland Institute,
October 1st, 1877, with additions. [Birmingham?,
1878?] 25 pp.
  Inscription.

U

UNIAKE, CROFTON. A letter to the Lord Chancellor, on the necessity and practicability of forming a code of the laws of England: to which is annexed the new bankrupt law. Boston: Hilliard, Gray, Little, and Wilkins, 1827. 52 pp.

The Unitarian advocate and religious miscellany conducted by an association of gentlemen. New ser. v. 1-4, Jan. 1830—Dec. 1831. Boston: Leonard C. Bowles, 4 v. in 2.

Unitarian affirmations: seven discourses given in Washington, D. C., by Unitarian ministers. Boston: American Unitarian Association, 1879. 175 pp.
    Signature: Lydian Emerson.

———. ———. Copy 2.

U. S. BUREAU OF EDUCATION. Public libraries in the United States of America, their history, condition, and management; special report, Dept. of the Interior, Bureau of Education. Part I. Washington: Govt. Print. Off., 1876. xxxv, 1178 pp.

———. Report of the Commissioner of Education made to the Secretary of the interior for the year 1870, with accompanying papers. Washington: Govt. Print. Off., 1870. 579 pp.

———. Special report of the Commissioner of Education on the condition and improvement of public schools

in the District of Columbia, submitted to the Senate,
June, 1868, and to the House, with additions,
June 13, 1870.   Washington: Govt. Print. Off., 1871.
912 pp.

U. S. BUREAU OF STATISTICS.   Special report on immigration; accompanying information for immigrants relative
to the prices and rentals of land, the staple products,
facilities of access to market, cost of farm stock,
kind of labor in demand in the western and southern
states, etc., etc.   To which are appended tables
showing the average weekly wages paid in the several
states and sections for factory, mechanical, and farm
labor; the cost of provisions, groceries, dry goods,
and house rent in the various manufacturing districts
of the country, in the year 1869-'70.   By Edward
Young, Chief of the Bureau.   Washington: Govt.
Print. Off., 1872.   xxvii, 232 pp.

U. S. BUREAU OF TOPOGRAPHICAL ENGINEERS.   Map of the
state of Florida comp. from the most recent authorities, and prepared by order of Jeff. Davis, Secretary
of War, in conformity with a resolution of the Senate
of the 11th of Feby. 1856, calling for "a general map
of the Peninsula of Florida, illustrative of the recent
surveys for a canal, executed by virtue of the appro-
priations made for that purpose."   Washington,
D. C.: C. B. Graham, 1856.   map.

U. S. CENSUS OFFICE.   *7th census, 1850.*   The seventh
census of the United States: 1850.   Embracing a
statistical view of each of the states and territories,
arranged by counties, towns, etc. . . . and an appendix
embracing notes upon the tables of each of the states,
etc. . . .   J. D. B. De Bow, Superintendent of the
United States Census.   Washington: R. Armstrong,
Public Printer, 1853.   cxxxvi, 1022 pp.

_____ .   *8th census, 1860.*   Manufacturers of the United
States in 1860; comp. from the original returns of the

eighth Census, under the direction of the Secretary of the Interior. Washington: Govt. Print. Off., 1865. ccxvii, 745 pp.

——— . Population of the United States in 1860; comp. from the original returns of the eighth Census, under the direction of the Secretary of the Interior, by Joseph C. G. Kennedy, Superintendent of Census. Washington: Govt. Print. Off., 1864. cvii, 694 pp.

——— . *9th census, 1870.* A compendium of the ninth Census, (June 1, 1870), comp. pursuant to a concurrent resolution of Congress, and under the direction of the Secretary of the Interior, by Francis A. Walker, Superintendent of Census. Washington: Govt. Print. Off., 1872. vii, 942 pp.

——— . ——— . Copy 2.
Given to Concord Free Public Library by Ralph Waldo Emerson in June 1873 (Cameron, III, 869).

——— . Ninth census. vol. I–[III] ... Comp. from the original returns of the ninth Census, (June 1, 1870) under the direction of the Secretary of the Interior, by Francis A. Walker, Superintendent of Census. Washington: Govt. Print. Off., 1872. 3 v. maps.

——— . ——— . Copy 2.
Given to the Concord Free Public Library by Ralph Waldo Emerson in June 1873 (Cameron, III, 869).

——— . Ninth census of the United States. Statistics of population. Tables I to VIII, inclusive ... Washington: Govt. Print. Off., 1872. 391 pp.

U. S. COAST AND GEODETIC SURVEY. Map of Central America comp. from materials furnished by the Committee on Foreign Relations of the Senate of the U. S. Executed at the Office of the U. S. Coast Survey, A. D. Bache, Sup[dt], under special direction of W. R. Palmer, U. S. Top[l]. Eng[ns]. Assist. in charge ad. in. March 1856. N. Y.: Lith. by J. Bien, L. D. Williams, 1856. map.

_____ . Report of the Superintendent of the Coast Survey, showing the progress of the survey during the
year 1861.   Washington: Govt. Print. Off., 1862.
vii, 270 pp.

U. S. CONGRESS.   The Congressional globe: containing
the debates and proceedings of the second session
of the thirty-seventh Congress, by John C. Rives.
[Pt. 1, 3–4.]   Washington: Congressional Globe Office, 1862.   3 v.
  Notes, pt. 3.   Signature: pt. 4, R. W. Emerson.

_____ . The Congressional globe: containing the debates
and proceedings of the second session of the thirty-
eighth Congress: also of the special session of the
Senate, by F. and J. Rives.   Washington: Congressional Globe Office, 1865.   li, 816 pp.

_____ . The Congressional globe: containing the debates
and proceedings of the first session fortieth congress,
by F. & J. Rives and George A. Bailey.   Washington:
Congressional Globe Office, 1867.   cxxii, 851,
51 pp.

_____ . The Congressional Globe ...   42d Congress,
with index.   Pts. 1, 3–6.   Washington, 1872.   5 v.
  Presented to the Concord Free Public Library by Ralph
Waldo Emerson in June 1873.   Withdrawn from circulation,
1933 (Cameron, III, 869).

_____ . Memorial addresses on the life and character of
Charles Sumner, (a Senator of Massachusetts), delivered in the Senate and House of Representatives,
forty-third Congress, first session, April 27, 1874,
with other congressional tributes of respect.   Published by order of Congress.   Washington: Govt.
Print. Off., 1874.   112 pp.

_____ . HOUSE.   Discussion of the Greek question, in
the House of Representatives by Mr. Webster,
Mr. Poinsett, Mr. Randolph, Mr. Cary, Mr. Wood,
Mr. Bartlett, Mr. Clay and Mr. Fuller.   [Boston:
Howard Gazette, 1824?]   48 pp.

Bound with: Webster, Daniel. A discourse delivered at Plymouth, December 22, 1820. Boston, 1821.

——— . JOINT SELECT COMMITTEE ON CONDITION OF AFFAIRS IN THE LATE INSURRECTIONARY STATES. Report of the joint select committee to inquire into the condition of affairs in the late insurrectionary states. Made to the two Houses of Congress, February 19, 1872. Washington: Govt. Print. Off., 1872. 632 pp.

——— . JOINT SELECT COMMITTEE ON RETRENCHMENT. The civil service. Report of Mr. Jenckes, of Rhode Island, made to the House of Representatives of the United States, May 14, 1868. Washington: Govt. Print. Off., 1868. vii, 219 pp.

——— . SENATE. Report of the Select Committee of the Senate of the United States on the sickness and mortality on board emigrant ships, August 2, 1854. Washington: Beverley Tucker, 1854. 147 pp.

U. S. DEPT. OF AGRICULTURE. Report of the Commissioner of Agriculture for the year 1863, 1868, 1871. Washington: Govt. Print. Off. 3 v.

——— . ——— . Copy 2. 1871.

——— . Report of the Commissioner of Agriculture on the diseases of cattle in the United States. Washington: Govt. Print. Off., 1871. 205 pp.

U. S. DEPT. OF STATE. Case of the Black Warrior, and other violations of the rights of American citizens by Spanish authorities. Washington: Beverley Tucker, 1854. 380 pp.

——— . Papers relating to foreign affairs accompanying the annual message of the President to the first session of the thirty-eighth Congress. Pt. I. Washington: Govt. Print. Off., 1864. xxxi, 688 pp.

——— . Papers relating to the foreign relations of the United States, transmitted to Congress with the annual message of the President, December 2, 1872. Pt. II. Washington: Govt. Print. Off., 1872. 5 v.

U. S. DEPARTMENT OF THE INTERIOR. Report of the
Secretary of the Interior. [1863.] Washington:
Govt. Print. Off. xxi, 739 pp.
Notes in R. W. E.'s hand.

U. S. ENGINEER DEPT. Report of an expedition down the
Zuni and Colorado rivers, by L. Sitgreaves, Corps
Topographical Engineers. Washington: Robert Arm-
strong, 1853. 198 pp.

———. Report on the exploration of the Yellowstone
River, by W. F. Raynolds. Communicated by the
Secretary of War, in compliance with a resolution
of Senate, February 13, 1866. Washington: Govt.
Print. Off., 1868. 174 pp.

———. Report upon the Colorado River of the West ex-
plored in 1857 and 1858 by Joseph C. Ives ... under
the direction of the Office of Explorations and Surveys, A. A. Humphreys, Captain, Topographical
Engineers, in charge. By order of the Secretary of
War. Washington: Govt. Print. Off., 1861. 1 v.
(various pagings).

U. S. GENERAL LAND OFFICE. Report on the geology of
the Lake Superior land district, by J. W. Foster and
J. D. Whitney ... Pt. II. The iron region together
with the general geology ... Washington: A. Boyd
Hamilton, 1851. xvi, 406 pp. and 3 maps.

U. S. GEOLOGICAL AND GEOGRAPHICAL SURVEY OF THE
TERRITORIES. Report of the United States Geologi-
cal and Geographical Survey of the Territories, by F.
V. Hayden, United States Geologist. 5th, 6th,
[1871], 1872. Washington: Govt. Print. Off. 2 v.
Vol. for 1871 presented to the Concord Free Public
Library by Ralph Waldo Emerson in June 1873. Withdrawn
from circulation, 1906 (Cameron, III, 869).

U. S. LAWS, STATUTES, ETC. Acts and resolutions of the
United States of America passed at the second session of the forty-second Congress, December 4,

1871—June 10, 1872.   Washington: Govt. Print.
Off., 1872.   531 pp.

U. S. MILITARY COMMISSION TO EUROPE, 1855-1856.
Military Commission to Europe, in 1855 and 1856.
Report of Alfred Mordecai, of the Ordnance Department.   Washington: G. W. Bowman, Printer, 1860.
vii, 232 pp.

U. S. NAVAL ASTRONOMICAL EXPEDITION, 1849-1852.
The U.S. Naval Astronomical expedition to the
southern hemisphere, during the years 1849-'50-
'51-'52.   J. M. Gilliss, Superintendent ...
Vol. II.   Washington: A. O. P. Nicholson, 1855.
ix, 300 pp.

U.S. NAVY DEPT.   Message of the President of the
United States, transmitting a report of the Secretary
of the Navy ... relative to the naval expedition to
Japan.   [Washington.], 1855.   195 pp.
Autograph.

———.   Report and charts of the cruise of the U. S. Brig
Dolphin, made under direction of the Navy Dept., by
S. P. Lee, United States Navy.   Washington: B.
Tucker, 1854.   vii, 331 pp.

———.   Report of the Secretary of the Navy, with an
appendix, containing bureau reports, etc.   December,
1867.   Washington: Govt. Print. Off., 1867.   vii,
311 pp.

U. S. PATENT OFFICE.   Report of the Commissioner of
Patents for the year 1854.   Arts and manufacturers.
Vol. I.   Text.   Washington: Beverley Tucker, 1855.
viii, 776 pp.

U. S. PRESIDENT.   *1853-1857 (Pierce)*.   Message from
the President of the United States to the two Houses
of Congress at the commencement of the second session of the thirty-third Congress ...   Pt. I.   Washington: Beverley Tucker, 1854.   629 pp.

_____ . Message from the President of the United States to the two Houses of Congress, at the commencement of the second session of the thirty third Congress. December 4, 1854 ... Pt. II. Washington: Govt. Print. Off., 1854. 712 pp.

_____ . *1861-1865 (Lincoln).* Message of the President of the United States and accompanying documents, to the two Houses of Congress, at the commencement of the first session of the thirty-eighth Congress. Washington: Govt. Print. Off., 1864. 222 pp.

_____ . *1865-1869 (Johnson).* Message of the President of the United States and accompanying documents, to the two Houses of Congress at the commencement of the second session of the fortieth Congress. Washington: Govt. Print. Off., 1867-68. 7v.

_____ . Message of the President of the United States, with accompanying documents, to the two Houses of Congress, at the commencement of the third session of the fortieth Congress. Pt. II. [Papers relating to foreign affairs.] Washington: Govt. Print. Off., 1869. xxx, 1080 pp.

_____ . *1869-1877 (Grant).* Message of the President of the United States and accompanying documents to the two Houses of Congress at the commencement of the third session of the forty-first Congress. Washington: Govt. Print. Off., 1870. 538 pp.

_____ . Message from the President of the United States to the two Houses of Congress at the commencement of the second session of the forty-second Congress, with the reports of the heads of departments and selections from accompanying documents. Ed. by Ben. Perley Poore, Clerk of Printing Records. Washington: Govt. Print. Off., 1872. 2 v.

_____ . Message from the President of the United States to the two Houses of Congress at the commencement

of the third session of the forty-second Congress,
with the reports of the heads of departments and selections from accompanying documents.   Ed. by Ben
Perley Poore, Clerk of Printing Records.   Washington: Govt. Print. Off., 1872.   772 pp.

_____ .   *1877-1881 (Hayes).*   Vetoes by the President
of the United States of the army bill, act to prohibit
military interference at elections and legislative appropriation bill.   Army bill, vetoed April 29, 1879.
Act to prohibit military interference at elections,
vetoed.   Legislative appropriation bill vetoed.
Washington, [1879].   16 pp.

U. S. WAR DEPT.   Exploration of the Red River of
Louisiana in the year 1852, by Randolph B. Marcy ...
assisted by George B. McClellan ...   With reports
on the natural history of the country.   Washington:
R. Armstrong, 1853.   xv, 320 pp. and 2 maps (portfolio).

_____ .   [Map of Gulf of California.   Plans named on
coast line West-East: Cabo de Lobas, Punta Robinson, Puerto de la Libertad, Punta de Kino.]   Head-
quarters, Dept. of New Mexico, Santa Fe, N. M.,
January 31, 1863.   Official copy.   Cyrus H. De Forrest. [Washington, 1863.]   map.

_____ .   Reports of explorations and surveys, to ascer-
tain the most practicable and economical route for a
railroad from the Mississippi River to the Pacific
Ocean.   Made under the direction of the Secretary of
War, in 1853-6 ...   Washington: Beverley Tucker,
1855-59.   10 v.
   Set incomplete: v. 4, 8, 9 wanting.
   Notes.

_____ .   Report on the art of war in Europe in 1854, 1855,
and 1856; by R. Delafield, from his notes and observations made as a member of a "Military Commission
to the Theatre of War in Europe," under the orders of

Jefferson Davis, Secretary of War. Washington: George W. Bowman, 1861. xxiv, 277 pp.

United States of America. Philada., Engraved by J. Watt, Jr., [18—?]. col. map.
   Autograph.
   Ms. note dated 1830.

UPANISHADS. TAITTIRIYA-UPANISHAD. The Taittiriya, Aitareya, Śvetaśvatara, Kéna, Iśa, Katha, Praśna, Mundaka and Ma'ndukya Upanishads. Tr. from the original Sanscrit by E. Röer. Calcutta: T. J. M'Arthur, 1853. 170 pp.
   Inscriptions: Henry D. Thoreau from Thomas Cholmondeley. R. W. Emerson from Henry D. Thoreau (in Emerson's hand). Notes.

UPHAM, THOMAS COGSWELL. Life and religious opinions and experience of Madame de La Mothe Guyon: together with some account of the personal history and religious opinions of Fenelon, Archbishop of Cambray. New York: Harper, 1847. 2 v.

_____ . The life of faith; in three parts; embracing some of the scriptural principles or doctrines of faith, the power or effects of faith in the regulation of man's inward nature, and the relation of faith to the divine guidance. Boston: Waite, Peirce, 1846. ix, 480 pp.

URQUHART, DAVID. The Sraddha, the keystone of the Brahminical, Buddhistic, and Arian religions, as illustrative of the dogma and duty of adoption among the princes and people of India. London: David Bryce, 1857. 44 pp.

_____ . _____ . Copy 2.

V

VACHEROT, ÉTIENNE. Histoire critique de l'école
d'Alexandrie. Paris: Librairie Philosophique de
Ladrange, 1846-51. 3 v.
  Notes in v. 1, 3.

[Valhalla, the myths of Norseland. n.p., 18—?]
156 pp.
  Copy imperfect: t.p. wanting.
  In verse.

VASARI, GIORGIO. The lives of the most eminent
painters, sculptors, and architects. Tr. from the
Italian of Giorgio Vasari. With notes and illus.,
chiefly selected from various commentators, by
Jonathan Foster. London: Henry G. Bohn, 1850-52.
5 v.
  Autographs and notes.

VAUGHAN, HENRY. Sacred poems and private ejacula-
tions. With a memoir by H. F. Lyte. Boston:
Little, Brown; New York: Evans and Dickerson, 1856.
vi, 307 pp.
  Autograph and notes.

VEDAS. RIGVEDA. *English*. Rig-Veda-Sanhitā. A collection of ancient Hindu hymns ... Tr. from the
original Sanskrit, by H. H. Wilson ... London: Wm.
H. Allen, 1854. 2 v.
  Set incomplete: v. 1 wanting.
  Inscription: Henry D. Thoreau from Thomas Cholmondeley.

VERGANI, ANGELO.   A new and complete Italian grammar
... London: Theophilus Barrois, Jr., 1818.   xix,
284 pp.
   Signature: R. W. Emerson.

VERGILUS MARO, PUBLIUS.   Bucolica Georgica et Aeneis.
Ex editione Petri Burman.   Glasguae: Robertus et
Andreas Foulis, 1758.   397 pp.

_____ .   Opera, et nonnulla opusscula, ex editione Chr.
G. Heyne, sedula recensione accurata.   Londini:
Rodwell et Martin, Law et Whittaker, 1818.   392 pp.
   Autograph.

_____ .   _____ .   Nova ed., notis brevioribus tabulisque
geographicis adornata.   Lugduni: J. B. Pelaguad et
Socii; Parisiis: Poussielgue-Rusand, 1851.   424 pp.

VERITY, ROBERT.   Subject and object; as connected with
our double brain, and a new theory of causation.
London: Longmans, Green, Reader, and Dyer, 1870.
86 pp.
   Caroline Tappan's copy, 1 Feb. 1873.

VERMONT.   Vermont state papers; being a collection of
records and documents, connected with the assump-
tion and establishment of government by the people
of Vermont; together with the journal of the Council
of Safety, the first constitution, the early Journals of
the General Assembly, and the laws from the year
1779 to 1786, inclusive.   To which are added the
Proceedings of the first and second Councils of
Censors.   Comp. and pub. by William Slade ...
Middlebury: J. W. Copeland, 1823.   xx, 567 pp.

Vermont [map].   Engraved for [Zadock] Thompson's
Gazetteer of Vermont.   Peabody, sc. [18-?].
   Inserted in: Tanner, Henry S.   New universal atlas.
   Philadelphia, 1845.

VERY, JONES.   Essays and poems.   Boston: C. C.
Little and J. Brown, 1839.   vii, 175 pp.
   Inscription: To M. M. E., from L. J. E.

_____ .   _____ .   Copy 2.

[VICK, JAMES, *firm, publishers.*] [Flower and vegetable
garden. Rochester, N. Y., 1876?] 119, [34] pp.

VIEYRA, ANTONIO. Novo diccionario portatil das linguas
portugueza e ingleza, em duas partes: Portugueza e
ingleza—Ingleza e portugueza; resumido do diccionario de Vieyra. Nova ed., rev. e consideravel-
mente augm., por J. P. Aillaud. Portuguez e
inglez. Paris: J.-P. Aillaud, Guillard, 1867. 2 v.
   Set incomplete: v. 2 wanting.

VIGNY, ALFRED VICTOR, *Comte* DE. Cinq-mars; ou, Une
conjuration sous Louis XIII ... 7. éd., précédée
de Réflexions sur la vérité dans l'art, accompagnée
de documents historiques. Paris: Calmann Lévy,
1880. 496 pp.

VINCENT, WILLIAM. The voyage of Nearchus from the
Indus to the Euphrates, collected from the original
journal preserved by Arrian, and illustrated by authorities ancient and modern ... To which are
added three dissertations: two, on the acronychal
rising of the Pleiades, by ... Samuel Horsley ...
and by William Wales ... and one by De La Ro-
chette, On the first meridian of Ptolemy ... London: T. Cadell, Jun. and W. Davies, 1797. xv, 530
pp.

VISHNUPURANA. The Vishṅu Puráṅa, a system of Hindu
mythology and tradition, tr. from the original Sanscrit, and illus. by notes derived chiefly from other
Puranas, by H. H. Wilson. London: John Murray,
1840. xci, 704 pp.
   Inscriptions: Henry D. Thoreau from Thomas Cholmondeley; R. W. Emerson, the bequest of Henry D. Thoreau.

VISVANATH PANCHANANA BHATTACHARYA. The Bhāshā
Parichchheda and its commentary The Siddhānta
Muktávalí, an exposition of the Nyāya philosophy
by Víswanātha Panchānana Bhaṭṭa, with an English
version, by J. R. Ballantyne. Printed for the use

of Benares College, by order of Government North
West Provinces.   Calcutta: Encyclopedia Press,
1851.   37 pp.
  Autograph.   Inscription: Henry D. Thoreau from Thomas
Cholmondeley.

[VOLDO, VENIER.]   A song of America, and minor lyrics.
New York: Hanscom, 1876.   206 pp.
  Inscription: 6 Sept 1876.

VOLKER, C.   New-Pestalozzian Institution.   London,
1827.   8 pp.
  Bound with: Lane, Charles.   A classification of
science and arts.   London, 1826.

VOSBURG, JOHN HENRY.   Ralph Elmwood, a poem.
Philadelphia: Claxton, Remsen & Haffelfinger, 1874.
91 pp.
  Inscription: June 1874.

W

[WADDINGTON, GEORGE.] A history of the church, from the earliest ages to the reformation. Published under the superintendence of the Society for the Diffusion of Useful Knowledge. London: Baldwin and Cradock, 1831–33. 2 v.
    Set incomplete: v. 2 wanting.

WADSWORTH, BENJAMIN. Five sermons. ... Boston: Printed by J. Allen for Nicholas Buttolph, 1714. 168 pp.

[WALKER, JOHN. Rhyming dictionary. 3d ed. London, 1819.] 2 v.
    In 1821 Emerson lent a "rhyming dictionary" to one of his Harvard classmates. Cameron (III, 856) suggests that it was probably this edition.

——. ——. New ed. London: William Baynes; Edinburgh: H. S. Baynes, 1824. xxiii, 684 pp.

[——], ed. Letters written by eminent persons in the seventeenth and eighteenth centuries; to which are added, Hearne's Journeys to Reading, and to Whaddon Hall, the seat of Browne Willis, and Lives of eminent men, by John Aubrey. The whole now first published from the originals in the Bodeleian Library and Ashmolean Museum, with biographical and literary illustrations. London: Longman, Hurst, Rees, Orme, and Brown, 1813. 2 v. in 3.
    Autograph and notes.

WALKER, WILLIAM SIDNEY.   Corpus poetarum Latinorum.
 Londini: Henry G. Bohn, 1849.   vi, 1209 pp.
   Autograph and notes.

WALLER, EDMUND.   Works, in verse and prose.   Published by Mr. Fenton.   London: J. Tonson, 1730.
 clxiii, 295 pp.

WALLING, HENRY FRANCIS.   Map of the town of Concord,
 Middlesex County, Mass., surveyed by authority of
 the town.   H. F. Walling, civil engr.   Boston,
 1852.   map.

WALPOLE, HORACE, *Earl of Oxford*.   Correspondence
 with George Montagu ...   New ed.   London: Henry
 Colburn, 1837.   3 v.
   Set incomplete: v. 2 wanting.
   Signature: R. W. Emerson.

_____.   Reminiscences; written in 1788, for the amuse-
 ment of Miss Mary and Miss Agnes B*** Y.   Boston: Wells and Lilly, 1820.   2 v. in 1.

WALTON. IZAAK.   The lives of Donne, Wotton, Hooker,
 Herbert, and Sanderson.   With some account of the
 author and his writings.   Boston: Hilliard, Gray;
 Cambridge: Brown, Shattuck, 1832.   2 v.
   Autographs.

WARD, JAMES WARNER.   Woman, a poem.   Cincinnati:
 Ward & Taylor; New York: G. P. Putnam, 1852.   41
 pp.

WARD, WILLIAM.   On the propagation of evil, by genera-
 tion: addressed to all professing Christians.   London: The Author, [18—?].   15 pp.
   Bound with: Lane, Charles.   A classification of
 science and arts.   London, 1826.

_____.   What is truth?   Contrasted from no. 1 of the
 "Inquirer" for January, 1838.   London: Harvey and
 Darton, [18—?].   12 pp.
   Bound with: Lane, Charles.   A classification of
 science and arts.   London, 1826.

WARDER, GEORGE WOODWARD.   Eden Dell; or, Love's
   wanderings, and other poems.   Kansas City: Ram-
   sey, Millett & Hudson, 1878.   vi, 358 pp.
   Inscription by author: Mar. 10, 1879.

WARE, HENRY.   The connection between the duties of
   the pulpit and the pastoral office.   An introductory
   address delivered to the members of the Theological
   School in Cambridge, October 18 and 25, 1830.
   Cambridge: Hilliard and Brown, 1830.   28 pp.
   Inscription.

———.   ———.   Copy 2.

———.   On the formation of the Christian character,
   addressed to those who are seeking to lead a religious life.   8th ed.   Boston: Hilliard, Gray; Cambridge: Brown Shattuck, 1832.   viii, 176 pp.
   Autograph: Ellen T. Emerson, 1856.

WARE, JOHN.   Memoir of the life of Henry Ware, Jr.
   Boston: J. Munroe, 1846.   xii, 484 pp.
   Inscription: Mrs. Ruth Emerson, from her friend
   A. Adams.

WARE, WILLIAM.   American Unitarian biography.
   Memoirs of individuals who have been distinguished
   by their writings, character, and efforts in the cause
   of liberal Christianity.   Boston: James Munroe;
   London: Edward T. Whitfield, 1851.
   Autograph.

WARING, ANNA LETITIA.   Hymns and meditations.   With
   an introduction by F. D. Huntington.   From the 8th
   London ed.   Boston: E. P. Dutton; New York: Hurd
   and Houghton, 1866.   107 pp.
   Inscription: Mama with love from Edith, New Years
   1871, and notes.

WARNER, ANNA BARTLETT.   Casper and his friends, by
   Amy Lothrop [pseud.].   New York: Robert Carter,
   1871.   262 pp.
   Autograph: Ellen T. Emerson.

WARNER, SUSAN. The wide, wide, world. New York: Lovell, Coryell, [18—?]. 592 pp.
Autograph: Ellen T. Emerson.

WASHBURN, FRANCIS TUCKER. Sermons and essays. With extracts from a memorial pamphlet. Boston: G. H. Ellis, 1876. 195 pp.

WASHBURN, WILLIAM TUCKER. Poems. New York: Jesse Haney, 1878. 2 v.
Set incomplete: v. 1 wanting.

Waters's roads; London to Dover. London: Tornbleson, 1833. col. map.
Broadside.

[WATSON, S. H.] [Fancies. n.p., 186-?] 35 pp.
Inscription: M. H. Watson. To Mrs. Emerson.

WATSON, SAMUEL JAMES. The legend of the roses, a poem. Ravlan, a drama. Toronto: Hunter Rose, 1876. 228 pp.
Inscription. Letter, Jan. 29, 1879, from author to Emerson, presenting a book, inserted.

WATTS, ISAAC. Horae lyricae. Poems, chiefly of the lyric kind. In three books. Sacred. I. To devotion and piety. II. To virtue, honour, and friendship. III. To the memory of the dead. Boston: S. Hall for B. Larkin, J. White, D. West, and E. Larkin, 1790. xxxviii, 252 pp.
———. ———. New ed. To which are added a supplement, containing translations of all the Latin poems, with notes, by Thomas Gibbons. London: Printed for G. Wilkie, J. Walker, etc., 1805. xlvi, 300 pp.
———. The Psalms of David, imitated in the language of the New Testament, and applied to the Christian state and worship, by I. Watts. Boston: Nathaniel Willis, 1813. xi, 468 pp.
Signatures: Ezra Ripley, Ruth Emerson, 1832.

WATTS, JOHN.   The facts of the cotton famine.   London: Simpkin, Marshall, 1866.   472 pp.
Given to Concord Free Public Library by Ralph Waldo Emerson in Feb. 1874. Withdrawn from circulation, 1906 (Cameron, III, 869).

WAYLAND, FRANCIS.   A discourse on the philosophy of analogy, delivered before the Phi Beta Kappa Society of Rhode Island, September 7, 1831.   Boston: Hilliard, Gray, Little, and Wilkins, 1831.   32 pp.
Bound with: Webster, Daniel.   Speech ... on the 14th January, 1814.   Alexandria, 1814.

_____.   The limitations of human responsibility. Boston: Gould, Kendall and Lincoln, 1838.   188 pp.

WEBSTER, DANIEL.   An address delivered at the laying of the corner stone of the Bunker Hill Monument. Boston: Cummings, Hilliard, 1825.   40 pp.
Bound with the author's A discourse, delivered at Plymouth, December 22, 1820.   Boston, 1826.

_____.   _____.   4th ed.   Boston: Cummings, Hilliard, 1825.   40 pp.
Bound with: Everett, Edward.   An oration delivered at Plymouth, December 22, 1824.   Boston, 1825.

_____.   A discourse delivered at Plymouth, December 22, 1820.   In commemoration of the first settlement of New England.   Boston: Wells and Lilly, 1821. 104 pp.
Signature: R. W. Emerson.

_____.   _____.   4th ed.   Boston: Wells and Lilly, 1826.   60 pp.

_____.   A discourse in commemoration of the lives and services of John Adams and Thomas Jefferson, delivered in Faneuil Hall, Boston, August 2, 1826.   Boston: Cummings, Hilliard, 1826. 62 pp.
Bound with the author's A discourse, delivered at Plymouth, December 22, 1820.   Boston, 1826.

———. ———. Copy 2.
Bound with: Everett, Edward. An oration delivered at Plymouth, December 22, 1824. Boston, 1825.

———. Second speech, delivered in the Senate of the United States, January 26, 1830. With a sketch of the preceding debate on the resolution of Mr. Foot, respecting the sale, &c., of public lands. Boston: Carter and Hendee, 1830. 76 pp.
Bound with: Everett, Edward. An oration delivered at Plymouth, December 22, 1824. Boston, 1825.

———. Speech at the National Republican Convention, in Worcester, Oct. 12, 1832. Boston: Stimpson & Clapp, 1832. 43 pp.
Bound with the author's Speech ... on the 14th January, 1814. Alexandria, 1814.

———. Speech delivered in the House of Representatives of the United States, on the 14th January, 1814, on a bill making further provision for filling the ranks of the regular army, encouraging enlistments, and authorising the enlistments for larger periods of men whose terms of service are about to expire. Alexandria: Snowden & Simms, 1814. 13 pp.
Autograph.

———. Speech in the Senate of the United States, on the President's veto of the bank bill, July 11, 1832. Boston: J. E. Hinckley, 1832. 32 pp.
Bound with the author's Speech ... on the 14th January, 1814. Alexandria, 1814.

———. Speech on the Greek Revolution. From the Washington ed. Boston: Cummings, Hilliard, 1824. 39 pp.
Bound with the author's A discourse delivered at Plymouth, December 22, 1820. Boston, 1826.

WEBSTER, JOHN. Works. With some account of the author, and notes, by Alexander Dyce. New ed., rev. and cor. London, New York: G. Routledge, 1871. xxix, 383 pp.

WEBSTER, NOAH.   An American dictionary of the English
language ...   Rev. and enl., by Chauncey A. Goodrich.   Springfield, Mass.: George and Charles
Merriam, 1861.   ccxliv, 1512 [i.e. 1758] pp.

———.   ———.   Thoroughly revised and greatly en-
larged and improved by Chauncey A. Goodrich ...
and Noah Porter ...   Cambridge: G. & C. Merriam,
[1864].   2 v.
    Set incomplete: v. 1 wanting.
    Inscription from the publishers: 12 Aug., 1878.

The wedding gift; or, The duties and pleasures of
domestic life.   Boston: Gould, Kendall & Lincoln,
[1843].   vi, 128 pp.
    Inscription: quotations in [?'s] hand on wedding day.

The weekly visitor.   [v. 2], no 89, June 24, 1834.
London: John Davis.   232 pp.
    Bound with: Lane, Charles.   A classification of
    science and arts.   London, 1826.

[WEIDEMEYER, JOHN WILLIAM.]   Themes and translations, by John W. Montclair, [pseud.].   New York,
1867.   xi, 167 pp.
    Inscribed on half-title: To Mr. R. W. Emerson with the
    compliments of the author.

WEISS, JOHN.   Life and correspondence of Theodore
Parker, minister of the Twenty-eighth Congregational
Society, Boston.   New York: D. Appleton, 1864.
2 v.
    Inscription from Joseph Lyman; autograph.   Portrait
    laid in.

———.   Wit, humor, and Shakespeare, twelve essays.
Boston: Roberts Bros., 1876.   428 pp.

WELD, THEODORE DWIGHT.   In memory: Angelina Grimké
Weld.   Born in Charleston, South Carolina, February
20, 1805.   Died in Hyde Park, Massachusetts,
October 26, 1879.   Printed only for private circulation.   Boston: George H. Ellis, 1880.   81 pp.

WELLS, ANNA MARIA (FOSTER). Poems and juvenile
sketches. Boston: Carter, Hendee & Babcock,
1830. 104 pp.

WELSH, ALFRED HIX. English literature in the eighteenth century. With an introduction, by R. G.
Hutchins. Columbus, Ohio: G. J. Brand, 1880.
viii, 158 pp.
Inscription. Letter from author, 7 July 1880, tipped in.

WENDTÉ, CHARLES WILLIAM, AND PERKINS, H. S. The
sunny side: a book of religious songs for the Sunday
school and the home. With original poetical contributions ... [and] music, original and selected ...
together with a careful selection of German folk and
child songs. New York: William A. Pond, [1875].
137 pp.
Bookplate of Sunday-School Library, Unitarian Society
in Concord.

WERDER, KARL. Vorlesungen über Shakespeare's Ham-
let, gehalten an der Universität zu Berlin (zuerst im
Winter-Semester 1859–1860, zuletzt 1871–1872).
Berlin: Wilhelm Hertz, 1875. 252 pp.
Autograph.

The Westminster review. New series. no. 3, 8; July,
1852; Oct. 1853. London: John Chapman. 2 v.

WHATELY, RICHARD. Elements of rhetoric. Comprising
the substance of the article in the Encylopaedia
metropolitana: with additions, etc. 3d ed. Oxford:
W. Baxter, 1830. xxi, 447 pp.
Autograph.

WHEILDON, WILLIAM WILLDER. Contributions to thought.
Concord, Mass.: Author's Private Print. Off., 1874.
236 pp.

_____. Curiosities of history: Boston, September
seventeenth, 1630–1880. 2d ed. Boston: Lee and
Shepard; New York: C. T. Dillingham, 1880. x,
141 pp.
Inscription: Dec. 1880.

———. History of Paul Revere's signal lanterns April 18, 1775, in the steeple of the North Church; with an account of the tablet on Christ Church and the monuments at Highland Park and Dorchester Heights. Concord: Author's Private Print. Off., 1878.   63 pp.

WHIPPLE, EDWIN PERCY.   Character and characteristic men.   Boston: Ticknor and Fields, 1866.   324 pp.
  Presented to Concord Free Public Library by Ralph Waldo Emerson in Feb. 1874 (Cameron, III, 869).

———. Eulogy on John Albion Andrew, with an appendix, containing the proceedings of the City Council and an account of the services in Music Hall.   Boston: Alfred Mudge, 1867.   36 pp.
  Inscription.

———. Success and its conditions.   Boston: James R. Osgood, 1871.   iv, 333 pp.
  Inscription: 24 Mar. 1871.

WHIPPLE, S.   The way to happiness: being an essay on the motives to human actions, and the fundamental principles of morality.   Utica, N. Y.: H. H. Curtiss, 1847.   269 pp.
  Inscription.

WHITE, EDWARD L.   The Sunday school singing book: being a collection of hymns with appropriate music, designed as a guide and assistant to the devotional exercises of Sabbath schools and families; comprising also, the elements of music, with directions for a good development of the voice, and vocal exercises. 6th ed.   Boston: William Crosby and H. P. Nichols, 1851.   112 pp.
  Notes.

———. ———. Copy 2.
  Notes.

WHITE, HENRY KIRKE.   The remains of Henry Kirke White ... with an account of his life, by Robert Southey.   Boston: Bedlington and Ewer, 1823.   2 v.

WHITEFIELD, EDWIN.   The homes of our forefathers; being a collection of the oldest and most interesting
buildings in Massachusetts, from original drawings.
With historical memoranda.   Boston: A. Williams,
1879.

[WHITER, WALTER.]   Etymologicon magnum; or, Universal
etymological dictionary on a new plan.   With illustrations drawn from various languages ...   Part the
first.   Cambridge, [Eng.]: Francis Hodson, 1800.
xl, 507, xxix pp.
No more published.

WHITING, WILLIAM.   War powers under the Constitution
of the United States.   Military armists, reconstruction, and military government.   Also, now first published, War claims of aliens.   With notes on the
acts of the executive and legislative departments
during our Civil War, and a collection of cases de-
cided in the national courts.   Boston: Lee and
Shepard; New York: Lee, Shepard and Dillingham,
1871.   xxviii, 695 pp.
Presentation inscription inserted.

WHITLOCK, NATHANIEL.   The microcosm of Oxford, containing a series of views of the churches, colleges,
halls and other public buildings of the University
and City of Oxford.   Accompanied with brief notices
of founders, benefactors, dates of buildings, and
other subjects, explanatory of the several drawings.
Oxford: N. Whitlock; London: J. Bumpus, Hinton, &
H. Harris, [18—?].   40 pp.

WHITMAN, JOHN W., *reporter*.   Massachusetts: Supreme
Judicial Court.   Trial of the case of the Commonwealth versus David Lee Child, for publishing in the
Massachusetts journal, a libel on John Keyes, before
the Supreme Judicial Court, holden at Cambridge, in
the County of Middlesex.   October term, 1828.
Boston: Dutton and Wentworth, 1829.   119 pp.

WHITMAN, WALT.   Drum-taps.   New York, 1865.   iv,
72 pp.
   Issued without Sequel, which was added to most copies
of this title after Lincoln's death.

——.   Leaves of grass.   Brooklyn, N. Y., 1855.
95 pp.
   Emerson gave this copy to Franklin Benjamin Sanborn
on the eve of the Civil War.   It is now in the library of
the University of Michigan at Ann Arbor (Cameron, III,
857).

WHITNEY, ADELINE DUTTON (TRAIN).   Just how: a key to
the cook-books.   Boston: Houghton, Osgood, 1879.
xviii, 311 pp.

WHITTIER, DANIEL BODWELL.   Genealogy of two
branches of the Whittier family from 1620 to 1873.
Boston: Alfred Mudge, 1873.   22 pp.

WHITTIER, JOHN GREENLEAF.   Home ballads and poems.
Boston: Ticknor and Fields, 1861.   vi, 206 pp.
   Autograph.

——.   The king's missive, and other poems.   Boston:
Houghton, Mifflin, 1881.   vi, 99 pp.

——.   The panorama, and other poems.   Boston:
Ticknor and Fields, 1856.   vi, 141 pp.
   Inscription: From the author (in Whittier's hand); To
R. W. Emerson (in Emerson's hand).

——.   Snow-bound, a winter idyl.   Boston; Ticknor
and Fields, 1866.   51 pp.
   Autograph.

——.   ——.   Boston: James R. Osgood, 1875.   82
pp.

WILBY, FRANCIS.   Pestalozzian maxims, on the requi-
site conditions to be presented by the mother in the
education of her child.   London: Pestalozzian
Academy, 1839.   12 pp.
   Bound with: Lane, Charles.   A classification of
science and arts.   London, 1826.

WILKINS, SIR CHARLES, *tr.*   The Heetopades of Veesh-
noo Sarma, in a series of connected fables, inter-
spersed with moral, prudential and political maxims;
tr. from an ancient manuscript in the Sanskreet language with explanatory notes.   Bath: Printed by
R. Cruttwell, 1787.   xx, 334 pp.
  Autograph and notes.

WILKINS, JOHN HUBBARD.   Elements of astronomy, illustrated with plates, for the use of schools and academies, with questions.   3d ed.   Boston: Cummings,
Hilliard, 1825.   151 pp.

WILKINSON, JAMES JOHN GARTH.   Emanuel Swedenborg,
a biography.   Boston: Otis Clapp, 1849.   vi, 270
pp.
  Inscription.

_____.   The human body and its connexion with man,
illustrated by the principal organs.   London: Chapman and Hall, 1851,   xxxi, 491 pp.
  Inscription of author: June 14, 1851.

_____.   Human science, good and evil and its works;
and on divine revelation and its works and sciences.   London: James Spiers, 1876.   xxi, 590 pp.

_____.   Improvisations from the spirit.   London: W.
White, 1857.   viii, 408 pp.
  Inscription: 10 July 1857.

_____.   Remarks on Swedenborg's economy of the
animal kingdom.   London: Walton and Mitchell.
1846.   86 pp.
  Inscription By author to R. W. E., May 14, 1846.

_____.   Unlicensed medicine with a plan for extending
homoeopathy.   London: R. Theobald; Manchester
H. Turner, 1855.   32 pp.
  Inscription.

WILKINSON, SIR JOHN GARDNER.   A popular account of the
   ancient Egyptians.   Rev. and abridged from his
   larger work.   Illus. with five hundred woodcuts.
   London: John Murray, 1854.   2 v.
   Set incomplete v. 2 wanting.
   Note and autograph.

WILLIAMS, WELLINGTON.   Appletons' southern and western travellers' guide: with new and authentic maps,
   illustrating those divisions of the country; and containing sectional maps of the Mississippi and Ohio
   rivers; with plans of cities, views, etc.   Forming a
   complete guide to the Falls of St. Anthony; Mammoth
   Cave, Ky.; Virginia springs; the tour of the great
   rivers of the West; the Great Lakes; the copper
   region of Lake Superior, etc; and containing full and
   accurate descriptions of the principal cities, towns,
   and villages, with distances, fares, etc.   New York:
   D. Appleton, 1850.   140 pp.
   Notes.

WILLISON, JOHN.   The afflicted man's companion; or, A
   directory for families and persons afflicted with
   sickness and other distress.   With directions to the
   sick, both under and after affliction.   Also to the
   friends of the sick, and others who visit them: and
   likewise to all, how to prepare both for sickness and
   death, and how to be exercised at the time of dying.
   With a collection of dying words of many choice and
   eminent saints.   Necessary for families.   Edinburgh: Silvester Doig, 1793.   xx, 251 pp.
   Signature on slip pasted in: William Emerson.

WILLSON, FORCEYTHE.   The old sergeant; being the car-
   rier's very humble offering.   January 1, 1863.
   Cambridge: Priv. Re-issued, 1866.   18 pp.
   Inscription, with initials: F. W.

———.   The old sergeant, and other poems.   Boston:
   Ticknor and Fields, 1867.   vi, 115 pp.
   Autograph.

WILSON, ALEXANDER.   Notes, questions and answers on
Our Lord's parables.   7th thousand, rev. and enl.
London: National Society's Depository, [1860].
171 pp.

WILSON, ALEXANDER STEPHEN.   A creed of tomorrow.
London: Longmans, Green, Reader, and Dyer, 1872.
xvi, 283 pp.
Inscription: From the author.

WILSON, SIR DANIEL.   Historical footprints in America.
[Toronto], 1864.   28 pp.
"From the Canadian journal for September, 1864."
Inscription.

WILSON, HENRY.   History of the rise and fall of the
slave power in America.   Boston: James R. Osgood,
1874.   2 v.
Set incomplete: v. 1 wanting.

WILSON, HORACE HAYMAN.   Select specimens of the
theatre of the Hindus, tr. from the original Sanskrit.
2d ed.   London: Parbury, Allen, 1835.   2 v.
Inscription: v. 2, Henry D. Thoreau from Thomas
Cholmondeley. Autograph: v. 1, H. D. T.

WILSON, JOHN ALBERT.   The paradox, and other poems.
New York: G. P. Putnam's Sons, 1877.   viii, 226 pp.
Inscription: To R. W. E. by author, Xmas, 1877.

WILSON, THOMAS.   A short and plain instruction for the
better understanding of the Lord's supper.   New
York: Pott and Emery, [18—?].   vii, 160 pp.

WINCKELMANN, JOHANN JOACHIM.   The history of ancient
art.   Tr. from the German by G. Henry Lodge, with
the life of Winckelmann, by the editor.   Boston:
Little, Brown, 1856.   2 v.
Inscription from E. R. Hoar; autograph and notes.

WINKLEY, SAMUEL HOBART.   A study of the scriptures...
Boston: Walker, Wise, 1863.   2 pts. in 1 v.
Autograph: Ellen T. Emerson, 19 Oct. 1863, and notes.

————. ————. Copy 2.
Autograph and notes.

WINKWORTH, CATHERINE. Lyra Germanica. 2d series:
The Christian life. Tr. from the German. New
York: Anson D. F. Randolph, 1858. xvi, 300 pp.
Inscription: Ellen T. Emerson, Feb. 24, 1859, from her
mother.

————. Lyra Germanica. Hymns for the Sundays and
chief festivals of the Christian year. Tr. from the
German. New ed. Boston: E. P. Dutton, 1862.
xxiii, 258 pp.

[WINSOR, HENRY.] Montrose, and other biographical
sketches. Boston: Soule and Williams, 1861. 400
pp.
Inscription.

WITHINGTON, WILLIAM. The growth of thought as affect-
ing the progress of society. Boston: A. Forbes,
1851. viii, 72 pp.

WOLSELEY, GARNET JOSEPH WOLSELEY, *1st Viscount.*
Field pocket-book for the auxiliary forces. London:
Macmillan, 1873. vi, 101 pp.

WOODHOUSELEE, ALEXANDER FRASER TYLER, *Lord.* Elements of general history, ancient and modern. To
which are added a table of chronology, and a comparative view of ancient and modern geography.
Philadelphia: F. Nichols, 1809. xix, 387 pp.

WOOLMAN, JOHN. A journal of the life, gospel labours,
and Christian experiences of that faithful minister of
Jesus Christ, John Woolman ... To which are
added his last epistle, and other writings. Warring-
ton: Thomas Hurst, 1840. xii, 339 pp.
Autograph: J. G. Whittier. Inscription: R. W. Emerson
from his friend J. G. Whittier 10th mo. 29, 1853 (in Emerson's hand).

WOOLSON, ABBA (GOOLD). Browsing among books, and other essays. Boston: Roberts Bros., 1881. 243 pp.
> Inscription: 14 Feb. 1882.

WORCESTER, JOSEPH EMERSON. An historical atlas, containing the following [10] charts ... 3 ed. Boston: Hilliard, Gray, Little, and Wilkins, 1828. 20 pp.
> Autograph.

Words in a Sunday school. Boston: Benjamin H. Greene, 1842. 194 pp.
> Autograph: L. J. Emerson.

_____. _____. Copy 2.
> Autograph: Lydian Emerson.

WORDSWORTH, CHRISTOPHER, *Bp. of Lincoln*. Memoirs of William Wordsworth, poet-laureate. Ed. by Henry Reed. Boston: Ticknor, Reed, and Fields, 1851. 2 v.
> Autographs.

WORDSWORTH, WILLIAM. Pastoral poems. New York: D. Appleton, 1859. 55 pp. illus.

_____. Poems. New ed. London: Edward Moxon, 1851. xxiv, 619 pp.
> Inscription: W. E.—E. W. E.; R. W. E.'s notes.

_____. Poems for the young. With fifty illus. by John MacWhirter and John Pettie and a vignette by J. E. Millais. Engraved by Dalziel Bros. London: Alexander Strahan, 1863. x, 91 pp.
> Autograph: Edith Emerson Forbes.

_____. Poetical works. Boston: Cummings, Hilliard, 1824. 4 v.
> Inscription: v. 1, R. W. E. from L. P. P. (in R. W. E.'s hand).
> Autographs, v. 1–4.

———. The prelude; or, Growth of a poet's mind; an autobiographical poem. New York: D. Appleton; Philadelphia: George S. Appleton, 1850. viii, 374 pp.

> Autograph and notes.

———. Yarrow revisited, and other poems. Boston: James Munroe, 1835. xii, 244 pp.

> Autograph and notes.

[WORTHMANN, FERD.] Ein Separatvolum zu Shakspeare's "Othello." [Druck von Grenzboten, Bd. 3, 1873.] [121]–136 pp.

WOTTON, SIR HENRY. Reliquiae Wottonianae; or, A collection of lives, letters, poems; with characters of sundry personages: and their incomparable pieces of language and art. Also additional letters to several persons, not before printed. 4th ed., with additions of several letters to the Lord Zouch, never publish'd till now. London: B. Tooke and T. Sawbridge, 1685. 43, 713 pp.

> Notes. Note on slip laid in at p. 473.

WRIGHT, CHAUNCEY. Letters. With some account of his life, by James Bradley Thayer. Privately printed. Cambridge: J. Wilson, 1878. 392 pp.

WRIGHT, H. G. Educational establishment, conducted by Mr. and Miss Wright, at Horn Common, near Richmond Park. Prospectus. [n.p., 18—?] 4 pp.

> Bound with: Lane, Charles. A classification of science and arts. London, 1826.

———. Exposition of an educative effort at Alcott House, Horn Common, near Richmond, Surrey. Conductors Mr. and Miss Wright, and assistants. [London: J. King, Printer,] 1839. 16 pp.

> Bound with: Lane, Charles. A classification of science and arts. London, 1826.

_____.   Marriage and its sanctions.   [Cheltenham: Harper, Printer, 1840?]   8 pp.

Bound with: Lane, Charles.   A classification of science and arts.   London, 1826.

_____.   _____.   4th thousand.   London: B. D. Cousins, and J. Cleave, 1840.   8 pp.

Bound with: Lane, Charles.   A classification of science and arts.   London, 1826.

_____.   Retrospective sketch of an educative attempt, at Alcott House, Horn Common, near Richmond, Surrey, by Mr. & Miss Wright.   London: V. Tornas, 1840.   7 pp.

Bound with: Lane, Charles.   A classification of science and arts.   London, 1826.

WRIGHT, WILLIAM BULL.   The brook, and other poems. New York: Scribner, Armstrong, 1873.   167 pp.

_____.   Highland rambles, a poem.   Boston: Adams, 1868.   vi, 183 pp.

Inscription: From the Author (in R. W. E's hand).

WYCHERLEY, WILLIAM.   The dramatic works of Wycherley, Congreve, Vanbrugh, and Farquhar.   With biographical and critical notices, by Leigh Hunt.   New ed.   London, New York: George Routledge, 1871. lxxxiv, 668 pp.

Note.

WYMAN, THOMAS BELLOWS.   Genealogy of the name and family of Hunt, early established in America from Europe.   Exhibiting pedigrees of ten thousand persons ...   Authorized by W. L. G. Hunt.   Comp. by T. B. Wyman, Jr.   Boston: J. Wilson, 1862-63. xv, 414 pp.

X

XENOPHON.　Minor works: vis., Memoirs of Socrates;
The banquet; Hiero, on the condition of royalty; and
Economics, or the science of good husbandry.　Tr.
from the Greek, by several hands.　London: J.
Walker, 1813.　vii, 467 pp.
　　Autograph.

Y

YONGE, CHARLOTTE MARY. Little Lucy's wonderful
globe. Pictured by L. Frolich, and narrated by
Charlotte M. Yonge ... London, New York: Macmillan, 1871. viii, 74 pp.

_____. Musings over the "Christian year" and "Lyra
innocentium," together with a few gleanings of
recollections of John Keble, gathered by several
friends ... New York: D. Appleton, 1871. 431 pp.

YOUMANS, EDWARD LIVINGSTON. The correlation and
conservation of forces; a series of expositions, by
Prof. Grove, Prof. Helmholtz, Dr. Mayer, Dr. Fara-
day, Prof. Liebig and Dr. Carpenter. With an introduction and brief biographical notices of the chief
promoters of the new views. New York: D. Appleton, 1867. xlii, 438 pp.
Autograph.

YOUNG, EDWARD. The complaint; or, Night-thoughts on
life, death and immortality. To which is prefixed
the life of the author ... Glasgow: R. Scott, 1798.
2 v.
Set incomplete: v. 2 wanting.
Inscriptions: v. 1, C. C. Emerson.

_____. Night thoughts on life, death & immortality.
New York: R. & W. A. Bartow, 1819. vi, 301 pp.
Stamped: R. W. Emerson.

Z

ZACHARIAS, OTTO; *i. e.*, EMIL OTTO. Zur Entwicklungs-
theorie. Jena: Hermann Costenoble, 1876. 127 pp.

Index

Inasmuch as the entries comprising the text of this book are arranged alphabetically by authors or, for periodicals and anonymous works, by titles, these names and titles are not repeated in the index.